DISCARD

Favorite Animal Stories in Large Print

Other Anthologies Available in Large Print:

Best-Loved Poems in Large Print
Favorite Short Stories in Large Print
Favorite Poems in Large Print
Famous Detective Stories in Large Print
A Treasury of Humor in Large Print

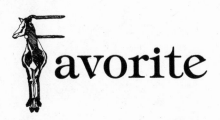

Favorite Animal Stories in Large Print

Edited by
Mary C. Allen

G.K.HALL &CO.
Boston, Massachusetts
1987

Copyright 1987 by G. K. Hall & Co.

G. K. Hall Large Print Book Series.

Animal alphabet copyright 1987 by
Kristina Hals and Lee Paradis.

Set in 16 pt Plantin.

Library of Congress Cataloging-in-Publication Data

Favorite animal stories in large print.

  (G. K. Hall large print book series)
  1. Animals—Fiction. 2. Short stories, English.
3. Short stories, American. 4. Large type books.
  I. Allen, Mary C.
[PR1309.A53F38 1987]   823'.01'0836   86–27025
ISBN 0–8161–4018–9

Acknowledgments

The editor gratefully acknowledges permission to reproduce the copyright material included in this volume. In the event of any error or omission, she will be pleased to make the necessary correction in future editions of this book.

Excerpt (chapter 4) from *The Story of Elsa* by Joy Adamson. © 1965 by Elsa Limited. Reprinted by permission of Harcourt Brace Jovanovich, Inc. Reprinted in Canada by permission of William Collins, Sons & Company Limited.

"The Lady of Leisure" by Helen Dore Boylston. Copyright 1932 by Harper & Brothers; renewed © 1960 by Helen Dore Boylston. Reprinted by permissions of Brandt & Brandt Literary Agents, Inc.

"A Hymn to Hawgs" by Louis Bromfield, from *Animals and Other People* by Louis Bromfield, copyright 1955 by Louis Bromfield. Reprinted by permission of Harper & Row, Publishers, Inc.

Excerpt from *The Incredible Journey: A Tale of Three Animals* by Sheila Burnford, © 1960, 1961 by Sheila Burnford. Reprinted by permission of Little, Brown and Company in association with The Atlantic Monthly Press. Reprinted in Canada by permission of Hodder and Stoughton Ltd.

"The Oracle of the Dog" by G. K. Chesterton, from *The Incredulity of Father Brown* by G. K. Chesterton. Reprinted by permission of Dodd, Mead & Company, Inc. Copyright 1926 by Dodd, Mead and Company Inc. Renewed © 1953 by Oliver Chesterton. Reprinted in Canada by permission of Miss D. E. Collins and A. P. Watt Ltd.

"A Tent in Agony" by Stephen Crane, from *Midnight Sketches* by Stephen Crane. Reprinted courtesy of Alfred A. Knopf, Inc.

"The Life and Death of Cholmondeley" by Gerald M. Durrell, from *The Overloaded Ark* by Gerald M. Durrell. Copyright 1953 by Gerald M. Durrell; renewed © 1981 by Gerald M. Durrell. Reprinted by permission of Viking Penguin, Inc.

Table of Contents

Editor's Note

Animal lovers abound, and for good reasons. Warm and abiding friendship often exists between animals and humans, and anyone who has lovingly observed animals is familiar with the delightful rewards of doing so. Many of the selections in this volume portray rich bonds between animals and people, or convey the delighted and often humorous observations of a seasoned animal watcher. A few, such as the two classic stories by Rudyard Kipling, depict animals themselves as characters able to talk and think like humans while still behaving like animals.

The selections span a broad range of tone and mood, from whimsical humor to moving drama; many, such as the piece from Marjorie Kinnan Rawling's *The Yearling*, almost palpably create a sense of the freshness of childhood and the love of nature. Some of the pieces collected are excerpted from books, and I have tried to choose excerpts which not only capture the flavor of the longer work but which also stand on their own.

I hope that readers of this anthology of animal stories in Large Print will spend many pleasurable hours — laughing, smiling, and perhaps shedding a few tears — with the stories and friends that follow.

Mary C. Allen
Cambridge, Massachusetts

Favorite Animal Stories
in Large Print

Safari to Lake Rudolf*
Joy Adamson

One afternoon, after we had returned to Isiolo, we met a herd of eland. Elsa instantly began to stalk them. These large antelope were grazing on a steep slope and had several young amongst them. One eland cow waited for her and before she got too close to the calves distracted her attention from the youngsters by playing hide and seek with her in the bushes. In this way, she kept her engaged until the herd and the calves had safely disappeared beyond the hillside. Then the eland cow galloped off at high speed, leaving poor Elsa standing.

Another case of animal diplomacy was fascinating to watch. We had taken Elsa up a hill behind the house, from the top of which we saw a herd of about eighty elephant with many small calves feeding below. Elsa saw them too and before we could shout "*No*" she went off downhill and, a few moments later, was advancing cautiously towards the herd.

Nearest to her was a cow with a small calf.

*From *The Story of Elsa,* the account of Joy Adamson's remarkable relationship with the lioness Elsa.

Elsa stalked it with great cunning, but the mother elephant was well aware of her intention. We watched, tense with anxiety, expecting a charge, but to our surprise the mother elephant moved quietly between Elsa and the calf, pushing it slowly towards some big bulls, keeping our lioness on the far side. Disappointed, Elsa looked for the next best playmate and used careful cover to join two feeding bulls. But again she was ignored. Then she tried to provoke other small groups of elephant, advancing to within a few yards of them. Still nothing happened. The sun was getting low; we shouted to her but she obstinately disregarded our calls. Finally we had no alternative but to return home without her. She certainly intended to take her time and we could only rely on her intelligence to keep her out of trouble.

I waited for her inside the enclosure and became more and more worried. What could we do? Chaining Elsa up during the elephant season would only frustrate and infuriate her; indeed, it might end by making her dangerous. We had to let her learn her limitations by experience, allow her to weigh the fun against the boredom, or danger, of playing with these big animals. In doing so perhaps she would come to lose interest in them. By this time she was three hours overdue and I feared an accident, then suddenly I heard her familiar hnk-hnk and in she came, very thirsty indeed, yet before she went to her water-bowl she licked my face and sucked my thumbs as if to tell me how glad she was to be with me again. She smelled strongly of elephant, and I could well imagine how close she had been to them, and that she had rolled in their droppings. By the way she flung herself with a crash to the ground, I could also judge how tired she was. I felt very humble; here was my friend just returned from a world that was utterly denied to me, yet she was as affectionate as ever. Did she have any realisation of the extraordinary link she was between the two worlds?

Of all animals, giraffe were undoubtedly her favourites. Often she stalked them until both sides became tired. Then she would sit down waiting for the giraffe to return and sure enough, after a time they would approach again, advancing slowly step by step, facing Elsa, looking at her with their large sad eyes, while their slender necks arched in an inquisitive way. Then usually, browsing at their favourite acacia seeds as they went by, they would walk peacefully away. But, sometimes, Elsa would drive them in proper lion fashion. After spotting them, she would turn off at right angles down wind, crouching with her belly close to the ground, every muscle quivering, until she had encircled the herd, then she would drive it towards us. No doubt we were expected to wait in ambush and kill the victims she had so cleverly rounded up for us.

Other animals also attracted her attention; for instance, one day she sniffed the air and then dashed into a thick bush. Soon afterwards we heard crashing and snorting coming straight at us! Quickly we jumped out of the way as a wart-hog thundered past, with Elsa hot on his heels. Both disappeared at lightning speed and for a long time we heard them breaking through the wood. We were very worried for Elsa's safety, as the wart-hog has formidable tusks which he can use to kill, till she returned; the winner of the chase rubbed her head against our knees and told us about her new playmate.

Our next safari was to take us to Lake Rudolf, a stretch of brackish water, some one hundred and eighty miles long, reaching to the Ethiopian frontier. We were to be away for seven weeks and most of the time we should travel on foot with pack donkeys and mules. It would be Elsa's first experience of a foot safari in the company of donkeys and we could only hope that both sides would accept each other. We were quite a party: George and myself, Julian, a Game Warden from a neighbouring territory, Herbert, who was again our guest, as well as Game Scouts, drivers and personal servants, six sheep to feed Elsa on the way, and thirty-five donkeys and mules. The pack animals were sent off three weeks ahead to meet us on the shores of the Lake, while we travelled the distance of about three hundred miles by motor transport.

It was a big convoy: two Land-Rovers, my one-and-a-half-ton truck with Elsa in the back of it, and two three-ton lorries. The latter were necessary to enable us to carry, as well as the men, sufficient food and petrol for the weeks we should be away, also eighty gallons of water. Our first one hundred and eighty miles led us through the sandy, hot and dusty plains of the Kaisut desert. Then we ascended the volcanic slopes of the Marsabit mountain, an isolated volcanic mass rising to 4,500 feet out of the surrounding desert. Clothed in thick, cool, lichen-covered forest, and often enveloped in mist, it presented a welcome contrast to the hot arid country below. It is a game paradise and harbours elephant carrying some of the finest ivory in Africa, besides rhino, buffalo, the greater kudu, lion and lesser game. Here was the last administrative post.

From now on we made our way through practically uninhabited country and were cut off from any contact with the outside world. Nothing broke the monotony of the sand gullies and lava ridges. The only incident was a crash which nearly broke my car in half. One back wheel left us and we came to an abrupt stop. Poor Elsa; it took hours to repair the damage and she had to spend the time inside the car, since it provided the only shade from the fierce sun which she hated. However she was most co-operative and although she did not like strange Africans, obligingly put up with the jabbering crowd of our people, who pressed close to the car trying to be helpful. When we were mobile again, we climbed up the most shocking track into the Hurri hills on the Ethiopian border. These are desolate and, though higher than Marsabit, attract

5

less moisture. An enervating gale blows across their slopes and, in consequence, they are barren of forest. Elsa was quite bewildered by the fierce wind and had to spend the night in the truck, well protected with canvas curtains from its icy blast.

George's purpose in visiting these hills was to examine the game situation and to see whether there were any signs of poaching by the Gabbra tribesmen. After a few days spent in patrolling the country we turned westwards, crossing the most depressing, desolate lava country, where sharp rocks jerked the car mercilessly, and Elsa had a tough time as we pushed the vehicles through deep sandy river beds or ground our way carefully between boulders, jostling against the large stones. At last we came out on to the Chalbi desert, a dry ancient lake bed some eighty miles in length, with a smooth fairly firm surface on which a vehicle can travel at full speed. Mirages are the most remarkable feature of this area: great expanses of water with palm trees reflected in their surface appear but swiftly vanish as one approaches them. Here, too, gazelles assume the proportions of elephants and appear to be walking on the waters. It is a land of thirst and grilling heat. At the western end of Chalbi lies the oasis of North Horr, where there is a Police Post, and where thousands of camels, sheep and goats belonging to the Rendile tribe come to water. Another remarkable sight to be seen there in the morning is that of thousands of sand grouse flying in to drink at the few pools. Now soon, as there was nothing to keep us at North Horr, we filled our water containers and continued on our way.

At last, after two hundred and thirty miles of hustling and bumping, we reached Loyongalane, an oasis of fresh-water springs in a grove of doum-palms near the south of Lake Rudolf. Here we found our donkeys waiting for us. We took Elsa at once to the lake, which was two miles distant. She rushed into the water as though to throw off the strain of the journey and plunged in right among the crocodiles, which are very plentiful in Lake Rudolf. Luckily they were not aggressive, but all the same we tried to scare them away. During our safari, their floating, horny shapes, silhouetted all along the shore, were to make bathing, at least for us, a dubious pleasure.

At Loyongalane we established our base camp and spent the next three days in repairing saddlery and packing donkey loads. Each load weighed approximately fifty pounds, two to each donkey. At last all was ready. There were eighteen donkeys loaded with food and camping gear, four with water containers, one riding mule for anyone who went weak or lame, and five spare donkeys. I was worried about what Elsa's attitude towards the donkeys was going to be. She watched all our repacking with restrained interest, then when we started loading she had to be chained up, for the sight of so much lovely meat braying and kicking and rolling in the sand in an endeavour to throw off unwanted burdens, with shouting Africans rushing about trying to bring order into the chaos, made her tense with excitement. The main cavalcade started off in the morning and we followed with Elsa later in the day when it was cooler. Our march was northwards along the shore line. Elsa was very excited and rushed like a puppy from one to the other of us, then she dashed in among the flocks of flamingoes, retrieved a duck we had shot, and finally went swimming in the lake, where one of us had to cover her with a rifle on account of the crocodiles. Later, when we passed a herd of camels, I was obliged to put her on the chain; this made her furious and her efforts to meet these new friends nearly pulled my arms off. I however, had no wish to see a stampeding, panic-stricken herd of camels falling over each other, bellowing, gurgling, legs intertwined, and Elsa in their midst. Fortunately these were the last livestock we met along the shore.

When night fell, we saw the fires of the camp by the lake. Again I put Elsa on the chain for fear that she might have enough energy left to chase our donkeys. When we arrived we found camp already pitched and everything laid out for dinner. While we had a belated sundowner we decided that at dawn each morning the lion party — George and I, Nuru, a Game Scout as guide — and Elsa would start off, while camp was being struck and the animals saddled and loaded.

In this way, we would benefit by the cooler hours and the pack animals would follow at a safe distance, dispensing us from any need to keep Elsa on the chain. Then about nine-thirty, we would look for a shady place where we could rest during the heat of the day and where the donkeys could get some grazing. As soon as these were sighted, we would put Elsa on the chain. In the afternoon we would reverse our routine, the donkey party leaving two hours before the lion party and pitching camp before dark. We kept to this routine during the whole safari and it worked out very well, for it kept Elsa and the donkeys apart, except during the midday rest, when she was chained up and very sleepy. As it turned out, both parties soon learned to take each other for granted and to accept that everything which formed part of the safari must be tolerated.

We found that Elsa marched well until about nine in the morning, then she began to feel the heat and kept stopping wherever a rock or bush gave shade. In the afternoon, she was reluctant to move before five; after that, once her pads had hardened, she could have gone on all night. On an average she trotted from seven to eight hours daily, and kept in wonderful condition. She dipped herself in the lake and swam as often as possible, often only six or eight feet from the crocodiles; no shouting or waving on my part would bring her back till she felt like doing so. Usually we reached camp between eight and nine in the evening; often the donkey party would fire Very lights to guide us.

The second day out we left the last human habitation behind us; it was a small fishing village of the primitive El Molo tribe. This tribe numbers about eighty souls who live almost entirely on fish, varied occasionally by crocodile and hippo meat. As a result of this badly balanced diet and of inter-breeding many of them are deformed and show signs of rickets. Perhaps also owing to malnutrition, or, more likely, to the fact that the lake water contains a high proportion of natron and other minerals, they also suffer from bad teeth and gums. They are a friendly and generous people and a stranger is always welcomed with a gift of fresh fish. Their fishing is mostly carried on by means of nets, which they make out of doum-palm fibre, the only fibre that does not rot in the alkaline water; while the giant Nile perch, which runs up to two hundred pounds and over, and crocodile and hippo, are harpooned from rafts made from three palm logs lashed roughly together. These unwieldy craft are poled along in the shallows and never venture far out for fear of the violent winds which often sweep the lake and sometimes attain a velocity of over ninety miles an hour. Indeed it is the wind which makes life thoroughly uncomfortable for any traveller in this region. It is impossible to pitch a tent, food is either blown out of the plate before one can eat it, or so covered with grit as to be inedible. Sleep is almost impossible because of the tearing gusts which fill eyes, nose and ears with sand and almost lift up the bed. Yet, in spite of these torments, the lake has real beauty in its quieter moments, and exercises a fascination difficult to describe, which makes one want to return again and again.

The first ten days took us along its shore. The country around was grim: lava, and more lava, only the consistency of the lava differed. Sometimes it was cinder-fine dust, at others sharp-edged so that our feet became sore from slipping and sliding over the uneven ground. In certain places there was deep sand, and as we waded along each step was an effort. Or again, we had to make our way across coarse grit or pebbles and at all times the hot wind blew, sapping our energy and making us feel dizzy. There was little vegetation, only a few thorny meagre plants which pricked, and razor-edged grass, which cut the skin.

To keep Elsa's paws in good condition, I had often to grease them, an act which she seemed to understand and to like. During the midday rest, I usually lay on my camp bed so as to be able to relax in more comfort than the hard pebbles provided. Elsa saw the point of this, adopted my idea and joined me. Soon I could consider myself fortunate if she left me a small corner, and sometimes I was unlucky and had to sit on the ground while she stretched herself full-length on the bed. But as a rule we curled up together on the bed, I hoping that it might not

11

break beneath our combined weight. During our long marches Nuru always carried drinking-water and a bowl for Elsa; she had her evening meal towards nine o'clock and afterwards slept heavily, tied up near my bed.

One evening we lost our way and were guided by Very lights to the camp, which we reached late at night. Elsa seemed exhausted, so I left her unchained to recover; but although she looked sleepy she suddenly rushed at full speed to the thorn enclosure in which the donkeys spent the night, and crashed through the fence in real feline style. Braying, panic and pandemonium ensued and before we could intervene, all the donkeys had bolted into the darkness. Luckily, we soon caught Elsa and I gave her a good hiding. She seemed to understand that she deserved it and, as far as she could, showed that she was sorry. I felt guilty at having underestimated her natural instinct and the tremendous temptation that a nice-smelling donkey herd must be to her, especially at an hour when the hunting spirit is most alive in wild animals.

Luckily only one poor donkey had received scratches and these were not serious. I dressed them and they soon healed, but this episode was a warning to me never to leave her unguarded.

Fish were plentiful and, as a rule, George and Julian were able to keep the camp supplied with delicious fish called giant *tilapia*, a *spécialité* unique to Lake Rudolf. These they caught either by rod or line, or by stunning them with a rifle bullet.

The Game Scouts seemed to prefer the ugly-looking cat-fish which lay in the shallows and which they were able to kill with sticks and stones. Elsa was always ready to join in the fun and sometimes she would retrieve a cat-fish, soon to drop it and wrinkle up her nose in disgust. One day we saw Nuru, who always carried a shotgun, lifting it up by the barrel and clubbing a cat-fish with it. He did this with such force that the stock split through in many places, broke and projected at right angles to the barrel. Nuru was so delighted with his cat-fish that he was quite oblivious to the damage he had done. When George pointed it out to him he replied calmly, "Oh, Mungo [God] will help you to get another gun." Elsa, however, took her revenge, for she ran off with Nuru's sandals which he had left on the shore, and galloped away with them; it was a funny sight to watch the two trying to outwit each other. In the end, the sandals were in poor shape when their owner got them back.

Before we reached Alia Bay some hundred miles to the north it was necessary to cross the long Longondoti range. In several places the hills fell straight into the lake, so the donkeys with their bulky loads had to make a detour inland, while the lion party struggled across the rocks and kept to the shore. At one point we looked like being defeated by a difficult corner, where Elsa, to wade round the point, had the choice of either jumping down a fifteen foot cliff, covered with a slippery deposit on which it was impossible for her to get any grip, to land in the shallow water below, or ambling down an equally steep rock to land in the foaming waters which shed against its foot. The water was in fact only about her own depth, but the foam made it look very dangerous and she did not know what to do. She tried every ledge of the rock, padding desperately on her small platform, bravely she jumped into the lashing waves and finally, coaxed by us, reached dry ground. It was touching to see how delighted and proud she was of her achievement and also at having pleased us.

For most of the way we had to drink and to cook with brackish lake water which, although harmless and so soft that it is beautiful for bathing and does not need soap for washing, has a disagreeable taste and tainted all our food. So it was indeed a pleasant surprise to find a little spring of fresh water at the foot of the hills called Moiti.

The route we took along the western foot of these hills had, so far as we knew, never before been travelled by a European; the few who had visited this region in the past had kept well to the east. Nine days out of Loyongalane, we camped at the northern end of the hills. As usual, we had sent a party of Game Scouts ahead to spy out the country and keep a lookout for poachers. Early in the afternoon they returned and reported seeing a large body of men in canoes. The only tribe on the lake which possesses roper dug-out canoes is the Galubba, a turbulent people, well supplied with rifles, who constantly carry out raids from across the Ethiopian border into our territory, looting and murdering. The band which the Scouts had seen might be either a raiding party, or a poaching and fishing expedition. In any case, they had no right to be there. Elsa and I remained in camp, with four Game Scouts armed with rifles to protect us, while the rest of the party went off to reconnoitre.

When they had reached the top of a ridge which overlooked the bay, they saw three canoes with twelve men on board, close in shore, paddling in the direction of our camp. However, they at once spotted our party, so that by the time George and the other men had reached the water's edge the canoes were a good two hundred yards out, making for a small island and paddling madly. They did not appear to have firearms, though, of course, they might have had rifles concealed in the canoes. Looking through glasses, George saw a body of at least forty men on the island and several canoes drawn up on its shore. He watched the canoes reach the beach and an obviously exicted group gather round them. Then — since without a boat there was nothing much that they could do — the party returned to camp. We packed up at once and moved to the bay below, as close as possible to the island. That night, extra sentries were posted and every man slept with his rifle, loaded, beside him. When dawn broke, we saw that the island was deserted. Evidently the Galubba had not liked the look of us and had decided to get away during the hours of darkness, in spite of a heavy gale which had blown up during the night. To make sure that they really had gone, George sent patrols along the shore. Soon after sun-up we saw a multitude of vultures and marabous descending upon the island; this led us to suppose that the Galubba had been on a poaching and fishing expedition and had no doubt killed several hippo, on the remains of which the vultures and storks had come to feast.

At about eleven in the morning two canoes suddenly issued out of a dense belt of reeds, to the south of the camp, and made for open water. To discourage them, George put a few bullets across their bows, which sent them back into the reeds in a hurry. He then sent some Scouts to try to make contact with the Galubba and persuade them to come ashore. But, although the Scouts managed to get within hailing distance, the poachers would not respond and retreated farther into the swamp. Throughout the day, we could see their heads bobbing above the reeds to inspect us. We estimated that there were four canoes in the reeds, probably stragglers from the main body. Since it was impossible to reach them, George thought the next best thing was to encourage them to make for home so, as soon as it was dark, he fired tracer bullets and a few Very lights at intervals over the swamp.

By now our supplies were running low and it was time to turn back. As it turned out, the first part of the safari was luxury compared to the second because we had had plenty of water from the lake. Now, instead of retracing our steps, we decided to take an inland route. Goite, our Turkana guide, did not seem very sure of the way and, what was worse, was not certain whether we should find water when needed. For the region was dependent on waterholes, which at this dry season were few and far between. George, however, calculated that we should never be more than a long day's march from the lake so, if pressed for water, could make for it. We missed the cooling breeze off the lake, and there were times when we felt nearly dehydrated by the heat. The country here was even more desolate than the one we had passed through on our outward march. There was nothing but lava, so, understandably, there was little game and no population. Luckily we had bought sheep at Loyongalane and, though Elsa's living larder was rapidly dwindling away, it was sufficient to solve her feeding problem. But all of us lost most of our surplus weight during this time. Our march back was rapid, because the donkeys were now carrying less weight and, much of the route being waterless, we had to do longer marches.

After eighteen days we got back to Loyongalane and spent three days there, refitting, mending saddlery, etc., in preparation for the second part of our safari, the ascent of Mount Kulal. This mountain which lies twenty miles east of the lake rises out of the surrounding desert to about 7,500 feet, catches all the moisture from the monsoon on its upper levels and has developed rich forest on its summit. It is a narrow volcano, twenty-eight miles long, with a crater in the centre about four miles wide. This crater is split in half and divides the mountain into a southern and northern portion. There is a theory that, after the volcano became extinct, an earthquake broke Kulal into deep crevasses, and cracked the awe-inspiring fissure through the crater. Its smooth walls are split like the peel of an orange when it is cut. These deep ridges fall 3,000 feet from the crater's lip. At the bottom, invisible from the top, is a gorge called Il Sigata which leads into the heart of the mountain. Its sheer walls tower hundreds of feet high and the opening is in places so narrow that the sky above is only visible through a slit. We tried to explore the gorge, entering from the only accessible opening, which lies towards the eastern foot of Kulal, but we were defeated, after a few hours, by huge rocks and deep waterpools which blocked the way.

To cover the mountain thoroughly it was necessary to go up one half, down again to the bottom and then up the second part.

The object of the safari was to find out whether the game on the mountain was holding its own, or decreasing as a result of poaching, by comparing the present situation with that found by George, when twelve years previously he had last visited the area. In particular, we wanted to investigate the state of the greater kudu.

18

Kulal does not look impressive from below: a long stretching mountain, with broad ridges leading to its summit; as we were to discover, these ridges became so narrow that the approaches for pack animals are very limited.

The first day's march, over thickly strewn lava boulders, was extremely arduous for laden animals. Later the ascent up knife-edged ridges was, in many places, very difficult to negotiate and we found it necessary to offload the donkeys and manhandle the loads.

On the second night we were two-thirds of the way up the mountain and camped in a precipitous valley choked with lava boulders, near a little spring which provided just sufficient water for one animal at a time. It was very late before the last donkey had its much needed drink. This was one of the few waterholes on Kulal and so it was naturally a vital centre for the Samburu tribesmen who bring their livestock up to Kulal in the dry season.

It must have been difficult for Elsa, to meet these large herds of camels, cattle, goats and sheep around this and other waterholes; but she was intelligent and good-natured and, apparently realising what the situation was, she put up with the tantalising smell of these animals which often passed within a few feet of her. On these occasions we put her on the chain but she made no attempt to attack and only wanted to get away from the dust and the noise.

The route up Kalal was steep and the climate

became arctic as we reached the higher slopes. We walked over saddles, crossed deep ravines and struggled along precipices. Here the bush was lower and then it changed into beautiful alpine flora.

Next morning we reached the top of Kulal; it was a relief to be walking on more or less even ground. Camp was pitched in a beautiful little glade, close to a rather muddy spring, fouled by the cattle of the Samburu tribesmen. Their astonishment was great at finding a nearly fully grown lion in our camp.

In the dense forest belt near the top on most mornings there was heavy mist, so we made a blazing cedar-log fire to keep us warm. At night it was so cold that I kept Elsa in my small tent, made her a nest of lichen and covered her with my warmest blanket. Most of my night was usually spent replacing it as it fell off continually and Elsa would begin to shiver. When I did this, she always licked my arm. She never made any attempt to tear the tent and get out; on the contrary she remained in it long after her usual waking hour, snuggling in her nest, where she was warm and cosy, whereas outside there was a blasting gale and wet mist. But as soon as the sun had cleared the fog away, she came to life and enjoyed the invigorating mountain air. Indeed she loved the place, for the ground was soft and cool, the forest gave thick shade and there were plenty of buffalo droppings to roll in.

Because of the shade and altitude, walking

during the heat of the day was no effort in this region, and she was able to explore the mountain with us. She watched the eagles circling high in the air and was annoyed by the crows who followed her and dived low to tease her, and on one occasion woke a buffalo out of his sleep and chased him. She had excellent scent, hearing and eyesight and never lost herself in the thick undergrowth. One afternoon we were following the advance party, which had gone well ahead through the forest, and Elsa was ambushing us in a playful way from behind every bush, when suddenly, from the direction in which she had just disappeared, we heard a panic-stricken bray. A moment later a donkey broke through the wood with Elsa clinging to it and mauling it. Fortunately the forest was so thick that they could not go very fast, so we quickly reached the struggling pair and gave Elsa the beating we thought she deserved; she had never done anything of this sort before, and I was very much alarmed, for I had prided myself on the fact that she always obeyed my call instead of chasing an animal unduly. But again I could only blame myself for not putting Elsa on the lead.

One day we stood on the lip of the crater which divides the mountain and looked across to the northern part which was not more than four miles distant, though we knew that it would take us a full two days' march to get there. Nonchalantly Elsa balanced herself on the edge of the two thousand foot precipice, a sight which nearly sent me into hysterics. But animals seem to have no fear of heights. The following day we descended and the safari reached the mouth of the greal Il Sigata gorge; there we made camp.

During the day thousands of camels, goats and sheep herded by tall, good-looking Rendile tribesmen, passed by on their way to water four miles up the gorge. They were followed by women leading strings of camels tied nose to tail loaded with water containers. These held about six gallons each and were made of closely woven fibre. We walked up the cleft, or rather, literally *into* the mountain. The floor of the gorge is a dry watercourse which, for about five miles, rises gently between towering walls which climb sharply on each side; when one penetrates still farther these walls attain some fifteen hundred feet in height and are sheer precipice. In places the gorge is so narrow that two laden camels cannot pass abreast and the cliffs overhang, shutting out the sky. We went far beyond the watering place of the stock, where the trickle of water becomes a sizable brook, with many rockbound pools of clear water. Finally we were halted by a sheer fall of thirty feet. Herbert, who is a mountaineer, managed to get up it only to find another high fall beyond.

The Il Sigata used to be a favourite place for poachers since it was easy to lie in wait for animals going to water. In fact, once an animal had entered the trap it was doomed, since there was no way out except that which led past the waiting hunters.

From Il Sigata it was a day and a half's march to the top of the northern massif, which we found to be more thickly inhabited by the Samburu and their livestock than the southern part. So Elsa's liberty had here to be curtailed.

We saw little game. Buffalo, of which there used to be a lot, had not, we were told, visited the northern end of the mountain for the last six years. There were also no greater kudu to be seen, though we observed the spoor of a few. George considered that this absence of game was probably due to the great number of Samburu stock which were eating up the grazing and rapidly denuding the mountain.

Owing to sharp broken lava, the descent to Loyongalane was a most exhausting struggle and not even the superb view of Lake Rudolf far below, reflecting the setting sun in its lead-coloured surface against deep indigo hills and an orange-yellow sky, could compensate us for our tumbles, which grew more and more frequent.

Elsa kept looking back at the mountain and cool forest and started to run towards them, so we had to put her on the chain.

Towards nightfall we lost our way in the dark. Elsa lay down every few yards, making it very plain that she had had enough. Although she was nearly full-grown, she still liked to suck my thumb when she felt nervous, and there was a lot of thumb-sucking that night. At last some tracer bullets, fired by the advance party, guided us to the camp. When we staggered in after our nightmare march, Elsa refused food and only wanted to be near me. I also could not eat from exhaustion and could well imagine the effort it had cost Elsa to carry on. She, of course, could not know why we were doing such a senseless thing as to struggle across sharp lava at night, and it was only her affection for us and her trust that kept her going. In spite of the hardships she had endured on this safari, in the course of which she had walked well over three hundred miles, the bond between us had only been strengthened. As long as she was with us and knew herself to be loved and secure, she was happy. It was very touching to watch her trying to control the strong forces within her and to adapt herself to our way of life in order to please us. Her good-natured temperament was certainly due in part to her character, but part too may have come from the fact that neither force nor frustration was ever used to adapt her to our way of life. For we tried by kindness alone to help her to overcome the differences that lie between our two worlds.

In natural life, as long as he finds food, a lion does not wander over great distances, and certainly Elsa had seen more of the world than she would have done living with a pride. Yet she knew her home, and whenever we returned from safari she would go straight back to her habits and usual routine.

The Lady of Leisure

Helen Dore Boylston

wo horses, with rider, came up the highway by the pasture, their hoofs clopping in cheerful rhythm on the hard surface. Molly ran along with fence beside them, her head and tail very high and her black body shining in the sun. If it had not been for the fence she could have outrun them easily. But the fence was there. Molly watched them until they grew small in the distance, then she swung around and ambled slowly back to the end of the pasture.

She was very clean. No speck of dust lurked beneath the sheen of her coat. Her mane and tail were free of burs and tangles. Her hoofs had been newly oiled.

At the margin of the frog pond she paused. Her ears pricked forward and she *wooshed* softly through her nose. The water was brackish and muddy and covered with a green slime. Molly never drank there, preferring the spring under the apple trees, but now she went unhesitatingly to the water and splashed in. When the gray ooze reached her knees she turned sidewise to the bank and lay down with a grunt. She rolled, floundered up, turned, and rolled again. When at last she rose, dripping, the cool clay lay thickly on her back and sides and plastered her legs. A lily pad was caught in her tail and her mane was festooned with wreaths of green slime. Molly shook herself gingerly and clambered up the bank.

A cowpath wandered through a tangle of weeds and long grass and straggled away under the apple trees, to the barn. It was soft under foot and the grasses were sweet and juicy. Molly browsed a little here and there and snuffed at the clover-scented wind.

The barn windows were open and Molly stopped, very casually, beneath one. She waited for a moment, and then, hearing the swish of a tail inside, laid her ears flat to her head and snorted. There was a sound of trampling, and Molly wheeled. But when the brown head and wondering eyes of Governor, the three-year-old gelding, appeared in the window, Molly was standing quietly with drooping head and eyes half closed. A wisp of green slime dangled from one ear. Her back was just within reach of Governor's nose.

He stretched his head out of the window, all eagerness, and sniffed at Molly's wet flank. Then he sprank back squealing. Molly's heels had missed his nose by a scant half inch. She lashed out again, her hoofs ringing against the side of the barn. There was a splintering crash inside, more trampling, another crash, and a long enraged squeal. Molly kicked at the barn once more.

Governor returned the kick with fury.

"*Molly!*"

It was Bruce. Molly moved away from the window and stared over the pasture gate at the overalled figure in the garage doorway. The clamor in the barn ceased. Molly's eyes shone with honesty. Her ears stood up in astonished innocence. Her little forefeet were planted close together. She waited primly, clay daubed and virtuous. Bruce grinned and after a moment went back into the garage.

The wind whispered in the oaks and an acorn fell with a sharp thwack on the barn roof. Governor was silent. A leaf blew across the barnyard and a puff-ball of a kitten rushed after it, tail twirking. A sound of hammering came from the garage. Molly stretched out a soft black nose and fumbled with the wooden button that fastened the gate. It did not move easily and it was splintery. Molly tried her teeth on it and at last it turned. She pushed at the gate, but nothing happened.

The hammering in the garage stopped and Bruce appeared suddenly in the door. Molly drowsed hastily. Bruce crossed to the house, got something from the back porch, and returned to the garage.

After a minute Molly tried the gate again. It refused to open. She nosed around the latch and presently encountered the cold iron of a hook. It was a fairly loose hook. Molly worked at it with short lifting drives of her nose until it fell, tapping, against the gate, which opened a little way of itself, and then caught against the sod. Molly scraped through, broke into a gallop, and thundered across the lawn to the driveway. She clattered before the door of the garage.

Bruce ran out, grimly silent.

Molly cavorted in front of him but not too near. She plunged and whirled and rocked and plunged, her hoofs beating a tattoo on the gravel. Her wet mane flapped against her neck. Lumps of clay fell from her. The lily pad in her tail swung in lively circles behind her. With a final superb fling of heels into the air she raced down the slope to the gorge, jumped lightly across the brook, and began the climb up the steep wooded hill on the other side.

Bruce followed, panting. He would try to cut her off and head her back. Molly kept well ahead of him. She wound in and out among the oaks, stopping now and again to look back and see what progress Bruce was making. He wasn't making much. The hill was very steep.

Molly continued on, up, her tail switching vigorously from side to side. Bruce was crashing through the underbrush below her as she came out on the crest of the ridge. She tore off a mouthful of leaves from a passing branch and stopped to wait. Bruce was nowhere in sight.

Down the ridge on the other side the valley began in green and gold and melted away into the plum-colored hills. Their outlines wavered in the heat, but the breath of the wind on Molly's back was cool and fresh. She munched oak leaves in placid contentment and watched the cloud shadows trailing their purple across the floor of the valley. On the tiny yellow thread of the highway a car glittered for a moment and was gone. Its hum came back on the wind. A squirrel swore with violence from a branch above her head. There was silence below.

Molly moved off the path to the edge of the ravine and looked down. The oak leaves dropped unnoticed from her mouth. Bruce was going back down the hill!

Molly stared after him, round-eyed. Then she lifted a forefoot and stamped once. Her nostrils vibrated with the explosion of her breath.

The path curved sharply and dipped down into the ravine. Molly stepped down cautiously, threw herself back on her haunches, forefeet braced, and slid, plowing up the matting of leaves and leaving a furrow of black loam behind her. One leap and she was across the brook. Her hoofs rang on the flagstone steps that led up the bank to the side of the garage. Bruce was inside. She could hear him moving. On the lawn she stopped, ready to run, but Bruce did not come out.

Molly bit off the top of a nearby hollyhock, mumbled it and let it drop. She moved forward along the side of the garage to where, by stretching her neck to the uttermost, she could just see the doorsill. There was no one there. She stamped. Silence. Briskly, with a determined switch of the tail, Molly tramped across a flower bed and went up to the door. The inside of the garage was dark after the bright sunlight, and Molly blinked and stretched and peered, but she saw nothing but a stairway, outlined against a dusty windowpane. It was too much. Molly took one more step and put her head in at the door.

The rope dropped without a sound, settling neatly behind her ears. Molly knew better than to fight it. She followed Bruce across the yard and through the pasture gate. She watched while he buttoned the gate, hooked it, and bound the hook in place with wire. He went away. That was that.

There was nothing to do. The early windfall apples didn't taste right. The grass was dusty. The sun was hot, and the drying clay on her back and sides was beginning to be itchy. Molly knelt, rolled experimentally once or twice, got a good swing, and rolled completely over. Triumphant, she rolled all the way back, and rose in a shower of dust and twigs.

There was nothing left to do but stand. Molly stood, growing sleepy. At last a hen wandering across the pasture caught her eye. She brightened. There were more hens scratching around in the grass under the willows. Molly's ears went back, her head lifted, and her tail went up. She galloped down the flock, and it scattered, fluttering and squawking. Molly dashed back and forth, her teeth snapping, turning back the stragglers, and bunching them together. She drove them into the corner where the fence joined the barn.

It wasn't a very good place. One hen skimmed under the fence and escaped. Molly nagged with teeth and heels and drove the rest, a compact and jittering little group, round to the back of the barn. There was no good place there to hold them either. She headed them down the wagon road toward the orchard in a shrieking procession that sowed the ruts with feathers. Molly capered behind.

"Molly! For God sake!"

Molly veered away from the flock and thundered past them, mane and tail streaming. Under the apple trees she stopped and swung around to look back, neck arched and head high. Bruce was climbing slowly back over the fence. Molly snorted.

When he had gone Molly cropped a little grass, but languidly. It was too dusty. She knocked a fly off her foreleg with her nose. It returned and buzzed about her. Molly stood waiting, listening to it, her eyes furious. It lit on her shoulder. Molly snapped, and the fly dropped to the ground.

The shadows were growing long down the hillside at the head of the ravine, and swarms of gnats jigged about her ears. It would soon be time to eat. Molly turned suddenly and trotted back to the barn. The door was open and the sweet musty smell of the hay blew out upon her. She stepped across the threshold and went straight to the door of the feed room. It was not that she expected to get it open, these days, but she

31

could always try. She tried. Miracle of miracles, it opened! Someone had left off the wire which had held it fast for a year, against all Molly's attempts.

The top of the feed box was up!

Molly's eyes bulged. She took one step farther in and buried her nose in the whispering oats. In the loft overhead the hay ticked faintly. A mouse ran along a beam and paused to look, bright-eyed and trembling. From somewhere came the thin mewing of new kittens. Governor stamped in his stall. Molly ate intensely, lifting her head only at rare intervals to munch more leisurely. A fly, caught in a spider web by the window, droned endlessly. The line of oats against the side of the feed box sifted lower and lower.

When it was impossible to crowd in another oat Molly raised her head and sighed, a gusty sigh of repletion. She backed out of the feed room a little awkwardly and went out into the barnyard and down the orchard road. The grasses brushed her knees and from force of habit she bit off a mouthful, but she chewed without swallowing and without interest.

The spring lay crystal clear under the trees, the green foliage mirrored in its heart. Molly lowered her head and drank for a long time, sucking up the water in great thirsty gulps. The coolness flowed around her nostrils and down her dusty throat. She lifted her head and stood for a moment, motionless. Then she drank again.

She felt a little heavy and cold inside when she at last stopped drinking, and she turned away from the spring with an effort. A strange sharp pain was beginning in her middle. It darted around, stabbing her, and Molly bit at her side. She heard Bruce's shout from the window of the feed room, but it was too much trouble to dodge when he ran down the road, a halter in his hand. He seemed agitated. Molly felt the agitation in his hands when he slopped the halter over her head.

He led her gently back to the barn, tied her by the door, and stood looking at her. "Oh, Molly, Molly! You've killed yourself!" he said. Molly rolled an eye at him. She was very uncomfortable. He touched her side and she flinched. Bruce went away through the barn, running.

Molly's head hung nearly to her knees.

Bruce returned presently and paced back and forth beside her. He usually moved rather slowly, but now he walked with quick short steps and he watched her sharply. It was irritating, and Molly felt uneasy. But the pain in her middle seemed to be going away. She hadn't that heavy sensation any more either.

A car roared out in front of the barn and then stopped roaring. A long narrow man came through the back door of the barn with a bag in his hand. Molly stiffened. She knew him. He was the one who had pried her mouth open once and had rasped at her back teeth most unpleasantly. The pain in her inside was practically gone now.

The long man and Bruce were both looking at her and their voices rose and fell. Molly switched her tail uneasily. The bag was on the ground and it had an evil smell. The long man went to it and took out a bottle. His movements were unhurried as he approached Molly and his touch on her neck was sure and kind. Molly relaxed a little. He spoke to her and his tone was light. It had been like that before. Molly jerked her head away from his hands but they followed her. There was no escape. Molly stood, rigid and motionless.

It took only a few seconds. The stuff burned in her throat for a short time, but that was all. Bruce untied her and let her go free. They watched her as she turned away and stood quietly at a little distance from them. She was still breathing hard and she was prepared to run if they came toward her, but they didn't. She rambled across the barnyard to a clump of grass and picked at it. She would have gone down to the end of the pasture, but they couldn't catch her now anyway, and she hated to miss anything.

They stayed there for a long time, just waiting, and not doing anything at all, except once, when Molly considered rolling. Then they both ran toward her. But when she scrambled up they only stared at her, their mouths making little round holes in their faces.

The sun went down behind the hill, leaving it black against the lemon-yellow sky. A smell of wood smoke and damp earth drifted down the breeze. Across the fields a whippoorwill called.

Suddenly Molly flung up her head. She wheeled and raced to the end of the pasture, circled, and raced back, pounding up to Bruce with her ears flattened and her eyes rolling viciously.

The long man sprang for the safety of the barn door, but Bruce didn't move. A slow grin spread across his face. He held out his hand and Molly dropped her nose into it. The long man shook his head, laughing, picked up his bag, and vanished into the darkness. The car roared again and a finger of light swept across the willows.

Molly tossed her head. Very gently she reached down and took Bruce's sleeve into her mouth. A long-drawn loop of sound came up Wolf Creek — a fox hound trying his voice — and a rabbit leaped out of a briar patch and fled, zig-zagging down the orchard road, its white tuft of tail bobbing in the starlight. Bruce's other hand crept up Molly's cheek, patting and patting in quick little movements.

"Come, Molly."

Molly drew a deep breath. It had been a very dull day. She rubbed her face against Bruce's sleeve and then, shoulder to shoulder, they crossed the yard and went into the warm darkness of the barn.

A Hymn To Hawgs*

Louis Bromfield

hoever has really looked into the eye of a shrewd old sow should feel humility. It is a bright clear eye, more like the eye of a human than the eye of any other animal. It looks at you quite directly, even with what might be described as a piercing gaze. The look sizes you up, appraises you and leaves you presently with the impression that the old sow has indeed a very low opinion of you, an opinion tempered by scorn and contempt and perhaps even a little animosity. Clearly she does not think that you amount to very much and that, given a difficult situation, she could cope with it far better than you could do. It is as if she said, "You think you can shut me up and confine me. Well, that's what you think! Ha! Ha! and again Ha! Ha!" And any farmer knows what she is thinking — that if she really wants to get out she'll find a way. Sometimes, I have a feeling that she is thinking, "You think you know how to manage me and bring up my litters with all

*This is the eleventh chapter of Louis Bromfield's *Animals and Other People*.

36

your disinfectants, your heat lamps, your violet rays, your antibiotics, your supplements, your inoculations, your vaccinations. Just let me alone and give me my freedom and I won't have any troubles nor will the pigs I feed."

Yet she can be friendly too and even understanding, as any farmer knows when a seven-hundred-pound sow comes running to have her back scratched. You don't have to scratch her back a dozen or a score of times. Once is enough and she gets the idea and after that she'll always be on hand when you enter the field. She may be using you and undoubtedly knows that she is, and there *may* be some affection involved, but I doubt that she ever really loses her scorn for you. In some ways, about many basic and fundamental things she knows, both by instinct and intelligence, quite a lot of things you don't know.

Animals at Malabar are likely to be well treated and most of them sooner or later come within the category of pets and sometimes very troublesome pets. Alton knows all his cows, what each one likes and doesn't like, the order in which they prefer to enter the milk parlor, which cows have best friends, which ones are bullies and which ones are timid and retiring. He knows the bad temper of Inez who just never could be milked without being tied down and the comic ways of Lauren who on more than one occasion was found shaking a barn cat in her mouth when the impudent cat attempted to walk across her parcel of feed. And he knows old Mary whom he rides home from pasture to the milking parlor as if she were a horse. There are no ill-treated animals at Malabar for the first consideration of employment in connection with any livestock is that the man must be able to imagine himself a cow, a pig or a chicken and so to know what would make that particular animal or bird happy and comfortable. And so you get to know animals pretty well and the more you know them the greater respect you have both for them and for God and Nature. The people who think all cows are exactly alike are merely stupid or ignorant; cows can sometimes be as individual as the people of any group and not infrequently more interesting.

But pets can be tiresome too, like the hand-raised lambs at Malabar who, growing up with the boxer dogs, came to believe they were dogs and not sheep at all. The most troublesome of all farm pets at Malabar were the goats which persecuted all of us and all visitors until they had to be sent away to Italian families who know better how to cope with them. If there is any animal more difficult to confine or to shut out than a pig, it is a goat. Both are certainly gifted with great powers of logic, reflection, judgment, deduction and mockery, qualities which man has usually and often mistakenly reserved for himself.

Out of an excessively busy life, pigs have cost me more time than fishing or golf or any of the usual activities in which men are accustomed to find relaxation, amusement and exasperation. When I am really busy, I dare not visit the pig lots, for inevitably I find myself standing there for indefinite amounts of time, watching the little pigs horsing about with their own games, listening to the conversation and gossip of the old sows, watching the pigs line up to feed, even on occasion watching a new litter arrive in this world to get up immediately on their feet, shake themselves and run around to their ouside source of supply in the new world which they have entered only a moment before. If I had ever doubted a pig's capacity to think things out, I lost it forever when I discovered one pig's trick of escaping through what was by every reasonable evidence a thoroughly pigtight fence.

He was one of some two hundred half-grown pigs enclosed for feeding in a ten-acre lot. Every day, week after week, this particular pig got outside the fence and no one was ever able to discover how he accomplished this feat, until late one afternoon as I stood in the far end of the field I saw what I found difficult to believe. At the opposite end of the field I saw a pig actually *climbing* the fence.

The fence was a typical hog fence with graduated openings from those too small for even the smallest pig to negotiate at the very bottom to openings at the top that were reasonably large. But the designer of the fence had reckoned without this special pig who possessed advanced powers of reasoning. He had discovered that the higher the openings were from the ground the larger they were and he managed to climb high enough to reach an opening big enough for him to slip through. With the greatest dexterity he worked his way upward until he reached an opening of sufficient size and then slipped down on the opposite side of the fence.

I watched the whole operation, even to his scuttling across the road into a neighboring cornfield where he was just able to reach up and drag down the ears of corn. I must add that so great was my weakness for pigs and my admiration for this particular pig, that I never betrayed the fact that I had learned his secret. The end of the story was that eventually he ate himself out of his freedom, for each day he grew fatter, heavier and larger in girth, until the day came when he was unable to find an opening large enough to permit his escape or to reach the top of the fence without falling backward again into the prison of his hog lot.

And there was the mentally handicapped pig who never did learn to use the self-feeder and who, as a consequence, developed a psychopathic and extremely bad and aggresive disposition. For the benefit of the city-bred who may be reading, a self-feeder is constructed with a kind of trap door which the average pig, or indeed every other pig I have ever known save this one, learns very quickly to raise by putting his snout beneath it and forcing it upward. Once he has his snout inside the feeder, the trap door rests on his snout or rather his forehead until he has eaten his fill. Then, as he backs away, the trap door falls down again by gravity and the feeder is closed. Just why this trap door is necessary or why it is supposed to be useful I do not know, unless some bright fellow believed that it saved feed, although any farmer knows that any good healthy pig allows no feed to be wasted whether it is in the feeder or outside on the ground. The self-feeder, however unnecessary, has been forced into the consciousness of the average farmer, like many another dubious agricultural equipment product, by high-pressure advertising and the general pressure in colleges, industrial plants and other places where new gadgets are constantly being thought up for farmers to buy. At this stage in the Malabar program, I was still naïve enough and inexperienced enough to believe that one could not raise hogs without a self-feeder, an idea which I long ago abandoned, for we at Malabar have never belonged to the school which invested in gadgets simply to make a hog lot or a building look "prettier."

In any case, we had in one lot of hogs this special backward pig who never learned to raise the trap door with his snout. He always took the lid between his teeth and raised it and always as he let loose of it the trap door fell shut again before he could get his snout under it to hold it open. I have watched him try again and again countless times to perform the operation so rapidly that he could outwit the falling trap door.

He never won and so in order to get his fill he turned, like many a delinquent and mental deficient, into a bully. He would approach the self-feeder, take up a stand and allow some innocent good-natured intelligent fellow pig to open the trap door with his snout. Then with a combination of a slashing and shouldering side movement, the backward pig would shove the innocent aside and thrust his snout into the opening to feed his fill. The odd thing was that he never learned, either by reasoning and logic as did our fence-climbing friend or simply by observing how the other pigs did it. He just never learned. But I think we need not be too critical or scornful of him; I have known a great many fellow men who suffered from the same handicap. He was the dumbest pig I have ever known and in fact the only "dumb" pig with whom I have ever been acquainted. He was also a bully, like many a human bully with a strong sense of inferiority — like Mussolini or Molotov.

Much discussion and argument has been spent regarding the ability or inability of animals to communicate with each other, but nowadays I believe there are few people or even experts who any longer doubt that animals have means of communication which are quite beyond our understanding. Turn a bull into the far side of a field away from a herd of cows and heifers with a hill or a woodlot in between. All he need do — and he always does it — is to give one loud bellow and all the cows and heifers, tails high in the air, leaping and cavorting coquettishly regardless of age, will come running. What man has ever had the eloquence or the blarney to command so easily such a harem? Beside the bull Don Juan was merely a piker.

Or what about the cantankerous cow who manages to ride down a fence or find an opening and who with a single bellow of peculiar volume and timbre will bring all the rest of the herd to join her in breaking out?

Again and again I have seen one of my dogs soundlessly communicate to the others that there is a strange dog on the place or in a visiting car which must be put in place or given the bum's rush. I have seen one of them tell the others that Lester the Cat was behind the greenhouse and in a vulnerable situation. A certain kind of bark surely communicates at least a certain variety or kind of information. But among all animals there is none which has such a variety of sounds designed obviously for the purposes of communication and even gossip as the pig.

Waste your time as I do, leaning on the fence, and you will see among the pigs everything from a directors' meeting to a ladies' discussion of the attractions of the visiting boar. There are the sounds which a sow makes when she feels it is time to feed her young, and there are the frightful squeals of discontent from her pigs when she will not give in to their demands and lie on her side to let them feed. And there is what is distinctly the most ferocious name-calling that can occur during the equivalent of a hair-pulling match between two old sows. Pick up a small pig and he will let out the most hair-raising shrieks for help that will bring running not only his own mother but all the sows in the neighborhood. He is the most blatant of small frauds, for the minute you put him down again on the ground the shrieks stop instantly and are replaced by the pleasant "oink! oink!" noises of a contented small pig. Come unexpectedly upon an old sow and her litter in a swamp or a thicket and, especially if there are dogs along, she will give the signal of alarm, gathering all the litter around her where they form a circle with all their small noses pointed outward like a Macedonian phalanx both for attack and defense, making at the same time the most threatening and bloodcurdling sounds.

These sounds made among pigs are not merely signals or crude symbols of speech. Observe a gathering of sows when they are not eating or feeding their pigs but are merely having a good gossip. The hog wallow is clearly a favorite spot for woman's talk — the kind of talk you might hear on "Ladies' Night" in a Turkish bath. There is a whole variety of sounds including not only pitch but intonation and the actual formation of given sounds. I once assisted at such a conversation among a group of sows who came to give advice at the birth of a new litter by one of their number.

The sow who was brought to bed was either taken unexpectedly in labor or was a plain fool, which is the more likely situation. She chose or (like a woman giving birth in a taxi) failed to start for the shelter of the barn in time and consequently had her litter in the middle of the hog lot on a day of great heat and blazing sunshine, something no sensible sow would dream of doing. In any case, the family came rapidly, all ten of them, popping up on their wobbly feet and going around at once to feed at the waiting cafeteria. The spectacle attracted several other sows who stood about clearly making comments of a disapproving nature. When the last of the pigs had entered this world, or, as the fashionable birth announcements in the French newspapers put it, "were given the light of day," the sow stood up and apparently either became aware of her foolishness in having her pigs in the midst of a hot field or heeded the reproaches and advice of the surrounding sows. She attempted to induce the pigs to follow her toward the shade of the near-by barn with no success, for the pigs were still so new to this world that, beyond the instinct of eating, they were without adjustment and clearly did not yet understand pig language. She made an astonishing variety of sounds, in which her friends joined — sounds that were now cajoling, now scolding, now clearly meant as commands. But the tiny shaky pink pigs merely wobbled about, aimlessly. Then abandoning temporarily all hope of getting them into the barn, she relaxed for a time and held what was clearly a discussion of her labor pains and prenatal condition with her friends. There was the most astonishing variety of sounds and intonations in which the other sows, their heads close together, all joined. This continued for some time with what was growing animation, for all the world like a group of women during a bridge game which has been interrupted by the more absorbing topic of whose labor pains were longest and hardest. Then after a time she returned to her futile efforts to herd the tiny pigs into the shade.

Nothing came of her efforts and I went to get Bob and Carl to help rescue the pigs. They were of the Yorkshire breed, naturally white in color and at this stage a delicate pearly color subject dangeriously to heat and to sunburn. By the time I returned, the other sows had apparently exhausted the subject of labor pains and wandered away, possibly with the conviction that their friend was a damned fool and there was nothing to be done about it.

To rescue the pigs and get them into the shade of the barn, we used age-old tactics well known to the experienced hog farmer. Bob fetched a bushel basket and put it over the head of the sow so that she would not attack. The bushel basket blinds her and her only impulse is to back away constantly from it to free herself, and as a sow can back only slowly, a fairly agile man can keep her under control for a limited length of time. While Bob controlled the sow, Carl scooped up the little pink pigs into two pails and headed as fast as possible for the barn, but like all small pigs they set up, even at their tender age which was not more than an hour, the most ungodly racket, bringing a whole troop of sympathetic mothers to the rescue. At the same time, the mother, excited by their devilish and unwarranted shrieks of distress, leapt forward to the fray instead of backing up as she was supposed to do, demolished the bushel basket, and set out in hot pursuit of Carl. Carl is a big and long-legged fellow but never has he made such speed as during that hundred-yard dash for the barn pursued by a whole troop of Yorkshire Niobes and Boadiceas, each one a sympathizing mother. The sounds they made were terrifying but Carl won his race. He managed to make the inside of the barn and drop both pails and clear the barrier of a feeding creep with scarcely an inch between the seat of his Levis and the gnashing of teeth of the outraged sows. Both Bob and myself had long ago cleared the fence, barbed wire and all.

At the same moment the wretched little devils spilled helter-skelter out of their baskets, stopped their shrieks and immediately began "oink-oinking!" in the most contented possible fashion while what was clearly a conversation of indignation and outrage broke out among the sympathetic sows.

Such an example as this taxicab foolishness is rare indeed among sows, but this one was only young and perhaps a little giddy and like many a young woman merely stayed out a little too long.

Few animals and indeed few people are quite as shrewd or gifted with such a remarkable natural instinct as a sow — instinct with regard to what to eat and how much, how to forage off the countryside, how to find shelter for herself and her young. Give a sow her freedom and she can take her litter right across the country feeding off the land. No animal has a diet so varied and so closely resembling that of man. The pig is both herbivorous and carnivorous. Our own pigs make most of their growth off alfalfa, brome grass and ladino clover. No animal, including man, can find a greater delight in good sweet corn, tomatoes, cantaloupe, cucumbers and watermelon, as many a farmer has long since discovered to his sorrow when the hogs raid the farm gardens. Like man, pigs thoroughly enjoy meat, eggs, cheese, milk and will even on occasion go off on hunting expeditions and bring home chickens, ducks and occasionally unwary wild animals.

But man and in particular the mean or ignorant farmer does not always give the hog or sow a chance to take care of their own comfort and needs. A hog is by nature the cleanest of animals and will never foul his own nest unless forced to do so by the laziness or ignorance of his owner. A sow, who is either properly fed or given her freedom, has never been known to eat her young. It is only the desperate sow shut into a dark and filthy sty without sufficient protein feeds and a lack of minerals which she cannot obtain by searching and rooting for them in the open field or swamp.

When we first took over the farms which now make up Malabar, we purchased the livestock as well. On one of the farms there was a sow shut up on concrete about to farrow. So bad was her forced diet owing to the ignorance of the farmer, that she was desperately tearing up the concrete with her teeth in order to obtain calcium and perhaps other minerals vital to the development of the pigs inside her.

Our own hogs are innocent of rings and their rooting activities are not worth notice; indeed the little rooting they do is good for the alfalfa, brome grass and actually stimulates their growth and increases the yield of good high protein forage.

The hog has followed man everywhere on his wildest pioneering ventures. Few frontiersmen ever set out into the wilderness without a sow and a boar pig and wherever he arrived, he had only to turn them loose to forage off the countryside until he could raise crops. Only an animal as big and as ferocious as a mountain lion or a bear was a match for the sow or boar, and even such formidable animals could never be sure of defeating the wits and the tusks of a boar or a ferocious old sow. Wherever man has gone, the pig has gone along to provide him with food, with litters which grew rapidly at very little cost or labor under adverse conditions.

And no animal has ever provided anywhere

near the variety of delicacies that can be obtained from the carcass of the hog. There is fresh pork and hams and bacon and sausage. There are pig's knuckles, and liver and headcheese and tenderloin and pork chops. Indeed less of the hog is wasted than any other animal. If I were forced to make a choice of a single meat (despite the offense such an opinion may give my beef cattle friends), it would always be pork. A good steak is fine and so is a good roast beef, but for my taste, both can become monotonous. Mutton is a meat that could best be described as "so-so." Lamb is a delicacy but one can grow sick of an unvaried diet of lamb, as many a sheepman knows.

By now it must be evident that this is one farmer who would not consider a farm a farm which did not include hogs in its program. They are the most utilitarian of animals and have justly been referred to as "mortgage raisers," even when uneconomically and badly raised and fed.

Much as I love pigs, much as they entertain me, there is one warning I would issue against them. Never take a pig as a pet. The dangers are far greater than the menace of a good bite from an old sow or being gashed by the long tusks of a boar. There are two principal difficulties and dangers. In the first place no animal comes more rapidly to think that he is "people," and, worst of all, a pig grows. The cute and funny little pig who follows you everywhere "oinking" affectionately will, before you realize it, be a tremendous animal weighing six or seven hundred pounds who thinks not only that he is "people" — indeed he is absolutely sure of it and you cannot dissuade him — but also thinks he is still a very small and charming pig. No animal is more easily housebroken but never let him get his foot in the door. If, by any chance, a small chubby pig does succeed in victimizing you, harden your heart, send him or her away for breeding purposes, preferably to some utterly unknown destination. Otherwise when, out of desperation, you put an end to his existence, you will suffer for the rest of your life from remorse as a cannibal and a murderer. Look at pigs over the fence but never bring a pig into your life. You will not have a chance, for a pig is even worse than a goat when he learns that he can push you around.

From all of this the reader has perhaps gathered the belief that the writer has a higher opinion of some hogs than he has of people; in this the reader would be quite right.

The Incredible Journey*
Sheila Burnford

ver two hundred miles now lay behind them, and as a group they were whole and intact, but of the three only the cat remained unscathed. The old dog, however, still plodded cheerfully and uncomplainingly along. It was the Labrador who was in really poor condition: his once beautiful gleaming coat was harsh and staring now, his grotesquely swollen face in horrible contrast to his gaunt frame, and the pain in his infected jaw made it almost impossible for him to open his mouth, so that he was virtually starving. The other two now allowed him first access to any newly killed and bleeding animal provided by the cat, and he lived solely on the fresh blood that could be licked from the carcass.

They had slipped into a steady routine during the day; the two dogs trotting along side by side, unconcerned and purposeful, might have seemed two family pets out for a neighborhood ramble.

*This is the ninth chapter of Sheila Burnford's famous novel, about the amazing homeward journey of two dogs and a cat through 250 miles of Canadian wilderness.

They were seen like this one morning by a timber-cruising forester returning to his jeep along an old tote road deep in the Ironmouth Range. They disappeared round a bend in the distance, and, preoccupied with tree problems, he did not give them a second thought. It was with a considerable shock that he remembered them later on in the day, his mind now registering the fact that there was no human habitation within thirty miles. He told the senior forester, who roared with laughter, then asked him if he had seen any elves skipping around toadstools too?

But inevitably the time was drawing nearer when the disappearance of the animals must be uncovered, the hue and cry begin, and every glimpse or smallest piece of evidence be of value. The forester was able to turn the laugh a week later when his chance encounter was proved to be no dream.

At Heron Lake John Longridge and his brother were making plans for the last trip of the season. In England the excited Hunter family were packed in readiness for the voyage home. Mrs. Oakes was busy in the old stone house, cleaning and polishing, while her husband stacked the wood cellar.

Soon all concerned would be back where they belonged, like pieces of a jigsaw puzzle being fitted together; and soon it must be discovered that three of the pieces were missing. . . .

Sublimely unaware of the commotion and worry, tears and heartbreak that their absence would cause, the three continued on their way.

The countryside was less wild now, and once or twice they saw small lonely hamlets in the distance. The young dog resolutely avoided these, keeping always to the woods and dense bush wherever possible — much to the disgust of the old dog, who had implicit faith in the helpfulness and loving kindness of human beings. But the young dog was the leader: however longingly the bull terrier looked towards a distant curl of smoke from a chimney he must turn away.

Late one afternoon they were followed for several miles by a single timber wolf who was probably curious about the cat and was no real menace: however hungry, it would never have risked an encounter with two dogs.

Like all his kind, however, the young dog hated and feared the wolf with some deep primeval instinct which must have had its origin in those mists of time when they shared a common ancestor. He was uneasy and disturbed by the slinking gray shape that merged into the undergrowth every time he looked back to snarl at it.

Unable to shake off the hateful shadow, and aware that the sun was sinking, irritable and exhausted with pain, he chose the lesser of two evils — leaving the bush for a quiet country road with small farms scattered at lonely intervals along it. He hurried his companions on, seeking protection for the night in the form of a barn or even an open field near a farm, sensing that the wolf would not follow within sight of human habitation.

They approached a small hamlet at dusk, a few small houses clustered around a schoolhouse and a white frame church. When the young dog would have skirted this too, the old terrier suddenly turned mutinous. He was, as usual, hungry; and the sight of the warm lights streaming out from the houses convinced him that this evening there was only one sensible way of obtaining food — from the hand of a human being! His eyes brightening at the thought, he ignored the young dog's warning growl, and trotted on unheeding down the forbidden road towards the houses, his rounded porcine quarters swinging defiantly, his ears laid back in stubborn disregard.

The young dog offered no further resistance. His whole head was throbbing violently with the pain of infection from the quills, and more than anything he wanted time to scratch and scratch, to rub the burning cheek along the ground.

The rebel passed the first few cottages, so snug and inviting to his comfort-loving soul — smoke rising in the still evening air, and the reassuring smell and sounds of humans everywhere. He paused before a small white cottage, snuffling ecstatically the wonderful aroma of cooking drifting out mingled with wood smoke. Licking his chops he walked up the steps, lifted a bold demanding paw and scratched at the door, then sat down, pricking his ears expectantly.

He was not disappointed. A widening stream of light from the opening door revealed a small girl. The old dog grinned hideously in pleasure, his slanted eyes blinking strangely in the sudden light. There is little to equal a bull terrier's grin, however charmingly presented, for sheer astonishing ugliness.

There was a moment's silence, followed by an urgent wail of "Dad. . . . " Then the door slammed shut in his face. Puzzled but persistent, he scratched again, cocking his head to one side, his big triangular ears erect, listening to footsteps scurrying around within. A face appeared at the window. He barked a polite reminder. Suddenly the door was thrown open again and a man rushed out, a bucket of water in his hand, his face convulsed with fury. He hurled the water full in the face of the astonished dog, then grabbed a broom.

"Get out! Get out of here!" yelled the man, brandishing his broom so menacingly that the terrier tucked his tail between his legs and fled, soaking and miserable, towards his waiting companions. He was not afraid, only deeply offended — never in his long life had human beings reacted in such a way to his friendly overtures. Justifiable fury he knew and expected when he had terrorized their pets in the old days; laughter, and sometimes nervousness — but never a crude, uncivilized reception like this.

Baffled and disappointed, he fell meekly in

behind his leader.

Two miles along the road they came to a winding cart track leading uphill to a farm. They crossed the dark fields, startling up an old white horse and some cows, heading for a group of outbuildings clustered together some distance from the farmhouse. A thin curl of smoke rose from the chimney of one. It was a smokehouse, where hams were smoking over a slow hickory fire. Pressing against the faint warmth at the base of the chimney they settled down for the night.

The young dog spent a restless night. The running sores on his face had been extended, by his continuous frantic clawing, into raw inflamed patches over the glands on one side of his neck; and the spreading infection was making him feverish and thirsty. Several times he left the others to drink from a small lake a short distance away, standing chest-deep in the cool, soothing water.

When the old dog woke shivering with cold he was alone. The cat was some distance away, belly to ground and tail twitching excitedly, stalking his breakfast. Stealing through the morning air came a familiar smell of smoke and something cooking — beckoning irresistibly.

The mists were rolling back from the valley, and a pale sun was lightening the sky when the old dog came through the windbreak of tall Norway pines and sat down outside the farmhouse door. His memory was short; already human beings were back on their rightful pedestals, cornucopias of dog food in their hands. He whined plaintively. At a second, louder whine, several cats appeared from the barn nearby and glared at him with tiger-eyed resentment. At any other time, he would have put them to instant flight; now he had more pressing business and chose to ignore them. The door swung open, a wondrous smell of bacon and eggs surged out, and the terrier drew up all the heavy artillery of his charm: with an ingratiating wag of his tail he glued his ears back, and wrinkled his nose in preparation for his disastrous winning leer. There was an astonished silence, broken by the deep, amused voice of a man. "Well!" said the owner of the voice, surveying his odd visitor, whose eyes were now rolled so far back that they had almost disappeared into his head. He called into the house, and was answered by the pleasant, warm voice of a woman. There was a sound of footsteps. The tail increased its tempo.

The woman stood for a moment in the doorway, looking down in silent astonishment at the white gargoyle on the step, and when he saw her face break into a smile the past master in the art of scrounging proferred a civil paw. She bent down and shook it, laughing helplessly, then invited him to follow her into the house.

Dignified, the old dog walked in, and gazed at the stove with bland confidence.

He was in luck this time, for there could not have been pleasanter people or a more welcoming house for miles around. They were an elderly couple, James Mackenzie and his wife Nell, living alone now in a big farmhouse which still held the atmosphere of a large, cheerful family living and laughing and growing up in it. They were well used to dogs, for there had been eight children in that house once upon a time, and a consequent succession of pets who had always started their adopted life out in the yard but invariably found their way into the household on the wildest pretexts of the children: misunderstood mongrels, orphaned kittens, sad strays, abandoned otter pups — Nell Mackenzie's soft heart had been as defenseless before them then as it was now.

She gave their visitor a bowl of scraps, which he bolted down in ravenous gulps, looking up then for more. "Why, he's starving!" she exclaimed in horror, and contributed her own breakfast. She petted and fussed over him, accepting him as though the years had rolled back and one of the children had brought home yet another half-starved stray. He basked in this affection, and emptied the bowl almost before it reached the ground. Without a word Mackenzie passed over his plate as well. Soon the toast was gone too, and a jug of milk; and at last, distended and happy, the old dog stretched out on a rug by the warmth of the stove while Nell cooked another breakfast.

"What is he?" she asked presently. "I've never seen anything quite so homely — he looks as though he had been squeezed into the wrong coat, somehow."

"He's an English bull," said her husband, "and a beauty too — a real old bruiser! I love them! He looks as though he'd been in a fight quite recently, yet he must be ten or eleven if he's a day!" And at the unqualified respect and admiration in the voice, so dear to the heart of a bull terrier — but so seldom forthcoming — the dog thumped his tail agreeably, then rose and thrust his bony head against his host's knee. Mackenzie looked down, chuckling appreciatively. "As cocksure as the devil — and as irresistible, aren't you? But what are we going to do with you?"

Nell passed her hand over the dog's shoulder and felt the scars, then examined them more closely. She looked up, suddenly puzzled. "These aren't from any dogfight," she said. "They're *claw* marks — like the ones bears leave on fresh wood, only smaller —"

In silence they looked down at the dog by their feet, digesting the implication, the unknown story behind the sinister scars; and they saw now, for the first time, the gathering cloudiness in the depths of the humorous little eyes; the too-thin neck shamed by the newly distended belly; and they saw that the indefatigable tail which thumped so happily on the floor was ragged and old, with a broken end. This was no bold, aggressive adventurer — only a weary old dog; hungry not only for food but for affection. There was no shadow of doubt in either what they would do

— keep him, if he would stay, and give him what he needed.

They searched unavailingly under the white coat and in the pink ears for an identifying registered tattoo, then decided that when Mackenzie went into Deepwater to fetch some new churns later in the day he would make some inquiries there, tell the Provincial Police, and possibly put an advertisement in a city paper. And if nothing came of that . . . "Then I guess we're landed with you for good, you disreputable old hobo!" said Mackenzie cheerfully, prodding his delighted audience with an experienced foot, so that the dog rolled over on his back with a blissful sigh and invited further attention under his forearms.

When he opened the door that morning Mackenzie had seen a flight of mallards going down in the direction of the small lake fed by the creek running through the farm. It was still early enough to walk over to see if they were still there, so he put a handful of shells in his pocket, took down an old pump gun from the wall and set off, leaving Nell stepping over and around the recumbent white form of their guest as she cleared the table. He noticed that an infinitesimal slit of eye followed her every movement.

Halfway over the still misty fields he stopped to load his gun, then walked quietly toward the cover of the alders fringing the little lake. Peering through the branches, he saw six mallards about halfway across, just out of range. With the wind the way it was he might wait all day for a shot, unless something startled them on the other side.

But even as he turned away he saw a disturbance in the reeds across the water. Simultaneously, quacking loudly in alarm, the mallards took off in a body. He fired twice as they came over, one bird plummeting into the water and the other landing with a thud on the shore nearby. He picked this one up, thinking that he would have to bring the light canoe for the other, when he saw to his astonishment a large head of a dog swimming towards it.

The sound of a shot and the splash of a duck had had the same effect on the Labrador as a trumpet call to an old war horse, and drew him as irresistibly. Without a second's hesitation he had plunged in for the retrieve, only to find that he was unable to open his mouth to grasp the heavy duck properly, and was forced to tow it ashore by a wingtip. He emerged from the water twenty feet from the man, the beautiful greenhead trailing from its outstretched wing, the sun striking the iridescent plumage. The Labrador looked doubtfully at the stranger, and Mackenzie stared back in open-mouthed amazement. For a moment the two were frozen in a silent tableau, then the man recovered himself.

"Good dog!" he said quietly, holding out one hand. "Well done! Now bring it to me." The dog advanced hesitantly, dragging the bird.

"Give!" said Mackenzie, as the dog still hesitated.

The dog walked slowly forward, releasing his hold, and now Mackenzie saw with horror that one side of his face was swollen out of all proportion, the skin stretched so tautly that the eyes were mere slits and one rigid lip pulled back over the teeth. Sticking out like evil little pins on a rounded cushion of raw skin were several quills, deeply embedded. Every rib showed up under the wet coat, and when the dog shook himself Mackenzie saw him stagger.

Mackenzie made up his mind quickly: no matter whose, this dog was desperately in need of urgent treatment; the quills must be extracted at once before the infection spread further. He picked up the ducks, patted the dog's head reassuringly, then "Heel!" he said firmly. To his relief the dog fell in behind unquestioningly, following him back to the farmhouse, his resistance weakened to the point where he longed only to be back in the well-ordered world of human beings, that solid world where men commanded and dogs obeyed.

Crossing the fields, the stranger padding trustingly at his heels, Mackenzie suddenly remembered the other dog, and frowned in bewilderment. How many more unlikely dogs in need of succor would he lead into the farmhouse kitchen today — a lame poodle this afternoon, a halt beagle tonight?

His long, early morning shadow fell over the woodpile, and the sleepy Siamese cat sunning himself there lay camouflaged by stillness as he passed, unobserved by the man, but acknowledged by the dog with a brief movement of his tail and head.

Mackenzie finished cleaning up the Labrador's face nearly an hour later. He had extracted the quills with a pair of pliers; one had worked its way into the mouth and had to be removed from within, but the dog had not growled once, only whimpering when the pain was most intense, and had shown pathetic gratitude when it was over, trying to lick the man's hands. The relief must have been wonderful, for the punctures were now draining freely, and already the swelling was subsiding.

All through the operation the door leading out of the kitchen to a back room had shaken and rattled to the accompaniment of piteous whining. The old dog had been so much in the way when Mackenzie was working, pushing against his hand and obviously worried that they were going to do his companion some harm, that Nell had finally enticed him out with a bone, then quickly shut the door on his unsuspecting face.

Now, still deeply suspicious of foul play, he was hurling himself against the door with all his weight, but they did not want to let him in yet until the other dog had finished a bowl of milk. Mackenzie went to wash his hands, and his wife listened to the anxious running feet and the thuds that followed until she could bear it no longer, certain that he would harm himself. She opened the door and the old dog shot out in a fury,

prepared to do battle on behalf of his friend —
but he drew up all standing, a comical, puzzled
expression on his face as he saw him peacefully
lapping up a bowl of milk. Presently they sat
down together by the door and the young dog
patiently sufered the attentions of the other.

It was evident by their recognition and devotion
that they came from the same home — a home
which did not deserve to have them, as Nell said
angrily, still upset by the gaunt travesty of a dog
that had appeared; but Mackenzie pointed out
that they must have known care and appreciation,
as both had such friendly, assured dispositions.
This made it all the harder to understand why
they should be roaming such solitary and
forbidding country, he admitted. But perhaps
their owner had died, and they had run away
together, or perhaps they had been lost from
some car traveling across country, and were
trying to make their way back to familiar territory.
The possibilities were endless, and only one thing
was certain — that they had been on the road
long enough for scars to heal and quills to work
their way inside a mouth; and long enough to
know starvation.

"So they could have come from a hundred
miles away or more," said Mackenzie. "From
Manitoba, even. I wonder what they can have
lived on all that time —"

"Hunting? Scrounging at other farms? Stealing,
perhaps?" suggested Nell, who had watched with
amusement in the kitchen mirror her early

morning visitor sliding a piece of bacon off a plate after breakfast when he thought her back was turned.

"Well, the pickings must have been pretty lean," said her husband thoughtfully. "The Labrador looks like a skeleton — he wouldn't have got much farther. I'll shut them in the stable when I go to Deepwater; we don't want them wandering off again. Now, Nell, are you quite sure that you want to take on two strange dogs? It may be a long time before they're traced — they may never be."

"I want them," she said simply, "for as long as they will stay. And in the meantime we must find something else to call them besides 'Hi!' or 'Good dog.' I'll think of something while you're away." she added, "and I'll take some more milk out to the stable during the morning."

From his sunny observation post on the woodpile, the cat had watched Mackenzie cross the yard and usher the two dogs into a warm, sweet-smelling stable, shutting the door carefully behind him. Shortly afterwards the truck rattled down the farm road, then all was quiet again. A few curious farm cats were emboldened to approach the woodpile, resenting this exotic stranger who had taken possession of their favorite sunning place. The stranger was not fond of other cats at the best of times, even his own breed, and farm cats were beyond the pale altogether. He surveyed them balefully, considering his strategy. After two or three well-executed skirmishes the band dispersed, and the black-masked pirate returned to his lair to sleep.

Halfway through the morning he awoke, stretched, and jumped down, looking warily around before stalking over to the stable door. He bleated plaintively and was answered by a rustle of straw within. Leisurely, he gathered himself for a spring, then leaped effortlessly at the latch on the door. But he was not quite quick enough; the latch remained in position. Annoyed, unused to failure, he sprang again, this time making sure of success. For a split second, almost in the same impetus as the spring, one paw was curved around the wooden block handle supporting his weight, while the other paw released the latch above and the door swung open. Purring with restrained pleasure, the cat walked in, suffering a boisterous welcome from his old friend before investigating the empty bowl. Disappointed, he left the stable, the two dogs following him into the sunlit yard, and disappeared into the henhouse. Several enraged and squawking fowls rushed out as he made his way towards the nesting-boxes. Curving his paws expertly around a warm brown egg, he held it firmly, then cracked it with a neat sideways tap from a long incisor tooth, the contents settling intact on the straw. He had brought this art to perfection after years of egg stealing. He lapped with delicate unhurried thoroughness, helping himself to two more before retiring to his woodpile again.

When Mackenzie drove into the farmyard later on in the afternoon he was surprised to see the two dogs sleeping in the sun by the shelter of the cattle trough. They stood by the truck wagging their tails in recognition as he unloaded, then followed him into the farmhouse.

"Did you let them out of the stable, Nell?" he asked, opening a parcel at the kitchen table and sheepishly dropping a meaty bone into the sharklike mouth that had opened beside him.

"Of course not," she answered in surprise. "I took them out some milk, but I remember being particularly careful to close the door."

"Perhaps the latch wasn't down properly," said Mackenzie. "Anyway, they're still here. The Lab's face looks better already — he'll be able to eat a decent meal by this evening, I hope; I'd like to get some meat on those bones."

Nothing was known of the runaways in Deepwater, he reported, but they must have come from the east, for a mink breeder at Archer Creek had spoken of chasing a white dog off his doorstep the night before, mistaking it for a local white mongrel well known for his thieving ways. Most men thought the Labrador could have been lost from a hunting trip, but nobody could account for an unlikely bull terrier as his companion. The Indian Agent had offered to take the Labrador if nobody turned up to claim him, as his own hunting dog had recently died . . .

"Indeed he will not!" Nell broke in indignantly.

"All right," said her husband laughing. "I told him we would never separate them, and of course we'll keep them as long as we can — I'd hate to think of one of my own dogs running loose at this time of year. But I warn you, Nell, that if they are heading somewhere with a purpose, nothing on earth will keep them here — even if they're dropping on their feet, the instinct will pull them on. All we can do is keep them shut in for a while and feed them up. Then, if they leave, at least we've given them a better start."

After supper that night the Mackenzies and their guests moved into the little back room: a cozy, pleasantly shabby place, its shelves still filled with childrens' books, tarnished trophies and photographs; while snowshoes, mounted fish and grandchildren's drawings jostled one another for space on the walls with award ribbons, pedigrees and a tomahawk. Mackenzie sat at a table, puffing peacefully on a pipe, and working at the minute, intricate rigging of a model schooner, while his wife read *Three Men in a Boat* aloud to him. The replete and satisfied Labrador had eaten ravenously that evening, cleaning up bowls of fresh milk and plates of food with a bottomless appetite. Now he lay stretched full length under the table in the deep sleep of exhaustion and security, and the terrier snored gently from the depths of an old leather sofa, his head pillowed on a cushion, four paws in the air.

The only disturbance during the evening was

the noise of a tremendous cat battle out in the yard. Both dogs sat up immediately and, to the astonishment of the elderly couple watching, wagged their tails in unison, wearing almost identical expressions of pleased and doting interest.

Later on they followed Mackenzie out quite willingly to the stable, where he piled some hay in a corner of a loose box for them, filled the bowl with water, then shut the door firmly behind him — satisfying himself that the latch was down and firmly in place, and would remain so even when the door was rattled. Shortly afterwards the lights downstairs in the farmhouse went out, followed in a little while by the bedroom light upstairs.

The dogs lay quietly in the darkness, waiting. Soon there was a soft scrabbling of paws on wood, the latch clicked, and the door opened a fraction, just enough to admit the slight body of the cat. He trampled and kneaded the hay for a while, purring in a deep rumble, before curling up in a ball at the old dog's chest. There were several contented sighs, then silence reigned in the stable.

When the young dog awoke in the cold hour before dawn only a few pale laggard stars were left to give the message which his heart already knew — it was time to go, time to press on westwards.

The yawning, stretching cat joined him at the

stable door; then the old dog, shivering in the cold dawn wind; and for a few minutes the three sat motionless, listening, looking across the still dark farmyard, where already they could hear the slight stirrings of the animals. It was time to be gone: there were many miles to be traveled before the first halt in the warmth of the sun. Silently they crossed the yard and entered the fields leading to the dark, massed shadows of the trees in the farthermost corner, their paws making three sets of tracks in the light rime of frost that covered the field; and even as they turned onto a deer trail leading westward through the bush, a light came on upstairs in the farmhouse. . . .

Ahead of them lay the last fifty miles of the journey. It was as well that they had been fed and rested. Most of the way now lay through the Strellon Game Reserve, country that was more desolate and rugged than anything they had yet encountered. The nights would be frosty, the going perilous and exhausting; there could be no help expected from any human agency. Worst of all, their leader was already weak and unfit.

The Oracle of the Dog

Gilbert K. Chesterton

"Yes," said Father Brown, "I always like a dog so long as he isn't spelled backwards."

Those who are quick in talking are not always quick in listening. Sometimes even their brilliancy produces a sort of stupidity. Father Brown's friend and companion was a young man with a stream of ideas and stories, an enthusiastic young man named Fiennes, with eager blue eyes and blond hair that seemed to be brushed back not merely with a hair-brush but with the wind of the world as he rushed through it. But he stopped in the torrent of his talk in a momentary bewilderment, before he saw the priest's very simple meaning.

"You mean that people make too much of them?" he said. "Well, I don't know. They're marvelous creatures. Sometimes I think they know a lot more that we do."

Father Brown said nothing; but continued to stroke the head of the big retriever in a half abstracted but apparently soothing fashion.

"Why," said Fiennes, warming again to his monologue, "there was a dog in the case I've come to see you about; what they call the 'Invisible Murderer Case,' you know. It's a strange story, but from my point of view the dog is about the strangest thing in it. Of course, there's the mystery of the crime itself, and how old Druce can have been killed by somebody else when he was all alone in the summer-house —"

The hand stroking the dog stopped for a moment in its rhythmic movement; and Father Brown said calmly,

"Oh, it was a summer-house, was it?"

"I thought you'd read all about it in the papers," answered Fiennes. "Stop a minute; I believe I've got a cutting that will give you all the particulars." He produced a strip of newspaper from his pocket and handed it to the priest who began to read it.

"Many mystery stories, about men murdered behind locked doors and windows and murderers escaping without means of entrance and exit, have come true in the course of the extraordinary events at Cranston on the coast of Yorkshire, where Colonel Druce was found stabbed from behind by a dagger that has entirely disappeared from the scene, and apparently even from the neighborhood. The summer-house in which he died was indeed accessible at one entrance — the ordinary doorway which looked down the central walk of the garden toward the house. But by a combination of events almost to be called a coincidence, it appears that both the path and the entrance were watched during the crucial time, and there is a chain of witnesses who confirm each other. The summer-house stands at the extreme end of the garden where there is no exit or entrance of any kind.

"The central garden path is a lane between two ranks of tall delphiniums, planted so close that a stray step off the path would leave its traces; and both path and plants run right up to the very mouth of the summer-house, so that no straying from that straight path could fail to be observed, and no other mode of entrance can be imagined.

"Oscar Floyd, secretary to the murdered man, testified that he had been in a position to overlook the whole garden from the time when Colonel Druce last appeared alive in the doorway to the time when he was found dead; as he, Floyd, had been on the top of a stepladder clipping the garden hedge. Janet Druce, the dead man's daughter, confirmed this, saying that she had sat on the terrace of the house throughout that time and had seen Floyd at his work. Touching some part of the time, this is again supported by Donald Druce, her brother, who overlooked the garden standing at his bedroom window in his dressing-gown, for he had risen late.

"Lastly the account is consistent with that given by Dr. Valentine, a neighbor, who called for a time to talk with Miss Druce on the terrace, and by the Colonel's solicitor, Mr. Aubrey Traill, who was apparently the last to see the murdered man alive — presumably with the exception of the murderer. All are agreed that the course of events is as follows: about half-past three in the afternoon Miss Druce went down the path to ask her father when he would like tea; but he said he did not want any and was waiting to see Traill, his lawyer, who was to be sent to him in the summer-house.

"The girl then came away and met Traill coming down the path; she directed him to her father and he went in as directed. About half an hour afterwards he came out again, the Colonel coming with him to the door and showing himself to all appearance in health and even in high spirits. He had been somewhat annoyed earlier in the day by his son's irregular hours, but seemed to recover his temper in a perfectly normal fashion; and had been rather markedly genial in receiving other visitors, including two of his nephews who came over for the day. But as these were out walking during the whole period of the tragedy, they had no evidence to give.

"It is said indeed that the Colonel was not on very good terms with Dr. Valentine, but that gentleman only had a brief interview with the daughter of the house, to whom he is supposed to be paying serious attentions. Triall, the solicitor, says he left the Colonel entirely alone in the summer-house, and this is confirmed by Floyd's bird's-eye view of the garden which showed nobody else passing the only entrance.

"Ten minutes later Miss Druce again went

down the garden and had not reached the end of the path when she saw her father, who was conspicuous by his white linen coat, lying in a heap on the floor. She uttered a scream which brought others to the spot; and on entering the place they found the Colonel lying dead beside his basket chair which was also upset. Dr. Valentine, who was still in the immediate neighborhood, testified that the wound was made by some sort of stiletto, entering under the shoulder blade and piercing the heart. The police have searched the neighborhood for such a weapon but no trace of it can be found."

"So Colonel Druce wore a white coat, did he?" said Father Brown as he put down the paper.

"Trick he learned in the tropics," replied Fiennes with some wonder. "He'd had some queer adventures there, by his own account; and I fancy this dislike of Valentine was connected with the doctor coming from the tropics, too. But it's all an infernal puzzle.

"The account there is pretty accurate; I didn't see the tragedy, in the sense of the discovery; I was out walking with the young nephews and the dog — the dog I wanted to tell you about. But I saw the stage set for it as described; the straight lane between the blue flowers right up to the dark entrance, and the lawyer going down it in his blacks and his silk hat, and the red head of the secretary showing high above the green hedge as he worked on it with his shears. This red-haired secretary Floyd is quite a character, a breathless bounding sort of fellow, always doing everybody's work as he was doing the gardener's."

"What about the lawyer?" asked Father Brown.

There was a silence and then Fiennes spoke quite slowly for him. 'Traill struck me as a singular man. In his fine black clothes he was almost foppish, yet you can hardly call him fashionable. For he wore a pair of long luxuriant black whiskers such as haven't been seen since Victorian times. He had rather a grave face and a fine grave manner, but every now and then he seemed to remember to smile. And when he showed his white teeth he seemed to lose a little of his dignity and there was something faintly fawning about him. It may have been only embarrassment, for he would also fidget with his cravat, and his tie pin, which were at once handsome and unusual, like himself.

"If I could think of anybody — but what's the good, when the whole thing's impossible? Nobody knows who did it. Nobody knows how it could be done. At least there's only one exception I'd make, and that's why I really mentioned the whole thing. The dog knows."

Father Brown sighed and then said absently, "You were there as a friend of young Donald, weren't you? He didn't go on your walk with you?"

"No," replied Fiennes smiling. "The young scoundrel had gone to bed that morning and got up that afternoon. I went with his cousins, two young officers from India; and our conversation was trivial enough. I remember the elder, whose name I think is Herbert Druce, and who is an authority on horse breeding, talked about nothing but a mare he had bought; while his brother Harry seemed to be brooding on his bad luck at Monte Carlo. I only mention it to show you, in the light of what happened on our walk, that there was nothing psychic about us. The dog was the only mystic in our company."

"What sort of a dog was he?" asked the priest.

"Same breed as that one," answered Fiennes. "He's a big black retriever named Nox, and a suggestive name too; for I think what he did more of a mystery than the murder.

"You know Druce's house and garden are by the sea; we walked about a mile from it along the sands and then turned back, going the other way. We passed a rather curious rock called the Rock of Fortune, famous in the neighborhood because it's one of those examples of one stone barely balanced on another, so that a touch would knock it over. It is not really very high, but the hanging outline of it makes it look a little wild and sinister. Just then the question arose of whether it was time to go back to tea, and even then I think I had a premonition that time counted for a good deal in the business.

"Neither Herbert Druce nor I had a watch; so we called out to his brother, who was some paces behind, having stopped to light his pipe under the hedge. Hence it happened that he shouted out the hour, which was twenty past four, in his big voice through the growing twilight; and somehow the loudness of it made it sound like the proclamation of something tremendous. According to Dr. Valentine's testimony, poor Druce had actually died just about half-past four.

"Well, they said we needn't go home for ten minutes and we walked a little farther along the sands doing nothing in particular; throwing stones for the dog and throwing sticks into the sea for him to swim after. And then the curious thing happened.

"Nox had just brought back Herbert's walking-stick out of the sea, and his brother had thrown his in also. The dog swam out again, but just about what must have been the stroke of the half hour, he stopped swimming. He came back again on to the shore and stood in front of us. Then he suddenly threw up his head and sent up a howl or wail of woe if ever I heard one in the world.

" 'What the devil's the matter with the dog?' asked Herbert, but none of us could answer. There was a long silence after the brute's wailing and whining died away on the desolate shore; and then the silence was broken. As I live, it was broken by a faint and far off shriek, like the shriek of a woman from beyond the hedges inland. We didn't know what it was then; but we knew afterwards. It was the cry the girl gave when she first saw the body of her father."

"You went back, I suppose," said Father Brown patiently. "What happened then?"

"I'll tell you what happened then," said Fiennes, with a grim emphasis. "When we got back into that garden the first thing we saw was Traill the lawyer; I can see him now with his black hat and black whiskers relieved against the perspective of the blue flowers stretching down to the summer-house with the sunset and the strange outline of the Rock of Fortune in the distance. His face and figure were in shadow against the sunset; but I swear the white teeth were showing in his head and he was smiling.

"The moment Nox saw the man, the dog dashed forward and stood in the middle of the path barking at him madly, murderously volleying out curses that were almost verbal in their dreadful distinctness of hatred. And the man doubled up and fled along the path between the flowers."

Father Brown sprang to his feet with a startling impatience.

"So the dog denounced him, did he?" he cried. "The oracle of the dog condemned him. Did you see what birds were flying, and are you sure whether they were on the right hand or the left? Did you consult the augurs about the sacrifices? Surely you didn't omit to cut open the dog, and examine his entrals. That is the sort of scientific test you heathen humanitarians seem to trust, when you are thinking of taking away the life and honor of a man."

Fiennes sat gaping for an instant before he found breath to say, "Why, what's the matter with you? What have I done now?"

A sort of anxiety came back into the priest's eyes.

"I'm most awfully sorry," he said, with sincere distress, "I beg your pardon for being so rude, pray forgive me."

Fiennes looked at him curiously. "I sometimes think you are more of a mystery than any of the mysteries," he said. 'But as for the lawyer, I don't go only by the dog; there are other curious details too. He struck me as a smooth, smiling, equivocal sort of person and one of his tricks seemed like a sort of hint. You know the doctor and the police were on the spot very quickly, Valentine was brought back when walking away from the house, and he telephoned instantly. That, with the secluded house, small numbers and enclosed space made it pretty possible to search everybody who could have been near; and everybody was thoroughly searched — for a weapon. The whole house, garden and shore were combed for a weapon. The disappearance of the dagger is almost as crazy as the disappearance of the man."

"The disappearance of the dagger," said Father Brown nodding. He seemed to have become suddenly attentive.

"Well," continued Fiennes, "I told you that man Traill had a trick of fidgeting with his tie and tie pin — especially his tie pin. His pin, like himself, was at once showy and old-fashioned. It had been one of those stones with concentric colored rings that look like an eye; and his own concentration on it got on my nerves, as if he had been a cyclops with one eye in the middle of his body. But the pin was not only large but long; and it occurred to me that his anxiety about its adjustment was because it was even longer than it looked, as long as a stiletto in fact."

Father Brown nodded thoughtfully. "Was any other instrument ever suggested?" he asked.

"There was another suggestion," answered Fiennes, "from one of the young Druces; the cousins I mean. Neither Herbert nor Harry Druce would have struck one at first as likely to be of assistance in scientific detection; but Harry had been in the Indian Police and knew something about such things. Indeed in his own way he was quite clever; and I rather fancy he had been too clever; I mean he had left the police through breaking some red-tape regulations and taking some sort of risk and responsibility of his own.

"Anyhow he was in some sense a detective out of work, and threw himself into this business with more than the ardor of an amateur and it was with him that I had an argument about the weapon, an argument that led to something new. It began by his countering my description of the dog barking at Traill; and he said that a dog at his worst didn't bark but growled."

"He was quite right there," observed the priest.

"This young fellow went on to say, that, if it came to that, he'd heard Nox growling at other people before then; and among others at Floyd the secretary. I retorted that his own argument answered itself; for the crime couldn't be brought home to two or three people, and least of all to Floyd who was as innocent as a harum scarum schoolboy, and had been seen by everybody all the time perched above the garden hedge.

" 'I know there's difficulties anyhow,' said my colleague, 'but I wish you'd come with me down the garden a minute. I want to show you something I don't think any one else has seen.' This was on the very day of the discovery, and the garden was just as it had been; the stepladder was still standing by the hedge; and just under the hedge my guide stooped and disentangled something from the deep grass. It was the shears used for clipping the hedge; and on the point of one of them was a smear of blood."

There was a short silence and then Father Brown said suddenly:

"What was the lawyer there for?"

"He told us the Colonel sent for him to alter his will," answered Fiennes. "The Colonel was a very wealthy man and his will was important. Traill wouldn't tell us the alternations at that stage; but I have since heard, only this morning in fact, that most of the money was transferred from the son to the daughter. I told you that Druce was wild with my friend Donald over his dissipated hours."

"The question of motive has been rather shadowed by the question of method," observed

Father Brown thoughtfully. "At that moment, apparently, Miss Druce was the immediate gainer by the death."

"Good God! What a cold-blooded way of talking," cried Fiennes, staring at him. "You don't really mean to hint that she —"

"Is going to marry that Dr. Valentine?" asked the other. "What sort of a man is he?"

"He — Valentine — man with a beard; very pale, very handsome; rather foreign looking. The name doesn't seem quite English somehow. But he is liked and respected in the place and is a skilled and devoted surgeon."

"So devoted a surgeon," said Father Brown, "that he had surgical instruments with him when he went to call on the young lady at tea time. For he must have used a lancet or something, and he never seems to have gone home."

Fiennes sprang to his feet and looked at him in a heat of inquiry. "You suggest he might have used the very same lancet —"

Father Brown shook his head. "All these suggestions are fancies just now," he said. "The problem is not who did it or what did it, but how it was done. We might find many men and even many tools; pins and shears and lancets. But how did a man get into the room? *How did even a pin get into it?*"

He was staring reflectively at the ceiling as he spoke.

"Well, what would you do about it?" asked the young man. "You have a lot of experience,

84

what would you advise now?"

"I'm afraid I'm not much use,' said Father Brown with a sigh. "I can't suggest very much without having ever been near the place or the people. For the moment you can only go on with local inquiries. I gather that your friend from the Indian Police is more or less in charge of your inquiry down there. I should run down and see how he is getting on. There may be news already."

As his guests, the biped and the quadruped, disappeared, Father Brown took up his pen and went back to his interrupted occupation of planning a course of lectures on the Encyclical De Rerum Novarum. The subject was a large one and he had to recast it more than once, so that he was somewhat similarly employed some two days later when the big black dog again came bounding into the room and sprawling all over him with enthusiasm and excitement. The master who followed the dog shared the excitement if not the enthusiasm. His blue eyes seemed to start from his head and his eager face was even a little pale.

"You told me," he said abruptly and without preface, "to find out what Harry Druce was doing. Do you know what he's done? He's killed himself."

Father Brown's lips moved only faintly and there was nothing practical about what he was saying; nothing that has anything to do with this story or this world.

"You give me the creeps sometimes," said Fiennes. "Did you — did you expect this?"

"I thought it possible," said Father Brown, "that was why I asked you to go and see what he was doing. I hoped you might not be too late."

"It was I who found him," said Fiennes rather huskily, "It was the ugliest and most uncanny thing I ever knew. I went down that old garden again and I knew there was something new and unnatural about it besides the murder. The flowers still tossed about in blue masses on each side of the black entrance into the old gray summer-house; but to me the blue flowers looked like blue devils dancing before some dark cavern of the underworld. The queer notion grew on me that there was something wrong with the very shape of the sky.

"And then I saw what it was. The Rock of Fortune always rose in the background beyond the garden hedge and against the sea. And the Rock of Fortune was gone."

Father Brown had lifted his head and was listening intently.

"It was as if a mountain had walked away out of a landscape or a moon fallen from the sky; though I knew, of course, that a touch at any time would have tipped the thing over. Something possessed me and I rushed down that garden path like the wind and went crashing through the hedge as if it were a spider's web. On the shore I found the loose rock fallen from its pedestal and poor Harry Druce lay like a wreck underneath it. One arm was thrown round it in a sort of embrace as if he had pulled it down on himself; and in the other hand was clenched a scrap of paper on which he had scrawled the words, 'The Rock of Fortune falls on the fool.' "

"It was the Colonel's will that did that," observed Father Brown. "The young man had staked everything on profiting himself by Donald's disgrace, especially when his uncle sent for him on the same day as the lawyer, and welcomed him with so much warmth. Otherwise he was dumb; he'd lost his police job; he was beggared at Monte Carlo. And he killed himself when he found he'd killed his kinsman for nothing. That's the whole story."

Fiennes stared. "But look here," he cried, "How do you come to know the whole story, or to be sure it's the true story? You've been sitting here a hundred miles away writing a sermon; do you mean to tell me you really know what happened already? If you've really come to the end, where in the world do you begin? What started you off with your own story?"

Father Brown jumped up.

"The dog!" he cried, "the dog, of course! You had the whole story in your hands in the business of the dog on the beach, if you'd only noticed the dog properly."

Fiennes stared still more. "But you told me just now that my feelings about the dog were all nonsense, and the dog had nothing to do with it!"

"The dog had everything to do with it," said Father Brown, "as you'd have found out if you'd only treated the dog as a dog, not as God Almighty, judging the souls of men."

He paused in an embarrased way for a moment, and then said, with a rather pathetic air of apology:

"The truth is that I happen to be awfully fond of dogs. And it seemed to me that in all this lurid halo of dog superstitions nobody was really thinking about the poor dog at all. To begin with a small point, about his barking at the lawyer or growling at the secretary. You asked how I could guess things a hundred miles away; but honestly it's mostly to your credit, for you described people so well that I know the types.

"A man like Traill who frowns usually and smiles suddenly, a man who fiddles with things, especially at his throat, is a nervous, easily embarrassed man. I shouldn't wonder if Floyd the efficient secretary is nervy and jumpy too; otherwise he wouldn't have cut his fingers on the shears and dropped them when he heard Janet Druce scream.

"Now dogs hate nervous people. I don't know whether they make the dog nervous too; or whether, being after all a brute, he is a bit of a bully. But anyhow there was nothing in poor Nox protesting against those people, except that he disliked them for being afraid of him.

"But when we come to that business by the seashore, things are much more interesting. I didn't understand that tale of the dog going in and out of the water; it didn't seem to me a doggy thing to do. If Nox had been very much upset about something else, he might possibly have refused to go after the stick at all. But when once a dog is actually chasing a thing, a stone or a stick or a rabbit, my experience is that he won't stop for anything but the most peremptory command, and not always for that. That he should turn round because his mood changed seems to me unthinkable."

"But he did turn around," insisted Fiennes, "and came back without the stick."

"He came back without the stick for the best reason in the world," replied the priest. "He came back because he couldn't find it. He whined because he couldn't find it. That's the sort of thing a dog really does whine about. He came back to complain seriously of the conduct of the stick. Never had such a thing happened before. Never had an eminent and distinguished dog been so treated by a rotten old walking stick."

"Why, what had the walking stick done?" inquired the young man.

"It had sunk," said Father Brown.

Fiennes said nothing but continued to stare, and it was the priest who continued, "It had sunk because it was not really a stick but a rod of steel with a very thin shell of cane and a sharp point. In other words, it was a sword stick. I

89

suppose a murderer never got rid of a bloody weapon so oddly and yet so naturally as by throwing it into the sea for a retriever."

"I begin to see what you mean," admitted Fiennes, "but even if a sword stick was used I have no guess of how it was used."

"I had a sort of guess," said Father Brown, "right at the beginning when you said the word summer-house. And another when you said that Druce wore a white coat."

He was leaning back, looking at the ceiling, and began like one going back to his own first thoughts and fundamentals.

"All that discussion about detective stories like the Yellow Room, about a man found dead in sealed chambers which no one could enter, does not apply to the present case; because it is a summer-house. When we talk of a Yellow Room, or any room, we imply walls that are really homogeneous and impenetrable. But a summer-house is not make like that; it is often made, as it was in this case, of closely interlaced but still separate boughs and strips of wood, in which there are chinks here and there. There was one of them just behind Druce's back as he sat in his chair up against the wall. But just as the room was a summer-house, so the chair was a basket chair. That also was a lattice of loop-holes.

"Lastly, the summer-house was close up under the hedge; and you have just told me that it was really a thin hedge. A man standing outside it could easily see, amid a network of twigs and branches and canes, one white spot of the Colonel's coat as plain as the white of a target.

"Now you left the geography a little vague; but it was possible to put two and two together. You said the Rock of Fortune was not really high; but you also said it could be seen dominating the garden like a mountain peak. In other words, it was very near the end of the garden, though your walk had taken you a long way round to it. Also, it isn't likely the young lady really howled so as to be heard half a mile. She gave an ordinary involuntary cry, and yet you heard it on the shore. And among other interesting things that you told me, may I remind you that you said Harry Druce had fallen behind to light his pipe under a hedge?"

Fiennes shuddered slightly. "You mean he drew his blade there and sent it through the hedge at the white spot? But surely it was a very odd chance and a very sudden choice. Besides, he couldn't be certain the old man's money had passed to him, and as a fact it hadn't."

Father Brown's face became animated.

"You misunderstand the man's character," he said, as if he himself had known the man all his life. "A curious but not unknown type of character. If he had really *known* the money would come to him, I seriously believe he wouldn't have done it."

"Isn't that rather paradoxical?" asked the other.

"This man was a gambler," said the priest,

"and a man in disgrace for having taken risks and anticipated orders. Now the temptation of that type of man is to do a mad thing precisely because the risk will be wonderful in retrospect. He wants to say, 'Nobody but I could have seized that chance or seen that it was then or never. Anybody would say I was mad to risk it; but that is how fortunes are made, by the man mad enough to have a little foresight.'

"In short, it is the vanity of guessing. It is the megalomania of the gambler. The more incongruous the coincidence, the more instantaneous the decision, the more likely he is to snatch the chance. The accident, the very triviality of the white speck and the hole in the hedge intoxicated him like a vision of the world's desire. Nobody clever enough to see such a combination of accidents could be cowardly enough not to use them! That is how the devil talks to the gambler."

Fiennes was musing.

"It's queer," he said, "that the dog really was in the story after all."

"The dog could almost have told you the story, if he could talk," said the priest. "All I complain of is that because he couldn't talk you made up his story for him and made him talk with the tongues of men and angels. It's part of something I've noticed more and more in the modern world, appearing in all sorts of newspaper rumors and conversational catchwords. People readily swallow the untested claims of this, that, or the other. It's drowning all your old rationalism and skepticism, it's coming in like a sea; and the name of it is superstition."

He stood up abruptly, his face heavy with a sort of frown, and went on talking almost as if he were alone. "It's the first effect of not believing in God that you lose your common sense, and can't see things as they are. A dog is an omen and a cat is a mystery and a pig is a mascot and a beetle is a scarab, calling up all the menagerie of polytheism from Egypt and old India; Dog Anubis and great green-eyed Pasht and all the holy howling Bulls of Bashan reeling back to the bestial gods of the beginning, escaping into elephants and snakes and crocodiles; and all because you are frightened of three words: Homo Factus Est."

The young man got up with a little embarrassment, almost as if he had overheard a soliloquy. He called to the dog and left the room with vague but breezy farewells.

But he had to call the dog twice; for the dog had remained behind quite motionless for a moment, looking up steadily at Father Brown as the wolf looked at St. Francis.

A Tent In Agony

Stephen Crane

Four men once came to a wet place in the roadless forest to fish. They pitched their tent fair upon the brow of a pine-clothed ridge of riven rocks whence a bowlder could be made to crash through the brush and whirl past the trees to the lake below. On fragrant hemlock boughs they slept the sleep of successful fishermen, for upon the lake alternately the sun made them lazy and the rain made them wet. Finally they ate the last bit of bacon, and smoked, and burned the last fearful and wonderful hoe-cake.

Immediately a little man volunteered to stay and hold the camp while the remaining three should go the Sullivan county miles to a farmhouse for supplies. They gazed at him dismally. "There's only one of you — the devil make a twin," they said in parting malediction, and disappeared down the hill in the known direction of a distant cabin. When it came night and the hemlocks began to sob, they had not returned. The little man sat close to his companion, the campfire, and encouraged it with logs. He puffed fiercely at a heavy built brier, and regarded a thousand shadows which were about to assault him. Suddenly he heard the approach of the unknown, crackling the twigs and rustling the dead leaves. The little man arose slowly to his feet, his clothes refused to fit his back, his pipe dropped from his mouth, his knees smote each other. "Hah!" he bellowed hoarsely in menace. A growl replied and a bear paced into the light of the fire. The little man supported himself upon a sapling and regarded his visitor.

The bear was evidently a veteran and a fighter, for the black of his coat had become tawny with age. There was confidence in his gait and arrogance in his small, twinkling eye. He rolled back his lips and disclosed his white teeth. The fire magnified the red of his mouth. The little man had never before confronted the terrible, and he could not wrest it from his breast. "Hah!" he roared. The bear interpreted this as the challenge of a gladiator. He approached warily. As he came near, the boots of fear were suddenly upon the little man's feet. He cried out and then darted around the campfire. "Ho!" said the bear to himself, "this thing won't fight — it runs. Well, suppose I catch it." So upon his features there fixed the animal look of going — somewhere. He started intensely around the campfire. The little man shrieked and ran furiously. Twice around they went.

The hand of heaven sometimes falls heavily upon the righteous. The bear gained.

In desperation the little man flew into the tent.

The bear stopped and sniffed at the entrance. He scented the scent of many men. Finally he ventured in.

The little man crouched in a distant corner. The bear advanced, creeping, his blood burning, his hair erect, his jowls dripping. The little man yelled and rustled clumsily under the flap at the end of the tent. The bear snarled awfully and made a jump and a grab at his disappearing game. The little man, now without the tent, felt a tremendous paw grab his coat tails. He squirmed and wriggled out of his coat like a schoolboy in the hands of an avenger. The bear howled triumphantly and jerked the coat into the tent and took two bites, a punch and a hug before he discovered his man was not in it. Then he grew not very angry, for a bear on a spree is not a black-haired pirate. He is merely a hoodlum. He lay down on his back, took the coat on his four paws and began to play uproariously with it. The most appalling, bloodcurdling whoops and yells came to where the little man was crying in a tree-top, and froze his blood. He moaned a little speech meant for a prayer and clung convulsively to the bending branches. He gazed with tearful wistfulness at where his comrade, the campfire, was giving dying flickers and crackles. Finally, there was a roar from the tent which eclipsed all roars; a snarl which it seemed would shake the stolid silence of the mountain and cause it to shrug its granite shoulders. The little man quaked and shriveled to a grip and a pair of eyes. In the glow of the embers he saw the white tent quiver and fall with a crash. The bear's merry play had disturbed the centre pole and brought a chaos of canvas upon his head.

Now the little man became the witness of a mighty scene. The tent began to flounder. It took flopping strides in the direction of the lake. Marvelous sounds came from within — rips and tears and great groans and pants. The little man went into giggling hysterics.

The entangled monster failed to extricate himself before he had walloped the tent frenziedly to the edge of the mountain. So it came to pass that three men, clambering up the hill with bundles and baskets, saw their tent approaching.

It seemed to them like a white-robed phantom pursued by hornets. Its moans riffled the hemlock twigs.

The three men dropped their bundles and scurried to one side, their eyes gleaming with fear. The canvas avalanche swept past them. They leaned, faint and dumb, against trees and listened, their blood stagnant. Below them it struck the base of a great pine tree, where it writhed and struggled. The three watched its convolutions a moment and then started terrifically for the top of the hill. As they disappeared, the bear cut loose with a mighty effort. He cast one disheveled and agonized look at the white thing and then started wildly for the inner recesses of the forest.

The three fear-stricken individuals ran to the

rebuilt fire. The little man reposed by it, calmly smoking. They sprang at him and overwhelmed him with interrogations. He contemplated darkness and took a long, pompous puff. "There's only one of me — and the devil made a twin." he said.

The Life and Death of Cholmondeley*

Gerald M. Durrell

Shortly before we left our hilltop hut at Bakebe and travelled down to our last camp at Kumba, we had with us a most unusual guest in the shape of Cholmondeley, known to his friends as Chumley.

Chumley was a full-grown chimpanzee; his owner, a District Officer, was finding the ape's large size rather awkward and wanted to send him to London Zoo as a present, so that he could visit the animal when he was back in England on leave. He wrote asking us if we would mind taking Chumley back with us when we left and depositing him at his new home in London, and we replied that we would not mind at all. I don't think that either John or myself had the least idea how big Chumley was: I know that I visualized an ape about three years old, standing about three feet high. I got a rude shock when Chumley moved in.

*This is the twelfth chapter of Gerald M. Durrell's *The Overloaded Ark*, an account of an expedition to Africa to collect rare animals and birds for British zoos.

He arrived in the back of a small van, seated sedately in a huge crate. When the doors of his crate were opened and Chumley stepped out with all the ease and self-confidence of a film star, I was considerably shaken; standing on his bow legs in a normal slouching chimp position, he came up to my waist, and if he had straightened up his head would have been on a level with my chest. He had huge arms and must have measured at least twice my size round his hairy chest. Owing to bad tooth growth, both sides of his face were swollen out of all proportion, and this gave him a weird pugilistic look. His eyes were small, deep-set, and intelligent; the top of his head was nearly bald, owing, I discovered later, to his habit of sitting and rubbing the palms of his hands backwards across his head, an exercise which seemed to afford him much pleasure and which he persisted in until the top of his skull was quite devoid of hair. This was no young chimp such as I had expected, but a veteran about eight or nine years old, fully mature, strong as a powerful man, and, to judge by his expression, with considerable experience of life. Although he was not exactly a nice chimp to look at (I had seen handsomer), he certainly had a terrific personality: it hit you as soon as you set eyes on him. His little eyes looked at you with great intelligence, and there seemed to be a glitter of ironic laughter in their depths that made one feel uncomfortable.

He stood on the ground and surveyed his

surroundings with a shrewd glance, and then he turned to me and held out one of his soft, pink-palmed hands to be shaken, with exactly that bored expression that one sees on the faces of professional hand-shakers. Round his neck was a thick chain, and its length drooped over the tailboard of the lorry and disappeared into the depths of his crate. With an animal of less personality than Chumley, this would have been a sign of his subjugation, of his captivity. But Chumley wore the chain with the superb air of a Lord Mayor; after shaking my hand so professionally, he turned and proceeded to pull the chain, which measured some fifteen feet, out of his crate. He gathered it up carefully into loops, hung it over one hand, and proceeded to walk into the hut as if he owned it. Thus, in the first few minutes of arrival, Chumley had made us feel inferior; he had moved in, not, we felt, because we wanted him to, but because he did. I almost felt I ought to apologize for the mess on the table.

He seated himself in a chair, dropped his chain on the floor, and then looked hopefully at me. It was quite obvious that he expected some sort of refreshment after his tiring journey. I roared out to the kitchen for someone to make a cup of tea, for I had been warned that Chumley had a great liking for the cup that cheers. Leaving him sitting in the chair and surveying our humble abode with ill-concealed disgust, I went out to his crate, and in it I found a tin plate and a battered tin mug of colossal proportions. When I returned to the hut bearing these, Chumley brightened considerably and even went so far as to praise me for my intelligence.

"Ooooooo, umph!" he said, and then crossed his legs and continued his inspection of the hut. I sat down opposite him and produced a packet of cigarettes. As I was selecting one a long black arm was stretched across the table, and Chumley grunted in delight. Wondering what he would do, I handed him a cigarette, and to my astonishment he put it carefully in the corner of his mouth. I lit my smoke and handed Chumley the matches, thinking that this would fool him. He opened the box, took out a match, struck it, lit his cigarette, threw the matches down on the table, crossed his legs again, and lay back in his chair, inhaling thankfully and blowing clouds of smoke out of his nose. Obviously he had vices in his make-up of which I had been kept in ignorance.

Just at that moment Pious entered bearing the tray of tea: the effect on him when he saw me sitting at the table with the chimp, smoking and apparently exchanging gossip, was considerable.

"Eh-aehh!" he gasped, backing away.

"Whar hooo," said Chumley, sighting the tea and waving one hand madly.

"Na whatee that, sah?" asked Pious from the doorway.

"This is Chumley," I explained. "He won't hurt you. Put the tea on the table."

102

Pious did as he was told and then retreated to the door again. As I poured tea and milk into Chumley's mug and added three tablespoons of sugar, he watched me with a glittering eye and made soft "ooing" noises to himself. I handed him the mug and he took it carefully in both hands. There was a moment's confusion when he tried to rid himself of the cigarette, which he found he could not hold along with the mug; he solved the problem by placing the cigarette on the table. Then he tested the tea carefully with one lip stuck out, to see if it was too hot. As it was, he sat there and blew on it until it was the right temperature, and then he drank it down. When he had finished the liquid there still remained the residue of syrupy sugar at the bottom, and as Chumley's motto was obviously waste not, want not, he balanced the mug on his nose and kept it there until the last of the sugar had trickled down into his mouth. Then he held it out for a refill.

Chumley's crate was placed at a convenient point about fifty yards from the hut, next to a great gnarled tree stump to which I attached his chain. From there he could get a good view of everything that went on in and around the hut, and as we were working he would shout comments to me and I would reply. That first day he created an uproar, for no sooner had I chained him up and gone into the hut to do some work than a frightful upheaval took place among the monkeys. All these were tethered on ropes under a palm-leaf shelter just opposite the hut. Chumley, after I had left him, felt bored; looking around, he perceived some sizable rocks lying about within easy reach. Arming himself with these, he proceeded to have a little underarm bowling practice. The first I knew of this was when I heard shrill screams and chatterings from the drills and guenons. I dashed out just in time to see a rock the size of a cabbage land in their midst, fortunately missing them all. If one of these rocks had hit a monkey it would have been squashed flat. Seizing a stick, I raced down upon Chumley, waving it and shouting at him, trying to appear fearsome, while all the time I was wondering what was going to happen if I tried to deal out punishment to an animal almost my own size and with twice my strength, when I was armed with only a short stick that seemed ridiculously flimsy. However, to my surprise, Chumley saw me coming and promptly lay down on the ground, covered his face and head with his long arms, and screamed loudly at the top of his voice. I gave him two cuts with the stick across his back, and it had about as much effect as if I had tried to demolish St. Paul's Cathedral with a toothpick. His back was broad and flat, solid muscle as hard as iron.

"You are a very wicked animal," I said sternly, and Chumley, realizing that punishment was apparently over, sat up and started to remove bits of leaf from himself.

"Whoooooo," he said, glancing up at me shyly.

"If you do that again I will have to give you a really good beating," I continued, wondering if anything short of a tree trunk would make any impression on him.

"Arrrrrr oooo," said Chumley. He shifted forward, squatted down, rolled up my trouser leg, and then began to search my calf for any spots, bits of dirt, or other microscopic blemishes. While he was thus engaged I called the animal staff and had them remove every rock from the vicinity. Later, after giving the beast yet another talking to, I left him, and shortly afterwards I noticed him digging hopefully in the earth near his crate, presumably in search of more rocks.

That night, when I carried Chumley's food and drink of tea out to him, he greeted me with loud "hoo hoos" of delight, and jogged up and down, beating his knuckles on the ground. Before he touched his dinner, however, he seized one of my hands in his and carried it to his mouth. With some trepidation I waited as he carefully put one of my fingers between his great teeth and very gently bit it. Then I understood: in the chimpanzee world, to place your finger between another ape's teeth is a greeting and a sign of trust, for to place a finger in such a vulnerable position is a sure display of your confidence in the other's friendliness. So Chumley was flattering my by treating me as he would another chimp. Then he set to and soon polished off his meal. When he had finished I sat beside him on the ground, and he went carefully through my pockets and examined everything I had on me.

When I decided that it was time he went to bed he refused to give back a handkerchief which he had removed. He held it behind his back and passed it from one hand to the other as I tried to get it. Then, thinking that the action would settle the matter, he stuffed it hurriedly into his mouth. I realized that if I gave in and let him keep the handkerchief he would think that he could get away with anything, so for half an hour I sat there pleading with him and cajoling him, until eventually, very reluctantly, he disgorged it, now very sodden and crumpled. After this I had no trouble with him: if he was playing with something I wanted I would simply hold out my hand and ask him for it, and he would give it to me without any fuss.

Now, I have known a great number of attractive and charming animals, from mice to elephants, but I have never seen one to compare with Chumley for force and charm of personality, or for intelligence. After knowing him for a while you ceased to look upon him as an animal; you regarded him more as a fascinating, mischievous, courtly old man, who had for some reason best known to himself disguised himself as a chimpanzee. His manners were perfect: he would never grab his food and start guzzling, as the other monkeys did, without first giving you a greeting, and thanking you with a series of his most expressive "hoo hoos." Then he would eat delicately and slowly, pushing those pieces he did not want to the side of his plate with his fingers. His only breach of table manners came at the end of a meal, for then he would seize his empty mug and plate and hurl them as far as possible.

He had, of course, many habits which made him seem almost human, and his smoking was one. He could light his cigarette with matches or a lighter with equal facility, and then he would lie down on the ground on his back, one arm under his head and his legs bent up and crossed, blowing great clouds of smoke into the sky, and occasionally examining the end of his cigarette professionally to see if the ash needed removing. If it did he would perform the operation carefully with one fingernail. Give him a bottle of lemonade and a glass, and he would pour himself out a drink with all the care and concentration of a world-famous barman mixing a cocktail. He was the only animal I have met that would think of sharing things with you: on many occasions, if I gave him a bunch of bananas or two or three mangoes, he would choose one and hold it out to me with an inquiring expression on his face, and he would grunt with satisfaction if I accepted it and sat down beside him on the ground to eat it.

Chumley had three aversions in life: African natives, giant millipedes, and snakes. Natives he would tolerate, and he got a great kick out of attracting them within range and then leaping at them with a ferocious scream. Not that I think he would ever have harmed them; he just liked to watch them run screaming in fear. But the trouble was that the natives would tease him if they got the chance, and Chumley would get more and more excited, his hair would stand on end, he would sway from side to side, swinging his powerful arms and baring his great teeth, and then heaven help the native who came too close.

Giant millipedes fascinated him, but he could never bring himself to trust them wholeheartedly. The giant millipede looks not unlike a thin black pudding, with a fringe of legs (a hundred or so pairs) arranged along the underside, and a pair of short feelers in front. They were completely harmless creatures that glided about on their numerous legs, their feelers waving, and liked nothing so much as a really rotten log of wood to feed on. However, their snakelike motion made them suspect in Chumley's eyes, although he seemed to realize that they were not snakes. If I placed a couple on his box he would sit and watch them for hours, his lips pursed, occasionally scratching himself. If one walked over the edge of the crate and fell to the ground and then started to walk in his direction, he would leap to his feet, retreat to the end of his chain, and scream loudly until I came and rescued him from the monster.

Snakes, of course, worried him a lot, and he would get really most upset if he saw me handling one, uttering plaintive cries and wringing his hands until I had put it down. If I showed him my hands after handling a snake he would always examine them carefully — I presume to make sure I had not been bitten. Whenever a snake slid towards him he would nearly have a fit; his hair would stand on end, he would moan, and, as it got closer, would throw bits of grass and twigs at it in a vain effort to stop its advance. One night he flatly refused to be shut in his box when it grew dark, a thing he had never done before. When I tried to force him in, thinking he was merely playing up, he led me to the door of the crate and, leaving me there, retreated, pointing with one hand and hoo-hooing loudly and in obvious fear. Investigating his blankets and banana-leaf bed, I discovered a small, blind, burrowing snake coiled up in the middle. This was a harmless creature, but Chumley was taking no chances.

Not long after Chumley's arrival he suddenly went off his food, lost all his interest in life, and would spend all day crouched in his crate. He would refuse all drink except about half a mugful of water a day. I was away at the time, and a frantic message from John brought me hurrying back, for John was not sure what the ape was suffering from or how ill he really was. On my return I tried everything I knew to tempt Chumley to eat, for he was growing visibly thinner. The staff was sent to search the countryside for ripe mangoes and paw-paws, and delicate fruit salads were concocted with great care by my own hands. But Chumley would not eat. This went on for nearly a week, until I was really beginning to think we should lose him. Every evening I would force him to take a walk with me, but he was so weak that he had to sit down and rest every few yards. But I knew it would be fatal to let him lose all interest in life, for once an ape does that he is doomed. One evening before I went to take Chumley for his walk I opened a tin of Ryvita biscuits and concealed a dozen or so in my pockets. When we had walked some distance Chumley sat down and I sat beside him. As we both examined the view I took a biscuit from my pocket and started to eat it. He watched me; I think he was rather surprised that I did not offer him any, as I usually did, but finished it up and smacked my lips appreciatively. He moved nearer and started to go through my pockets, which was in itself a good sign, for he had not done that since the first day he had been taken ill. He found a biscuit, pulled it out, sniffed it, and then, to my delight, ate it up. He again broached my pocket and got another, which he also ate. Altogether he ate six, and for the next four days he existed on water and Ryvita. Then came the morning when he accepted first his cup of tea and then two bananas. I knew he was going to be all right. His appetite came back with a rush, and he ate us out of house and home for about two weeks, and then he returned to narmal. I was very glad to have pulled him round, for we were due to leave for Kumba, and he was certainly in no condition to face the journey as thin as he had been.

The day of our departure from Bakebe dawned, and when Chumley saw the lorry arrive to load the collection he realized he was in for one of his favourite sports, a lorry ride. He hooted and yelled and danced on the end of his chain with excitement, and beat a wild tattoo on his crate, making as much noise as possible so that we should not overlook him. When everything else had been loaded his crate was hoisted on board, and then he climbed into it, hooting delightedly. We started off, and we had not gone far before the staff, all clinging to the back and sides of the vehicle, started to sing loudly, as they always did, and presently Chumley joined in with a prolonged and melodious hooting, which convulsed the staff. In fact, the cook-mate found a singing chimpanzee so amusing that he fell off the back of the lorry, and we had to stop and pick him up, covered with dust, but still mirthful. It was a good thing we were not going at any speed.

At Kumba, three schoolhouses belonging to the Basle Mission were put at our disposal, through the kindness of the Reverend Paul Schibler and his wife. On moving in, there was complete chaos for a while, as always happened when you made a fresh camp, and apart from numerous other things that had to be attended to, there was the question of water supply. While a suitable water-carrier was being employed, furnished with tins, and told to do his job at the double, Chumley made it quite clear that he was very thirsty indeed. He was chained outside, and had already attracted a large crowd of natives who had never seen a fully grown chimp before. In desperation I opened a bottle of beer and gave him that, and to my surprise he greeted its arrival with hoots of joy and smacked his lips over the froth. The lower the level fell in the bottle the more Chumley showed off, and the larger grew the crowd around him. Soon he was turning somersaults, and in between dancing a curious sort of side shuffle and clapping his hands. He was covered with beer froth, and enjoying himself hugely. But this drunken jig caused me a lot of trouble, for it took Chumley several hours to sober up and behave properly, and it took three policemen to disperse the crowd of two hundred people that was wedged around our houses, making entry and exit impossible. After that Chumley never had anything stronger than tea or lemonade, no matter how thirsty he became.

It was not long after we settled in at Kumba that Sue arrived. She was the youngest chimp I had ever seen: she could not walk and was the proud possessor of four teeth only. She arrived in a basket out of which she peered with wide-eyed interest, sucking her left foot. How she had been kept alive by her native owner, who had been feeding her on a diet of mashed coco yam, I don't know. Within an hour she was sucking away at a bottle full of warm milk, liberally laced with sugar and cod-liver oil. When I took her out to show her to Chumley he displayed no interest other than trying to poke her in the eye with his forefinger, so my hopes of a romantic attachment faded.

To any mother worn out with a squealing baby, I would be tempted to say, "Go and exchange it for a chimpanzee like Sue: it will be half the trouble and give you just as much pleasure." Sue spent the night in a warm basket, and the day on my bed, and there was never a murmur out of her. The only times she screamed, clenching her little fists and kicking her legs in gusts of fury, were on those occasions when I showed her the bottle and then discovered it was too hot for her to drink straightaway. This was a crime, and Sue let you know it. She had her first feeding at about seven o'clock in the morning, and her last feeding at midnight. She slept right through the night, a trick that is too uncommon among human babies. During the day, as I say, she would sprawl on my bed, lying there sucking her thumb or foot, or occasionally doing press-ups on the edge of the bed to get her arm muscles in trim for feeding time. Most of the day, however, she just slept.

Her face, hands, and feet were pink, and she had a thick coat of wiry black hair. On her head this looked as though it had been parted in the middle and then cut in a fringe over her large ears. She reminded me of a solemn-faced Japanese doll. At first sight her tender years (or months) had rather put me off, as I felt that she would

113

require endless attention which I had not the time to give her. But, as it turned out, she was considerably less trouble than any of the other animals. The animal staff were so captivated by her that they would fight for the privilege of giving her a bottle, and I even found John, on more than one occasion, prodding her fat middle and muttering baby talk at her, when he thought I was not within earshot.

Chumley was, I think a little jealous of Sue, but he was too much of a gentleman to show it. Not long after her arrival, however, the London Zoo's official collector arrived in the Cameroons, and with great regret I handed Chumley over to be transported back to England. I did not see him again for over four months, and then I went to visit him in the sanatorium at Regent's Park. He had a great straw-filled room to live in, and was immensely popular with the sanatorium staff. I did not think that he would recognize me, for when he had last seen me I had been clad in tropical kit and had sported a beard and moustache; now I was clean-shaven and wearing the garb of a civilized man. But recognize me he did, for he whirled around his room like a dervish when he saw me and then came rushing across to give me his old greeting, gently biting my finger. We sat in the straw and I gave him some sugar I had brought for him, and then we smoked a cigarette together while he removed my shoes and socks and examined my feet and legs to make sure there was nothing wrong with them.

Then he took his cigarette butt and carefully put it out in one corner of his room, well away from the straw. When the time came to go, he shook hands with me formally and watched my departure through the crack in the door. Shortly after he was moved to the monkey house, and so could receive no more visitors in his private room.

I never saw Chumley again, but I know his history: he became a great television star, going down to Alexandria Palace and doing his act in front of the cameras like an old trouper. Then his teeth started to worry him, and so he was moved from the monkey house back to the sanatorium to have an operation. One day, feeling bored with life, he broke out and sallied forth across Regent's Park. When he reached the main road he found a bus conveniently at hand, so he swung himself aboard; but his presence caused such horror amongst the occupants of the bus that he got excited and forgot himself so far as to bite someone. If only people would realize that to scream and panic is the best way of provoking an attack from any wild animal! Leaving the bus and its now bloodstained passengers, Chumley walked down the road, made a pass at a lady with a pram (who nearly fainted), and was wandering about to see what else he could do to liven life up for Londoners, when a member of the sanatorium staff arrived on the scene. By then I expect Chumley had realized that civilized people were no decent company for a well-brought-up chimp, so he took his keeper's hand and walked back home. After this he was branded as not safe and sent back to the monkey house. But he had not yet finished with publicity, for some time later he had to go back to the sanatorium for yet more treatment on his teeth, and he decided to repeat his little escapade.

It was Christmas Eve and Chumley obviously had memories of other and more convivial festivities, probably spent at some club in the depths of Africa. Anyway, he decided that if he had a walk around London on Christmas Eve, season of goodwill, he might run across someone who would offer him a beer. So he broke open his cage and set off once more across Regent's Park. At Gloucester Gate he looked about hopefully for a bus, but there was not one in sight. But there were some cars parked there and Chumley approached them and beat on the doors vigorously, in the hope that the occupants would open up and offer him a lift. Chumley loved a ride in any sort of conveyance. But the foolish humans misconstrued his actions: there he was, full of Christmas spirit, asking for a lift, and all they could do was to wind up their windows and yell for help. This, thought Chumley, was a damn poor way to show a fellow the traditional British hospitality. But before he had time to explain his mission to the car owners, a panting posse of keepers arrived, and he was bundled back to the Zoo. Chumley had escaped twice, and they were not going to risk it happening again. From being a fine, intelligent animal, good enough to be displayed on television, he had suddenly become (by reason of his escapades) a fierce and untrustworthy monster, who might escape yet again and bite some worthy citizen. To avoid this risk, Chumley was sentenced to death and shot.

The Night Raider

Walter D. Edmonds

The farm buildings stood in the river valley, with a rushing brook separating them from the big house in which we lived. My father liked to feel that someday the farm might pay for itself, and he had the idea that the bigger it was, the more likely it was to do so. He kept adding to the dairy herd until there were almost eighty head of milking cows. With old Woodlawn, the Holstein bull, and the calves and young stock the herd numbered one hundred. There were two farm teams and an odd horse to rake hay and pull the potato hiller and take the three great milk cans to the cheese factory.

In the carriage barn he kept three more horses. He had a hen house full of Rhode Island Reds and Plymouth Rocks, a hog house with Black Berkshire pigs, sheep that pastured on the uplands in summer, a flock of turkeys that also ranged on the uplands every day, Indian Runner ducks in the brook, and finally he acquired a flock of guinea hens. It was because of them that the raider was drawn to the farm.

I was seven then, and for me life began each morning only when I had crossed the brook to the farm buildings. I would stop first at the farmhouse where the superintendent, old Nelson, lived with his wife, Mrs. Goodwell, to find out what would be going on that day. Life on a big farm is a very complex operation, but Nelson had it all at his fingertips.

He was a tall, heavy-built, quiet-spoken man with shoulders so rounded that he seemed almost hunchbacked. As he explained it, his shoulders got that way during the battle of Gettysburg. He had been fourteen then, a slim, long-boned boy, who had volunteered to bring in wounded soldiers. According to Mrs. Goodwell he had worked without stopping, wheeling wounded soldiers in a wheelbarrow to the hospital stations, for three days and the best part of three nights, and his shoulders had never straightened up again. He was the most powerful man I had ever seen. Once, he picked up a threshing hand who was foul-mouthing our family and carried him over his head to the back door of the carriage barn and threw him out on the manure pile. I admired him more than anyone I knew.

When I went up on the farmhouse porch he would come out and list the day's activities. Eugene Wills, the teamster, who lived in the cottage over the lawn, might be cultivating the cornfield with the sulky cultivator behind the grey team, or driving the mowing machine or the reaper, or plowing, according to the season. De Witt Parks, who lived in the farmhouse along with his son D-D, and who tended the poultry, would be cleaning the hen house or fussing with the setting hens. He was a gaunt widower, too old for heavy work. D-D was already off with the spring wagon and the three great milk cans on his way to the cheese factory. Nelson himself was doing chores around the barn because one of the registered heifers, Jacqueline De Koll, was about due with her first calf.

So it went, and I could make my plans for my day — where I wanted to be, and when. I didn't want to miss anything worth seeing; I felt more at home among the farm animals and poultry than I did in my own family; and in my way I found plenty to do. The cows went out to day pasture before I got up, but most days I went up over the uplands to find them and bring them back. And when the young turkeys got big enough, my brother and I would drive the whole flock of maybe two hundred up on the flats where they fed on grasshoppers all day among the sheep. The turkeys, though, always brought themselves home at sunset. They would take off at the steep edge of the flats and come sailing down through the sunset air to land at the edge of the creek. As my father got the notion of putting a sleigh bell around the necks of most of the old hens and gobblers, you could hear the silvery notes dropping down through the evening sky from all over the farm.

During the summer months, their only danger came from the larger hawks. But the turkeys took care of that in their own way. Each day four or five of the hens and gobblers would be posted as sentinels. They stayed in the outskirts of the flock, one eye or the other continually cocked sidewise at the sky till one wondered why they didn't get permanent neck cramps. The minute they spotted a hawk they would cluck and holler till the entire flock had been alerted. The hens would turn on their young ones, pecking and beating their wings to drive them under the nearest thornapple bush. With the young ones under the thorny branches, the hens would ring the bush facing out, while the gobblers strutted around the perimeter with hoarse, half-gobbling challenges. No hawk ever tried to break down those defenses. I think they might even have baffled a fox. Big turkeys are great fighters, and I once saw two hens jump an osprey who had lit on a young bird, shove him over on his back, and kill him right there, though it took quite a bit of time. Turkeys have a lot of knowledge in ways that suit themselves. And nights they were always in their own poultry house.

But with the guinea hens it was entirely different.

My father, who liked doing things in an impressive way, had decided to start his flock of guinea hens by buying three dozen birds. He thought they would add to the picturesque side of the farm, with their pale blue faces, red wattles, and speckled grey plumage. There was also in his mind the image of broiled young guinea hens appearing on a platter in front of him on the dining table. In the beginning it looked like a fool-proof program. None of us, however, knew anything about their habits, if guinea hens can be said to have any habits at all.

They nested hit or miss, outdoors, wherever it fancied them to drop the first egg. I found most of these nests and marked them with a stake nearby fluttering a strip of red cotton, as a precaution against their not having hatched before the mowing started. Unfortunately, I did not find them all and we had casualties. But most did hatch out in good time, and after that we would see the adult birds whizzing up the drive in their strange, bent-forward run, or rushing through the barnyard, followed by a stream of tiny chicks like dark-brown mottled bumblebees. How the chicks ever managed to keep up was a mystery to everyone on the farm. The trouble was, however, that the adult birds were continually flying back and forth across the brook, and the babies, still in their soft down, had to swim as best they could with their little bare and stick-like feet. Nearly three-quarters of them, as far as we could tell, were drowned that way.

They had other irritating traits. They were always discussing with each other. You could hear their endless "pot-rack, pot-rack!" all over the place. When the young birds got old enough to stop peeping and "pot-rack" like their elders, the noise could be deafening. Along about midsummer they started coming over the brook and holding sunrise concourse on the front lawn, directly under my father's bedroom windows, and yelling there till he threw open the sash and began hurling sticks of firewood at them. This fazed them not at all. They merely withdrew from range and continued their clamor on a derisive note; and after three weeks, O'Toole, the coachman, whose duties included keeping the fireplaces stocked with wood, rebelled at bringing up another stick thrown out by no matter who, gave notice, and returned to the city.

So all of us learned to endure their rackety ways, and after my father stopped throwing wood out the window, they lost interest in our house and stayed mostly on the farm side of the brook.

August turned into September; the dark came earlier; the nights were cold enough for light upland frosts; and the tempo of the farm changed with the season. There were no grasshoppers left on the flats, and the turkeys stayed on the lower meadows. We no longer heard the cascade of sleigh bells as they planed down from the top of the hill. The dairy herd did not have to be hunted through the woods and glades at the back of the place; they would come winding down the sandy raod at twilight of their own accord and wait at the gate at the foot of the hill, so that whoever fetched them had only two hundred yards to walk. The men going to the barn to milk carried lighted lanterns, which they hung above the runway between the rows of stanchions.

The barn became a different place in lantern light, with the dust motes in the yellow air and only the rumps of the stanchioned cows clear to view, punctuated by the milkers and the soft slurring of the milk jets in the pails. You seemed to hear it much more clearly in the lantern light, with the big doors shut against the cold.

The early darkness also changed the nighttime habits of the poultry. The ducks clamored to get into the barn, where they had a pen in the hall-like space that separated the cowbarn from the horses' stable at the far end. The hens entered their house earlier than before, rooting around the chaff floor for the cracked corn and hopping sleepily to the roosting board as the shadows thickened. The turkey flock, depleted now by the sale of most of the young birds for broilers, were glad to go into their own house beyond the hog house on what was called the hog-house hill. But the biggest change took place among the guinea hens. All summer they had moved about in high independence of each other, perching anywhere their fancy struck them or squatting in a tuft of grass. Now all at once they joined in a single flock and every night marched in formation, in what was almost a parading of the guard, through the farm buildings and up the hog-house hill to a large black-cherry tree, on whose wide limbs they roosted in long lines. When the great, full October moon rose over the pond we could see their bumpy silhouettes stuck tight to the spreading branches.

The mornings too were slower to get started. I would hear the herd bells moving off along the road to day pasture as I was getting dressed, while in summer they were often gone before I woke. The routine of the farm seemed to contract, as if in preparation for the harsh constriction of our northern winter. Frost was not only on the uplands now; it crackled in the grass when I went out after breakfast, and if I walked up to the dam, as I often did, I could see the frost mists rising off the water, forming swaying pillars of white, like ghosts fading before day.

I was coming back from the dam one morning when I saw the first of the strange tubelike objects that mystified not only myself but everyone else on the place. It was about an inch and a half long and a quarter inch in diameter. I thought it was a worm, but when I picked it up it was rubbery and harder than a worm would be, and its ends were square, as if cut by a knife. Then I noticed a speckled grey guinea feather, and after a moment came on three more beyond it. But I saw no reason to connect them with the little pink tube.

Nor did my father, when I showed it to him. He didn't seem much interested. Nobody was. It was just one of those things that continually turned up on any farm. No one knew what it was, and it didn't matter, because you'd never see another. But the next morning I found another one, very nearly in the same spot. This time a lot of feathers were lying about, and it seemed obvious that something drastic had happened to a guinea hen there.

I brought the little piece of tubing back to the house and this time it aroused more interest and speculation; but nobody knew what it was. In my own mind I felt that something evil and terrible was coming out of the autumn woods after dark, and now De Witt Parks, the poultry-man, came to my father and said that he felt sure that something was getting at the guinea hens. He had found feathers for two nights under the cherry tree they roosted on, and to make sure, he had picked all the feathers up the night before, but this morning there had been a new batch of them.

For two days I found no more pink tubes. Then on the third day there was another up on the dam. I picked it up as I had the others. The dam was white with frost that morning, my feet had left plain black prints in it, and I realized that around the spot where I had picked up the tube, there was no other track. Whatever was responsible might have come early in the night, I supposed, and the frost fell heaviest towards morning, covering tracks. But that did not seem likely to me.

I went back to the house again with my find, but my father was busy talking to an old man he sometimes went hunting with. Birdy Morris had come around to see if Father would go off for an afternoon of partridge shooting and hoped also to arrange a deer-hunting party for next Sunday if Father would agree to let them hunt our land or, better yet, to join their party.

I could see them discussing this while I stood looking in through the living-room window, and presently Birdy caught my eye. I heard him say, "Your boy out there looks as if he wanted to see us."

"Oh, yes," my father said. "He's been finding some peculiar things around the place. He's probably found another."

They called me in and I showed the small pink piece of tubing to Birdy. He was a shortish man who looked even shorter because one shoulder was deformed. But his eyes were bright as the eyes of a wild thing peering from a thicket. He took the tubing from me and rolled it gently between thumb and finger.

"Yes," he said. "It's a piece of something's windpipe. Can't say what, with just it to look at."

"There were some guinea feathers," I said.

"That's it, then. You've got an owl raiding your guinea hens. Horn owl, it will be. That's how they kill. Two claws and cut a piece out of the windpipe clean as razors."

He went on to say that the horn owl wasn't afraid of anything that he had ever heard of. (Father later said that Birdy Morris should have called it a great horned owl; but you couldn't expect a backwoods type like him to know such things.) They were bigger than the barred owls and a tarnation sight more powerful. They'd go for just about anything. One once had gone for him.

"Got into my attic loft through a broke window. My wife — she was alive then — kept telling me to mend it, but you know how them things be. I heard a noise up there and went up through the trapdoor and the danged thing hit me. Lucky I had my hat on and he took that. You can bet I had the door shut before he found it wasn't me, and the next time I opened it I had my scatter gun poked through ahead of me."

Abruptly, as old men will, he lost interest in me and owls and turned to finish his business with my father. When I went out across the brook to tell Nelson and De Witt what Birdy had told us, I saw his bent-shouldered figure ambling down the river road.

I showed the windpipe to Nelson, who said he had never heard of such a thing, but was inclined to believe it, if Birdy said so. Birdy knew everything there was to know about the woods and the animals who lived among them. De Witt was skeptical. It did not seem a rational way for anything, wild or not, to kill some other thing. He was busy anyway giving the hen house its monthly cleanup and scattering the first winter layer of chaff over the floor.

But that afternoon, just before sundown, he came over the brook to talk to my father.

"There's something funny going on with the

guinea hens," he said. "They're standing under that cherry tree they roost on but there's not one flown up into it. They're all hollering and yelling. Seems almost they're hollering by turns."

Father told De Witt not to worry about it. In his opinion all the guinea hens were crazy.

De Witt shook his head. "Seems almost as if they wasn't going to roost there tonight, and they're trying to make up their minds where to go to instead."

"They haven't got any minds," my father said impatiently. Forget about them, De Witt."

But De Witt wasn't satisfied. And sure enough, when I went out with him to the barnyard, we saw the guinea hens coming down off the hog-house hill. They moved in close order at their usual running gait, whizzing around the corner of the big cowbarn and heading straight for the hen house.

"Just as if they knowed where they was going," De Witt said admiringly.

They obviously did know, for as they reached the hen-yard fence, the leading birds turned to face the rest of the flock. There was a brief, intense harangue. Then the leaders flew up and over the fence, followed in threes and fours by the rest. Inside the yard they formed up close and marched on the three small poultry openings that led into the house, running up the sloping boards that led to them and into the hen house. A moment later there was a protesting outcry from the hens. When De Witt and I looked through the door the hens were standing in a huddle on the floor, still protesting, and the guinea hens had taken over the roost.

"What are you going to do with them?" I asked.

"Nothing," De Witt said. "If we tried to get them out now, there'd be such a commotion the hens wouldn't come back into the house for a week, let alone lay an egg. You don't ever want any commotion around hens if you can help it. Their minds addle too easy." He took his hat off in order to scratch the top of his head. "Maybe Birdy Morris is right," he allowed. "And if it's an owl, I want to do something about getting rid of it. Come on, we'll go see your pa again."

We went back to the big house and found my father in the living room. De Witt told him about the guinea hens. "I can't get rid of them tonight, but I'll close the chicken doors tomorrow before they get down there. But Mr. Edmonds, we ought to take care of that owl, or whatever it is, before he goes after something else."

"What do you suggest, De Witt?"

"I want to take a Plymouth Rock pullet and wire her to a limb of that cherry tree and set a trap."

"Seems a shame to waste a pullet that way," my father said. "But go ahead if you think you can catch the owl."

So we went back across the brook, and while De Witt went to get a pullet, I hunted out Nelson and asked for an Oneida jump trap. Then I went up to the cherry tree on the hog-house hill.

De Witt was already there with a dead pullet and some fine wire. The bottom branch, which a large part of the guinea hen flock had used for roosting, was within his reach. He wired the body of the pullet to it and in what I considered an artful way. It rested breast down on the branch, and he had tucked its head underneath a wing. It looked for all the world like a pullet sleeping on its roost. Then he set the trap and with a piece of heavy thread tied it on the back of the dead pullet, passed the chain around the branch, and stapled the ring at the end of it solidly into the wood.

"I don't expect a bird's knowing about traps, like a fox or mink," De Witt said, as we walked back down the hill to the barn. "But we'll see in the morning."

As we were sitting at breakfast next morning a great to-do of gasping exclamations broke out in the kitchen, and Maggie, the waitress, hurried in to tell my father that De Witt had something to show him.

"Tell him to come in," my father said, and a moment later De Witt's gaunt, bony figure edged in through the pantry door. He was wearing Eugene the teamster's heaviest leather gloves and holding the legs of a great owl whose body was tucked under his arm.

I remember as if it were today the way the great bird looked, his golden eyes glaring at us, the tufts that got him his name of "horned" erect and stiff. Beneath De Witt's gloved hands the thickly feathered toes with their curved talons opened and closed. He may have been afraid but all I remember in his face was his scorn and hatred for us all. If he felt any fear, he did not let it show.

My mother turned quite pale. "Oh, De Witt," she said, "how dreadful!" And De Witt, who obviously did not think it was dreadful at all, said, "Yes, mam."

"What are you going to do with him?" Father asked.

"I have a chicken crate for him in Nelson's cellar," De Witt replied. "We can't let him go."

"No. Will he eat anything?" my father asked.

"We haven't tried," said De Witt.

"Well, put him back in it," my father said, "and we'll decide what to do."

De Witt took him away. Asking to be excused, I followed him. There was the same flutter among the maids. The cook thought the owl looked "fearful," but the waitress exclaimed, "Oh, no! He's beautiful. See the golden eyes on him!" Both of them seemed rather ridiculous to me, and I walked out behind De Witt and over the brook to the open bulkhead doors leading down into Nelson's cellar. Only two of the high, small windows in the foundation wall were open to the sky, and the cellar was dark enough for my eyes to take a minute to adjust themselves. Then I could see De Witt kneeling before a chicken crate, which for some reason was on its side, against the far wall. I could not think why until, with infinite carefulness to avoid the owl's beak, he maneuvered the bird through the door. The owl still snapped his beak at him through the bars of the crate; it made a thin, brittle, almost pathetically small sound, but its fierceness was unmistakable.

De Witt stood up and then I could see why the crate was on its side. Unless it had been, the owl could not have stood upright. As we drew back he seemed to compose himself. His wings, which had been spread an inch or two away from his body as he threatened De Witt through the bars of the crate, now closed. The owl stood perfectly still but his ferocity remained undiminished. As I turned to follow De Witt up the bulkhead steps I felt the bird's eyes staring after me. Even when I had closed the bulkhead doors I seemed to see them.

At noon there was another stir in the kitchen. The waitress had gone to see the owl in Nelson's cellar and, putting her hand too close to the crate, had had a piece taken out of the end of her finger.

"He'll have to be killed," my father said.

But that evening De Witt and Nelson came over to our house. De Witt carried the owl by its legs, barehanded. The bird hung inert, his wings limply spread. He had died of natural causes, Nelson and De Witt decided. If confinement in a chicken crate in a farmhouse cellar, with the stamp of people walking overhead, can be considered natural for an owl, maybe they were right. But it seemed to me that he had died of hatred and the dread he did not let us see.

The Gray Mules*

Ben K. Green

One winter I was feeding a bunch of steers on the Brazos River on a big old rough ranch — rough pasture and lots of canyons and draws. The river was winding, and it was a hard kind of country to get your feed out into the pasture to feed cattle. Of course, in those days we used wagons and teams for everything.

I had a young team of horses that were thrown in on the deal when I leased the ranch, and that were supposed to be unbroke. Well, that was putting it mildly. Generally when you say a team is unbroke, you are talking about young horses three or four or five years old that just never have been worked. When I got this team up, they were a pair of well-matched bay, bald-faced horses that weighed about fourteen hundred, and instead of being four or five years old and unbroke — they were eight or nine years old and had been broke *at*. But there was sure nobody had ever done much of a job of breaking them.

*From *Horse Tradin'*, a book of yarns from a Texas cowboy and horse trader.

135

They were the rankest, big draft-type horses that I had ever had any experience with. When you roped them, they choked and pawed and fought. Then when you got them up and got your hands on them, you would have to tie a foot up on each one to harness them — if you didn't, they would kick you from behind and paw you in front and bite you anytime you weren't looking. Generally, big horses are gentle, but these weren't.

Every morning after I'd load my feed wagon, I'd start to hitch up this team. That meant I'd have to rope them and tie them to a tree and try to get harness on them. And after I'd get them harnessed — each one separately — I'd have to get them up by the side of each other and hook them together and then run them over the wagon tongue — two or three times — before I ever got them to stop where I could draw them back in position to hook them to the wagon. After they were hooked to the wagon, they would either try to run away or try to balk and fly back two or three times when you tried to start them with a load.

I had been carrying on this kind of a battle every morning for about three weeks. It was taking me twice as long to tend to my steers as it should have, and I decided I had to have another work team. One Saturday morning I hooked them up to the wagon loaded with feed and started through the pasture gate; just as I got the gate open, they came through it and tried

136

to run away. They hung the back wheel on the gatepost, broke the coupling-pin, and ran off with the four wheels. It just happened they ran astraddle a tree — got it between them — and didn't get very far. But this was the final performance that made it easy for me to get rid of them.

The ranch was about thirty-five miles west of Fort Worth; so Sunday morning I saddled up a good saddle horse, led this pair of great big horses over to Fort Worth, took them to Ross Brothers Horse and Mule Barn, and checked them in to be sold the next day at the auction. I got a stall for my saddle horse and cleaned him off and fed him good before I went up to Mrs. Brown's boardinghouse to spend the night.

This was a big old boardinghouse on top of the hill overlooking the horse and mule barns, on the west end of Exchange Avenue. It was kind of horse traders' headquarters, and it was about the only place along about then that I knew to spend the night in Fort Worth — unless I went away over across town to the big hotels.

Next morning I was out at the horse and mule barns early, looking around to pick me out a good team that I knew would be safe and a sure-pull and wouldn't cause me any more grief through the winter while I was trying to tend to those steers. Since I had gotten in with my horses Sunday, they were in the early part of the sale Monday morning.

When they came in the ring, Jim Shelton was

doing the auctioneering. He looked down and saw my name on the ticket and said: "Ben, tell me about these horses."

I said: "Well, they're a big stout pair of green-broke horses." My name was Green and I had put the breakin' on them — what little they'd had — so I guessed I could say they were green-broke, although that usually just meant a pair of horses that hadn't been worked much. Anyway, they sold for more money than I had hoped to get for them.

I had been up and down the alleys and back of the barns and looked at some horses and some mules. I had watched them hook-in some various teams of mules to the try-wagon out in front, to see how they would work. I had decided that a good pair of steady mules would be better for me to try to finish feeding cattle through the winter than horses would be. Mules are always more dependable to a wagon in a hard pull, and they usually are quieter than horses are; so I had made up my mind that I'd buy me a nice pair of mules.

I sat there and watched horses and mules sell for three or four hours and got pretty well posted on what I thought mules like I wanted ought to bring when they'd come in the auction ring. About two-thirty in the afternoon I had already decided that I couldn't ride home and lead a team of mules that day — that I'd have to stay over; so I wasn't in too big a hurry to spend my money.

Late that afternoon a great big nice pair of dapple-gray mare mules came into the ring. They were well made and fat, they had good dispositions, and when the man led them around the ring he touched their ears to show they weren't shy about their ears when they were being bridled. Parker Jamison looked in their mouths — he was the ring man — and he hollered out loud: "The prettiest mouths you ever saw. Mark 'em about eight-year-olds."

Wad Ross started them at $200. A few people bid on them — people you could see were commenting on them. I couldn't hear what they were saying, but there was something unusual. The bidding went up to $240, and I bid $250. Didn't anybody else raise my bid. Two or three fellows turned around and looked where I was standing to see who it was bid the $250. I just thought to myself that they were looking at me because I knew a good team when I saw it.

Well, directly Jim Shelton — he was the auctioneer — knocked the mules off to me and hollered: "Sold!"

I watched them go out at the gate and run down the plank alley. They were so near alike, you would have thought they were twins. I saw the pen they turned into, and I had got the numbers off their hips while they were in the ring. When you bid on horses or mules and bought them, then a ticket boy would bring you a ticket. So when I got a ticket, I tore off down the barn alley to look at the mules I'd bought.

I walked in the pen and drove them out on the plank alley to themselves and stood there and looked at them and rubbed them a little bit with my hands. Oh, they were nice, well-made, beautifully dappled mules. I got ahold of the barn foreman and asked if he couldn't put them off in a separate pen where wouldn't anything happen to them — they wouldn't get skinned up or maybe kicked in the night.

He was real nice, said he knew I was proud of that pair of mules and he didn't blame me — he would be proud of them, too — and that he would put them over to one side in a pen to themselves. Of course he knew me, knew I was horseback. He said he would sure help me with them and I could go on and forget them.

Well, I had seen a lot of horse and mule selling that day and I was kind of tired of the barn; so I got on the streetcar and rode over to the big main part of Fort Worth to eat a big steak at the Siebold Hotel. I went up to the picture show — the Majestic Theater — and saw Richard Dix in *Cimarron*. Then I went back to Mrs. Brown's boardinghouse and went to bed about nine-thirty. I had a long ride ahead of me the next morning.

I got to the horse and mule barn by daylight. After two nights and one day's rest, my saddle horse was in good shape and ready to go. I got him saddled and rigged out and got my mules out. They had nice woven grass halters on them like used to come on horses and mules that were bought at auctions, and I tied a long lead rope to these halters. Somebody held my lead rope while I got on my saddle horse, handed me the lead rope, and I started out of the horse and mule market and up Exchange Avenue. I was going to hit the White Settlement Road and head out west. It was pretty chilly, but not real cold, and the sun not near in sight.

I was way out in the edge of town before it got good sun-up, and my horse settled down to a nice long sweeping walk. This was a good pair of mules, and they traveled nice and walked right up by my horse. I crossed plank bridges with them and they didn't shy or pull back — or get scared from meeting anybody — and the farther I went toward home with them, the better I liked them and the prouder I was of them. It was a little after dark when I rode into the ranch, and I put my new mules in a small pasture next to the barn and gave them plenty of feed. I turned my saddle horse loose and fed him and went to bed thinking how much nicer it was going to be to tend my cattle through the rest of the winter with the right kind of a work team.

This was about the nicest colored pair of dapple-gray mare mules anybody ever saw. The dappling was real smooth and beautiful and uniform over their hindquarters and up and down their sides and around their shoulders. Their heads and necks were just a little lighter color, just as they should be. Then their feet and legs from their knees and their hock joints to the ground were real dark, just the way they should be. They had a beautiful color for a pair of eight-year-old mare mules, just about as nice as anybody could ever have wished for. I don't believe a real good artist could have painted them any more perfect than they were.

In the meantime, I had left instructions to get my wagon brought in and fixed, and I had the wheels and the coupling-poles all ready to hook up to it that morning and start back to feeding my cattle. I got these mules out, and I had to let the harness out some to where it would fit them. They were a nice, big pair, and it took big harness to fit them. I had several collars, and I had to change around until I got the collars that would fit on them good — to where they could pull good and not hurt their shoulders. I just could hardly take my eyes off of them, they had such a beautiful dapple-gray color.

I hooked up to the wagon and drove them around the lot two or three times to the empty wagon. They didn't do a thing wrong. They didn't make a bobble or take a wrong step. And I backed them up to the crib of the barn where I loaded my feed, dropped my lines, and said: "Woah." They just stood there. As I threw feed into the wagon I made noise throwing the sacks around; they never moved. I finally had a team that were just broke to perfection.

I put on a big load of feed and started out through the pasture. It was a big old long rough pasture, some hills and bad places to pull over, and one place I went down into the valley and across the creek. It was the common way you forded a creek — no bridge or nothing — and coming out of the bank on the other side it was a little slick. The load was heavy, and these mules got down just as smooth and even and pulled with each other as steady as you every saw a team pull. It was quite a relief from the work team I'd had in that pair of horses.

I had my saddle horse leading behind, tied to the back of the wagon. I drove up to the feed grounds where generally I'd feed my cattle, and they weren't all there. I called and hollered a few times, and you could hear a few cattle bawl. Some were coming; some were up on the side of the mountain and weren't trying to get down there to the feed grounds. I left my new team standing with the lines done up, but not tied to any kind of a tree or post or hitched in any way. I thought: "This pair of mules is so perfect, they won't run off with the wagonload of feed."

I got on my saddle horse and loped up in the hills and started the cattle moving toward the feed ground. I circled around, and after I knew everything was coming in good, I rode back down to the wagon. There that pair of dapple-gray mules stood, just perfect. They hadn't offered to get scared or run off or twist around or try to graze or do anything that a good mule oughtn't to do.

I fed my cattle at this pasture and tied my horse to the back of the wagon again. I stepped in and took the lines down from the stick I had them wrapped around. Since I had unloaded some of my feed, I trotted my mules off in a pretty good trot and started over into another pasture about a mile away. This good pair of mules didn't mind trotting to the load. They stayed in step good, and it was a pleasure to stand up in the wagon and look over them and watch how nice they worked. It was just hard to believe an eight-year-old pair of mules would be so near perfect.

By the time I got to the next feed ground, they had begun to break a sweat a little around the collars and up and down the backbands and around where the breeching worked on their hindquarters. I didn't think a little sweat hurt a mule, so I just trotted them on to the next feed ground. I had to round the cattle up in this pasture, and I left my mules standing out in the feed ground, close to a feed trough. They were just perfect. They stood there until I got back. I rode up and put out the feed and tied my horse back to the wagon. I had one more pasture to feed.

I drove across the creek again and up the bank on the other side — pulled them pretty hard. I thought there was a little dirt working out of their hides and their hair maybe. I noticed some black lines coming along the backbands and around the collars where the sweat worked out. I didn't think much about it, only I just thought they sure were a nice pair of mules to be that dirty. I hadn't noticed too much dirt in their hides when I was harnessing them, but that didn't bother me much. I stopped them at the next feed ground to wind up my morning's work. It was kinda clouding up and misting a little bit, and these cattle came to feed better than the others had.

I did the reins up on my saddle horn. My saddle horse knew the way back to headquarters — he didn't have to follow the wagon — so he trotted on out the road in front of us, and I stepped the mules up to a good brisk trot. When they moved out, I noticed the backbands were working the sweat back and forth — and that every time they did, the hair got a little whiter around the backbands and a little bit more dirt piled up and down that ridge. There was a little sweat coming on their hind legs, and I noticed some black lines running down their legs. I didn't think much about that. I just thought these mules must have been wallowing somewhere in the blackland and just had a lot of dirt down next to the hide — and I hadn't noticed it.

When I went through the last pasture gate and started up to the house, a little shower came and sort of washed everything off. It was a quick little hard shower, and I pulled my jacket up over my head and rode along. The mules were trotting along good; my saddle horse was on ahead, probably to the barn by now; I wasn't looking too close — just letting the mules go, following the road at a good brisk trot. When we pulled up at the barn another pretty hard shower hit, and I ran in the barn. I thought I would stay until it let up, and then I would unhook my team.

Well, my team was pretty warm — of course, it wouldn't hurt a good mule to get rained on — so I stood in the feed room a few minutes until it slowed raining, and then I went out. I was keeping my head kinda ducked — to keep the rain from hitting me in the face — as I unhooked the traces and unhooked the coupling-pole and drove the mules up to the edge of the barn where the water wouldn't hit quite so much. I went to taking off the collars and the harness, and after I stripped it off and hung it up in the barn — I turned around and looked.

My mules had sure bleached out a batch — between getting sweaty and getting rained on! And I had a lot of stain all over my hands — and all over my sleeve where I had run my hand through the harness to carry it in and hang it up in the barn!

By this time I had forgot that it was misting rain, and I rubbed my hand down one mule's neck and across where the collar had worked — and I just rubbed off great, big, wide streaks of those beautiful dapples. And the farther I rubbed, the more dapples I rubbed. And the more I rubbed, the sicker I got. When it got through raining, and I got through rubbing, I had a pair of mules as white as gray mules can get in a lifetime. Now, they were just as white as white mules ever get to be! This was sure the first time

I ever lost $100 on a pair of mules in two days — without one of them dying.

Well, I had that color all over me, and I hadn't decided yet what kind it was. Anyway, I kinda washed my hands in a little puddle on the ground by the side of the barn where it dripped, and I opened one of these mules's mouths. She had a cup in the corner tooth like an eight-year-old ought to have; but her tooth was too long for an eight-year-old, it was too wide across the top, and it was too ridged up and down the side. My mules were a good thirteen or fourteen years old. Somebody had worked their mouths and made them an eight-year-old corner, and evidently somebody had given them a dye job. I didn't know what they were dyed with or how anybody did it. The dapples were so natural and so purple and so well shaped — nobody in the world could ever have guessed that they didn't belong to these mules.

Then it kinda began to dawn on me about that whispering and looking that those people did when I was bidding on this pair of mules. And I got to thinking how that barn foreman smiled when he said he would help me take care of them — that he knew I wouldn't want anything to happen to them. I don't know whether women had beauty parlors by then or not — but there was bound to have been a mule beauty parlor somewhere, because that pair had as nice a hair job done as could be done on any kind of animal.

They were a real nice work pair, and I was

busy wintering a bunch of cattle, and the weather was bad. I kinda hibernated and stayed at home and fed steers and worked my mules. There was just no fault in their working qualities or their dispositions. They stayed fat, and they were easy to shoe — never offered to kick or do anything wrong. There was just nothing wrong with them except that dye job. The color had made it pretty deceiving about how old they were. The dapple-gray color went with an eight-year-old tooth, but the white color they had now went with a mouth that looked about fourteen years old when you got to looking at it close. When Parker Jamison called the age on them, I don't know whether he knew the difference or not. I imagine he did, but he was trying to match the mouth up with the color.

I got to hunting through my vest pocket, and I found the ticket that showed who owned the mules when they were consigned to the sale. Of course, I never bothered about who bought that green-broke pair of horses — that was their trouble. What I was bothered about was that dye job on this pair of mules. I saw that the name on the ticket was that of a very prominent horse and mule man who lived off down about Hillsboro somewhere.

I went to two or three First-Monday trades around over the country, and I'd get into conversation with a bunch of road traders or old-time horse and mule men. I would just sort of bring up casual-like about: "Wouldn't it be nice if a dapple-gray mule could just keep its color like that all its life."

It generally didn't start much conversation, except that everybody would say: "Yeah, but the older they git the whiter they git." Which wasn't news to me.

I would just say: "Uh-huh," and walk off.

Hardly anybody knew about my mules because I had kept them at home and worked them, and I had got them home without anybody seeing them. Oh, maybe some of the neighbors had noticed they had whitened out on me, but it didn't ever dawn on them how come it. One man did say something about them turning awful white. I said: "Yeah, the hair has got out on them long, and I guess they'll blue back up when they shed in the spring."

I knew an Irish horse trader that was about a half-breed gypsy — been raised in a road camp. I kept laying for him, but it didn't seem like he was ever going to come through the country again. I figured he would know how you manage to do a blue job on a mule.

I took some saddle horses to Decatur one trades day, to trade maybe for something different. These horses weren't good and they weren't bad, it was just that once in a while you would want to change colors on your stock — or sizes, or ages, or something. Anyway, you needed to have a little variety among your livestock, some new experiences about what could be the matter or what could be good about some of them. So in Decatur, about the middle of the morning, I spied my old Irish horse trader friend.

He and I traded a few times in years past. It never had been anything big. We always hurrahed and tried to cheat each other if we could — but for a horse trader he was sort of on the honest side, and I was just a great big wild rough young boy and he kinda liked me. A time or two he had told me things I needed to know, so I propositioned him to let's go up town and eat some dinner. He lived in a road camp and ate his own cooking, or camp cooking, so he said he believed he'd like a little change and he believed he'd just take me up on my proposition.

We got some chile or some stew or something — I don't know. We ate a pretty good little batch of dinner and visited and talked about how the country looked and where he had been since I saw him last. By this time we were about to order pie and wind up the dinner; so I decided I'd better ease up on these gray mules. I said: "It's a pity that a nice dapple-gray mule or horse can't stay that color all its life."

"Yeah," he said, "but we all get gray when we get old."

"I know," I said, "You are getting a little gray, but I ain't worried about you — and it's a long way off for me — but I got some mules that got gray pretty soon."

He had a sharp black eye, and he glanced up at me real quick. A little twist came in the corner of his lip, and he said: "How do you mean?"

Well, I hadn't told anybody else, but I didn't think he would tell on me; so I explained to him what had happened about my mules. He thought it was real funny, and we had a good laugh. Then he said: "Where did the mules come from?"

I told him about this high-class horse and mule man from down around Hillsboro who had sent them to Fort Worth — that his name was on the ticket when I bought them.

"Oh, you mean him! I remember when he was a road trader — till he married that rich woman that had a good farm. Then," he said, "he got respectable. He's not supposed to remember any old tricks like that — much less play 'em on people that are buyin' work stock."

"What do you mean — old trick?"

So he described how the dapples looked on the mules, and sure enough, he knew. He knew that they were darker and bigger around on the sides and down on the lower part of the belly. And he knew that they were smaller and lighter up around their necks and shoulders. He just knew exactly how these mules were colored — and he never had seen them.

I said: "Damn, did this man from Hillsboro learn how to color them mules from you, or did you learn from him? Evidently you all are using the same color pattern."

He kinda laughed and said: "I'll tell you — I'll go down and look at your horses and see if there is anything I want to trade you out of that would be worth a little boot between mine and yours. Then I'll tell you how to recolor your mules — and call it boot."

We laughed, and I told him that would be sort of like blackmail, I reckoned, but it might not be anything new in the horse and mule business. We visited on — and I asked him where he was going from there. He said it didn't make much difference, that he could drift down south. He would kinda like to be in Waco in about a month, so he believed he would come by and see my mules in a few days.

I told him that sure would be fine, that I had a good little pasture he could camp in, and he wouldn't have to stake out his stock. He could let them run loose for a few days and fill up before he went on down the road. He said he thought that was a good proposition — for me not to worry too much about the color on my mules because they just might gain it back.

I said: "Well, I've heard of mules gaining weight back, growing out their manes and tails and things like that — but I've never heard of one gaining its color back."

"You boys," he said, "that stay at home and feed cattle — there's things you haven't heard about. Let's go on back down to the trade ground. If I don't see you no more there, I'll come by your place in two or three days."

He knew where I was ranching and how to get there. It wasn't too much out of his way if he was going to go on down into central Texas.

I traded a saddle horse or two that day —

didn't do anything too smart or too dumb, which was a fair average for me along about then. I started home along about the middle of the afternoon, rode by his wagon and waved at him, and told him I would be looking for him.

He said: "That's fine. Kill a yearling and get some fresh groceries and I'll stay a few days."

That was a common remark, and we both waved and laughed and I rode off thinking that maybe I was going to be able to lead my mules back through the fountain of youth after all. It was getting to be up in the spring of the year, and it was nice to travel horseback and have my bunch of trading stock on the road. They could graze along the way, and there was water in the road ditches.

Sure enough, in four or five days my Irish horse-trading friend pulled up to my ranch gate in the late afternoon. I saw him coming — I was out at the barn doing something — and I went and opened the gate and let his stock in and let him drive his wagon in. I waved to him to turn down toward the creek and some great big pecan trees to set up his camp. I walked alongside his wagon until he pulled up between two big trees where he would be in the shade all morning and afternoon both. I helped him unhitch and shuck the rigging off his team — untied the ones that were tied to his wagon and just turned them loose there in the small pasture.

We got through and sat down on the wagon tongue and talked a few minutes. "I want to see your changeable mules," he said.

"I don't know whether they are so changeable or not," I said. "They just changed once since I've had them — and it wasn't for the better."

We walked up to the barn where the mules were in the corral on the other side of the barn. Regardless of their color, they were still nice mules, and I had kept them fat and their feet were in good shape and their shoes weren't too worn. They were just good mules. I had let their manes grow out — I hadn't roached their manes or sheared their tails — and they looked a little ragged. But you couldn't make mules like them look too bad regardless of what you neglected about them.

This old Irish horse trader was, I guess, about sixty years old. He said: "Kid, you've sure got a pretty pair of mules, and it is a shame that they seem to have lost that youthful bloom so all of a sudden."

I started up again and I said: "Well, if there's any way to color a mule — and there's bound to be — then they had been colored. But I can't understand how you could get the dapples so smooth and even — and small where they needed to be and large where they needed to be. It's a mystery to me — it was just a work of art. I guess you might brush it on. But how would you get the mule to stand long enough?"

He just died laughing. "It's easy," he said.

We just sat there a few minutes on the feed trough out in the lot — just looking at our stock.

His horses and mules that he had brought in with his wagon — they had been to the creek and drunk and wallowed and had begun to graze. He said: "It's going to help my tradin' stock to get two or three days rest in here — in that good pasture."

I said: "Yeah, you needn't be in any hurry gettin' on down the road. Let 'em fill up."

"That might give me time to help the looks of your mules some, too."

I said: "Well, you know, the main reason I'd want the looks of these mules helped is — our friend down at Hillsboro must like this dapple-gray color of mules we are talking about, or else he wouldn't have colored this pair. And I just felt like maybe he'd like to have another pair back — if they were the right color."

He laughed and he said: "I don't believe that'll work. He's too sharp for that." We sat in silence a few minutes and then he said: "But I'll tell you what would work," and his face brightened up like he had just seen the light.

"What's that?"

He said, "He's got a son-in-law that's a-buyin' mules at Cleburne and a-usin' the old man's checkbook. The son-in-law, he's not too sharp a mule man, but his daddy-in-law has got to keep him up someway — so he lets him buy horses and mules for him and use his checkbook. He's a-stakin' him on the halves, hopin' he'll make half as much as it's costin' to keep him up."

I said: "Well, maybe we can make it be half-color and half-mules and have a little deal with the son-in-law — if you know how to put the blush back on them that they had when I got 'em."

"Kid, it's easy — if you know how."

"Yeah, you said that before, but you cut me out ever time you add that if-you-know-how to it. Besides that, if you was to put that cloudy color on 'em here, I don't know how I'd get 'em to Cleburne without it running on 'em."

He stayed around and we visited two or three days. His trading stock filled up, and he enjoyed resting under the big trees. He slept in his wagon and I slept at the house, but he ate with me and visited, and he told me a lot of things about trading that I never knew. He rode around the pasture with me, and he told me that when he was a young man he thought he would be a cow man. But, he said, he never could figure out how you would make any money just waiting for a cow to have a calf. He said if you went to trading in cattle you couldn't cheat anybody — because about the time you thought you knew all there was to know about a steer or a cow, all they had to do was weigh her and make a fool out of you. So far as he was concerned, he had rather have swapping stock than beef stock.

Along about now, that all made sense to me, too.

The afternoon he was ready to go, he never yet had told me how he was going to color that pair of mules — or how for me to color them. It seemed like a deep, dark-gray secret. All he would ever tell me when I would bring it up was: "It's easy, Kid. It's easy."

Well, that "Kid" with me and "it's easy" was about to drive me beyond the kid stage. I was aging fast from wondering how we would do it. He got all harnessed and hooked up one morning and pulled out in the road in front of the house and started to leave. I said: "You never have . . ."

"Yeah, I know, I never have," he said. "In about three nights from now I'll camp down close to Godley. That won't be far out of Cleburne. You bring your mules and spend the night at the wagon with me, and I'll get 'em in shape that you can take 'em to Cleburne the next morning and show 'em to this promisin' young mule buyer. The trip will be so short that I don't think the dye job will run on 'em."

Well, I'd finished the winter, and I'd fed my cattle, and I was through with the mules, and they were a year older by the calendar but six years whiter. So on the appointed day I saddled up, tied my mules to the saddle horn, and started off to find my Irish gypsy friend's wagon.

I went through Granbury and on down through Cresson and on over to Godley. My old Irish friend was camped down below Godley two or three miles — out by the side of the road where there was a little pond of water and some fresh grass, a nice place to camp and not too far from Cleburne. The next morning was Monday, and it would be a Trading Monday, which would be an ideal day to be in Cleburne.

I rode into camp and we had our "howdys" out, and I staked my mules over to one side where they wouldn't mix up with his. He had a fire going, and it was sort of late. He was frying up some meat and stuff and had a Dutch oven full of sour dough biscuits; so we sat down and ate a big supper. It was the spring of the year and it got a little chilly, so we sat around the fire a little while before we unrolled the bedrolls and went to sleep. I still didn't know about coloring these mules — but he knew I was there, so I wasn't going to bring it up.

The next morning was a bright, sunshiny morning and he said: "Well, this is a nice clear day for our little chore."

I said: "It don't seem to me like it's such a little chore."

"Oh," he said, "it won't take but just a little while. I got the fixin's the last town I came through."

I said: "Well, I'd still like to know about these fixin's."

"Oh," he said, "Don't let it bother you. It's easy. These mules are gentle?"

"Sure, they're gentle!"

Well, in the meantime I had roached their manes and sheared their tails up neat to their bodies, and they were looking good. I had trimmed a little of the long hair off around their fetlocks and under their chins. The mules were in good shape so far as dressing and brushing and currying were concerned. They just lacked that little tinting job.

We finished breakfast, and my Irish horse-trading friend set the black kettle off the fire, over to one side, and said he was going to have to let that cool. "I still don't know what you're doing," I said.

"Kid, don't worry. I know what I'm doing."

"I believe you," I said. "I'm just waiting for the demonstration."

He reached back in the wagon into a little box and brought out some black Easter egg dye. I told him, "Now this ain't Easter — and anybody knows that the bunny didn't bring these mules — and I don't see how that is gonna work."

He said: "Kid, don't let it bother you."

Well, he made up that black Easter egg dye in that pot with me asking: "How in the world are you gonna get it on 'em?"

"Oh," he said, "that's the simplest part about it."

He reached back in the cooking part of his old wagon and got three great big brown hen eggs. He didn't cook them, and he didn't crack them. He took those hen eggs and dipped them in that Easter egg dye. Where he wanted a little dapple, he would mash the small point of the egg into the hair and turn it around. That dye would come off the egg in a nice little round circle. Then where he wanted a big dapple, he would change ends and dip that egg in the dye and turn it around on the hair. The dye would come off

159

the egg to where the hair would stay white in the middle. Then if he wanted a long, oblong kind of dapple along the bottom of the belly, he would use the egg the long way. I stood and watched him, and he worked just as nimble and fast as anybody can ever imagine. In about an hour's time he had a nice pair of dapple-gray mules with the little dapples where they belonged, the big dapples where they belonged, the dark dapples where they belonged — and of course the lower parts of the legs were already black and didn't need any touching up.

When the sun got up higher and brighter and the dye dried on these mules, they were just simply beautiful. They were just as nice a pair of mules as I had bought before, and I thought about taking them back home with me. But I knew we might have another shower, or I might get them wet with sweat again. And too, the teeth hadn't changed any. They were still too long, and too rough, and too wide. That corner that had been put there changed their ages in part of their mouths only.

When he got them dappled out pretty he said: "Now, Kid, you'd better go back to the ranch and feed your cattle and see how much you can get 'em to weigh. This is a professional job, and I'd better wind it up for you."

I told him that I'd let him wind it up for me, but that I was going to go along to watch the show.

We pulled in on the trades square in Cleburne,

and it was the middle of the morning and lots of other traders were there. A good many mules were standing around, but it was still early enough in the spring that there was a good demand for mules, especially good stout heavy well-fed mules that could go to work. I sat around on my horse and watched. Didn't anybody know me much. I'd mosey around horseback from one wagon to the next. I didn't have any other trading stock with me.

Sure enough, after a while here comes this overly dressed son-in-law with a big diamond horseshoe stickpin and a great big diamond ring and a great big white hat — and a bigger mouth. He came to buy some mules for his father-in-law, and he was carrying that long checkbook. He walked around the wagon and talked to my Irish friend a few minutes. He picked out a brown mare and he picked out a bay horse. Then he said: "I think I'll have to have that pair of dapple-gray mules." He looked in their mouths and asked: "How much for them?"

My friend said: "$300."

"Aw — they're a nice pair of mules and they're ready, but they're not worth quite $300."

My old horse-trading friend said: "I don't get many mules with that quality, and I'm really not capable of knowin' what they're worth. What do you think you can give for 'em?"

"Well, I could give you $250."

My friend said: "I couldn't take that, but I'd take $275."

"Aw — that would be too much. I'll give you $265."

I was holding my breath, and my Irish friend was a-pawing around on the ground like a horse that was tied to something he didn't like, but directly he said: "I guess that'll be all right. You can just pay me."

The son-in-law whipped his big long checkbook out and made out a check for the bay horse and the brown mare and the gray mules. He hollered across the yard at a Negro to come and get them and lead them off for him. He wouldn't have wanted to get his gloves off or get them dirty leading that stock around. After all, he wasn't spending his own money.

So I waited until he got away with them, and I got down off my horse and leaned up against the wagon wheel and stood there and laughed a while.

My old Irish friend said: "You don't want this check. I've got the money on me, so I'll just pay you."

He gave me my $265. I told him that I had $250 in those mules, but I had worked them all winter, so I would take $225. I gave him back $40 for his trouble.

He said that was getting a pretty good price for Easter egg dye that early in the season, and he thanked me. I told him to come by and camp any time he was in my part of the country.

He told me that I'd better go back to making cattle get fat — then when I got cheated, it would be by weight and not by color.

A Friendly Rat

W. H. Hudson

Most of our animals, also many creeping things, such as our "wilde wormes in woods," common toads, natterjacks, newts, and lizards, and stranger still, many insects, have been tamed and kept as pets.

Badgers, otters, foxes, hares, and voles are easily dealt with; but that any person should desire to fondle so prickly a creature as a hedgehog, or so diabolical a mammalian as the bloodthirsty flat-headed little weasel, seems very odd. Spiders, too are uncomfortable pets; you can't caress them as you could a dormouse; the most you can do is to provide your spider with a clear glass bottle to live in, and teach him to come out in response to a musical sound, drawn from a banjo or fiddle, to take a fly from your fingers and go back again to its bottle.

An acquaintance of the writer is partial to adders as pets, and he handles them as freely as the schoolboy does his innocuous ringsnake; Mr. Benjamin Kidd once gave us a delightful account of his pet humble-bees, who used to fly about his room, and come at call to be fed, and who manifested an almost painful interest in his coat buttons, examining them every day as if anxious to find out their true significance. Then there was my old friend, Miss Hopely, the writer on reptiles, who died recently, aged 99 years, who tamed newts, but whose favourite pet was a slow-worm. She was never tired of expatiating on its lovable qualities. One finds Viscount Grey's pet squirrels more engaging, for these are wild squirrels in a wood in Northumberland, who quickly find out when he is at home and make their way to the house, scale the walls, and invade the library; then, jumping upon his writing-table, are rewarded with nuts, which they take from his hand. Another Northumbrian friend of the writer keeps, or kept, a pet cormorant, and finds him no less greedy in the domestic than in the wild state. After catching and swallowing fish all the morning in a neighbouring river, he wings his way home at meal-times, screaming to be fed, and ready to devour all the meat and pudding he can get.

The list of strange creatures might be extended indefinitely, even fishes included; but who has ever heard of a tame pet rat? Not the small white, pink-eyed variety, artificially bred, which one may buy at any dealer's, but a common brown rat, *Mus decumanus*, one of the commonest wild animals in England and certainly the most disliked. Yet this wonder has been witnessed recently in the village of Lelant, in West Cornwall. Here is the strange story, which is rather sad and at the same time a little funny.

This was not a case of "wild nature won by kindness"; the rat simply thrust itself and its friendship on the woman of the cottage: and she, being childless and much alone in her kitchen and livingroom, was not displeased at its visits: on the contrary, she fed it; in return the rat grew more and more friendly and familiar towards her, and the more familiar it grew, the more she liked the rat. The trouble was, she possessed a cat, a nice gentle animal not often at home, but it was dreadful to think of what might happen at any moment should pussy walk in when her visitor was with her. Then, one day, pussy did walk in when the rat was present, purring loudly, her tail held stiffly up, showing that she was in her usual sweet temper. On catching sight of the rat, she appeared to know intuitively that it was there as a privileged guest, while the rat on its part seemed to know, also by intuition, that it had nothing to fear. At all events these two quickly became friends and were evidently pleased to be together, as they now spent most of the time in the room, and would drink milk from the same saucer, and sleep bunched up together, and were extremely intimate.

By and by the rat began to busy herself making a nest in a corner of the kitchen under a cupboard, and it became evident that there would soon be an increase in the rat population. She now spent her time running about and gathering little straws, feathers, string, and anything of the kind she could pick up, also stealing or begging for strips of cotton, or bits of wool and thread from the workbasket. Now it happened that her friend was one of those cats with huge tufts of soft hair on the two sides of her face; a cat of that type, which is not uncommon, has a quaint resemblance to a Mid-Victorian gentleman with a pair of magnificent side-whiskers of a silky softness covering both cheeks and flowing down like a double beard. The rat suddenly discovered that this hair was just what she wanted to add a cushion-like lining to her nest, so that her naked pink little ratlings should be born into the softest of all possible worlds. At once she started plucking out the hairs, and the cat, taking it for a new kind of game, but a little too rough to please her, tried for a while to keep her head out of reach and to throw the rat off. But she wouldn't be thrown off, and as she persisted in flying back and jumping at the cat's face and plucking the hairs, the cat quite lost her temper and administered a blow with her claws unsheathed.

The rat fled to her refuge to lick her wounds, and was no doubt as much astonished at the sudden change in her friend's disposition as the cat had been at the rat's new way of showing her playfulness. The result was that when, after attending her scratches, she started upon her task of gathering soft materials, she left the cat severely alone. They were no longer friends; they simply ignored one another's presence in the room. The little ones, numbering about a dozen, presently came to light and were quietly removed by the woman's husband, who didn't mind his missis keeping a rat, but drew the line at one.

The rat quickly recovered from her loss and was the same nice affectionate little thing she had always been to her mistress; then a fresh wonder came to light — cat and rat were fast friends once more! This happy state of things lasted a few weeks; but, as we know, the rat was married, though her lord and master never appeared on the scene, indeed, he was not wanted; and very soon it became plain to see that more little rats were coming. The rat is an exceedingly prolific creature; she can give a month's start to a rabbit and beat her at the end by about 40 points.

Then came the building of the nest in the same old corner, and when it got to the last stage and the rat was busily running about in search of soft materials for the lining, she once more made the discovery that those beautiful tufts of hair on her friend's face were just what she wanted, and once more she set vigorously to work pulling the hairs out. Again, as on the former occasion, the cat tried to keep her friend off, hitting her right and left with her soft pads, and spitting a little, just to show that she didn't like it. But the rat was determined to have the hairs, and the more she was thrown off the more bent was she on getting them, until the breaking-point was reached and puss, in a sudden rage, let fly, dealing blow after blow with lightning rapidity and with all the claws out. The rat, shrieking with pain and terror, rushed out of the room and was never seen again, to the lasting grief of her mistress. But its memory will long remain like a fragrance in the cottage — perhaps the only cottage in all this land where kindly feelings for the rat are cherished.

Mowgli's Brothers*

Rudyard Kipling

Now Chil the Kite brings home the
    night
That Mang the Bat sets free —
The herds are shut in byre and hut,
    For loosed till dawn are we.
This is the hour of pride and power,
    Talon and tush and claw.
Oh, hear the call! — Good hunting all
    That keep the Jungle Law!
                    Night-Song in the Jungle.

It was seven o'clock of a very warm evening in
the Seeonee hills when Father Wolf woke up
from his day's rest, scratched himself, yawned,
and spread out his paws one after the other to
get rid of the sleepy feeling in their tips. Mother
Wolf lay with her big grey nose dropped across
her four tumbling, squealing cubs, and the moon
shone into the mouth of the cave where they all
lived. 'Augrh!' said Father Wolf, 'it is time to
hunt again'; and he was going to spring downhill when a little shadow with a bushy tail crossed

*From *The Jungle Book.*

the threshold and whined: 'Good luck go with you, O Chief of the Wolves; and good luck and strong white teeth go with the noble children, that they may never forget the hungry in this world.'

It was the jackal — Tabaqui, the Dish-licker — and the wolves of India despise Tabaqui because he runs about making mischief, and telling tales, and eating rags and pieces of leather from the village rubbish-heaps. But they are afraid of him too, because Tabaqui, more than any one else in the Jungle, is apt to go mad, and then he forgets that he was ever afraid of any one, and runs through the forest biting everything in his way. Even the tiger runs and hides when little Tabaqui goes mad, for madness is the most disgraceful thing that can overtake a wild creature. We call it hydrophobia, but they call it *dewanee* — the madness — and run.

'Enter, then, and look,' said Father Wolf stiffly; 'but there is no food here.'

'For a wolf, no,' said Tabaqui; 'but for so mean a person as myself a dry bone is a good feast. Who are we, the *Gidur-log* [the Jackal-People], to pick and choose?' He scuttled to the back of the cave, where he found the bone of a buck with some meat on it, and sat cracking the end merrily.

'All thanks for this good meal,' he said, licking his lips. 'How beautiful are the noble children! How large are their eyes! And so young too! Indeed, indeed, I might have remembered that the children of Kings are men from the beginning.'

Now, Tabaqui knew as well as any one else that there is nothing so unlucky as to compliment children to their faces; and it pleased him to see Mother and Father Wolf look uncomfortable.

Tabaqui sat still, rejoicing in the mischief that he had made: then he said spitefully:

'Shere Khan, the Big One, has shifted his hunting-grounds. He will hunt among these hills for the next moon, so he has told me.'

Shere Khan was the tiger who lived near the Waingunga River, twenty miles away.

'He has no right!' Father Wolf began angrily — 'By the Law of the Jungle he has no right to change his quarters without due warning. He will frighten every head of game within ten miles, and I — I have to kill for two, these days.'

'His mother did not call him Lungri [the Lame One] for nothing,' said Mother Wolf quietly. 'He has been lame in one foot from his birth. That is why he has only killed cattle. Now the villagers of the Waingunga are angry with him, and he has come here to make *our* villagers angry. They will scour the Jungle for him when he is far away, and we and our children must run when the grass is set alight. Indeed, we are very grateful to Shere Khan!'

'Shall I tell him of your gratitude?' said Tabaqui.

'Out!' snapped Father Wolf. 'Out and hunt with thy master. Thou hast done harm enough

171

for one night.'

'I go,' said Tabaqui quietly. 'Ye can hear Shere Khan below in the thickets. I might have saved myself the message.'

Father Wolf listened, and below in the valley that ran down to a little river, he heard the dry, angry, snarly, singsong whine of a tiger who has caught nothing and does not care if all the Jungle knows it.

'The fool!' said Father Wolf. 'To begin a night's work with that noise! Does he think that our buck are like his fat Waingunga bullocks?'

'H'sh! It is neither bullock nor buck he hunts to-night,' said Mother Wolf. 'It is Man.' The whine had changed to a sort of humming purr that seemed to come from every quarter of the compass. It was the noise that bewilders wood-cutters and gipsies sleeping in the open, and makes them run sometimes into the very mouth of the tiger.

'Man!' said Father Wolf, showing all his white teeth. 'Faugh! Are there not enough beetles and frogs in the tanks that he must eat Man, and on our ground too?'

The Law of the Jungle, which never orders anything without a reason, forbids every beast to eat Man except when he is killing to show his children how to kill, and then he must hunt outside the hunting-grounds of his pack or tribe. The real reason for this is that man-killing means, sooner or later, the arrival of white men on elephants, with guns, and hundreds of brown men with gongs and rockets and torches. Then everybody in the Jungle suffers. The reason the beasts give among themselves is that Man is the weakest and most defenceless of all living things, and it is unsportsmanlike to touch him. They say too — and it is true — that man-eaters become mangy, and lose their teeth.

The purr grew louder, and ended in the full-throated 'Aaarh!' of the tiger's charge.

Then there was a howl — an untigerish howl — from Shere Khan. 'He has missed,' said Mother Wolf. 'What is it?'

Father Wolf ran out a few paces and heard Shere Khan muttering and mumbling savagely, as he tumbled about in the scrub.

'The fool has had no more sense than to jump at a woodcutter's campfire, and has burned his feet,' said Father Wolf, with a grunt. 'Tabaqui is with him.'

'Something is coming uphill,' said Mother Wolf, twitching one ear. 'Get ready.'

The bushes rustled a little in the thicket, and Father Wolf dropped with his haunches under him, ready for his leap. Then, if you had been watching, you would have seen the most wonderful thing in the world — the wolf checked in mid-spring. He made his bound before he saw what it was he was jumping at, and then he tried to stop himself. The result was that he shot up straight into the air for four or five feet, landing almost where he left ground.

'Man!' he snapped. 'A man's cub. Look!'

Directly in front of him, holding on by a low branch, stood a naked brown baby who could just walk — as soft and as dimpled a little atom as ever came to a wolf's cave at night. He looked up into Father Wolf's face, and laughed.

'Is that a man's cub?' said Mother Wolf. 'I have never seen one. Bring it here.'

A wolf accustomed to moving his own cubs can, if necessary, mouth an egg without breaking it, and though Father Wolf's jaws closed right on the child's back not a tooth even scratched the skin, as he laid it down among the cubs.

'How little! How naked, and — how bold!' said Mother Wolf softly. The baby was pushing his way between the cubs to get close to the warm hide. *'Ahai!* He is taking his meal with the others. And so this is a man's cub. Now, was there ever a wolf that could boast of a man's cub among her children?'

'I have heard now and again of such a thing, but never in our Pack or in my time,' said Father Wolf. 'He is altogether without hair, and I could kill him with a touch of my foot. But see, he looks up and is not afraid.'

The moonlight was blocked out of the mouth of the cave, for Shere Khan's great square head and shoulders were thrust into the entrance. Tabaqui, behind him, was squeaking: 'My lord, my lord, it went in here!'

'Shere Khan does us great honour,' said Father Wolf, but his eyes were very angry. 'What does Shere Khan need?'

'My quarry. A man's cub went this way,' said Shere Khan. 'Its parents have run off. Give it to me.'

Shere Khan had jumped at a woodcutter's camp-fire, as Father Wolf had said, and was furious from the pain of his burned feet. But Father Wolf knew that the mouth of the cave was too narrow for a tiger to come in by. Even where he was, Shere Khan's shoulders and forepaws were cramped for want of room, as a man's would be if he tried to fight in a barrel.

'The Wolves are a free people,' said Father Wolf. 'They take orders from the Head of the Pack, and not from any striped cattle-killer. The man's cub is ours — to kill if we choose.'

'Ye choose and ye do not choose! What talk is this of choosing? By the bull that I killed, am I to stand nosing into your dog's den for my fair dues? It is I, Shere Khan, who speak!'

The tiger's roar filled the cave with thunder. Mother Wolf shook herself clear of the cubs and sprang forward, her eyes, like two green moons in the darkness, facing the blazing eyes of Shere Khan.

'And it is I, Raksha [The Demon], who answer. The man's cub is mine, Lungri — mine to me! He shall not be killed. He shall live to run with the Pack and to hunt with the Pack; and in the end, look you, hunter of little naked cubs — frog-eater — fish-killer — he shall hunt *thee!* Now get hence, or by the Sambhur that I killed (*I* eat no starved cattle), back thou goest to thy mother, burned beast of the jungle, lamer than ever thou camest into the world! Go!'

Father Wolf looked on amazed. He had almost forgotten the days when he won Mother Wolf in fair fight from five other wolves, when she ran in the Pack and was not called The Demon for compliment's sake. Shere Khan might have faced Father Wolf, but he could not stand up against Mother Wolf, for he knew that where he was she had all the advantage of the ground, and would fight to the death. So he backed out of the cave-mouth growling, and when he was clear he shouted: —

'Each dog barks in his own yard! We will see what the Pack will say to this fostering of man-cubs. The cub is mine, and to my teeth he will come in the end, O bush-tailed thieves!'

Mother Wolf threw herself down panting among the cubs, and Father Wolf said to her gravely: —

'Shere Khan speaks this much truth. The cub must be shown to the Pack. Wilt thou still keep him, Mother?'

'Keep him!' she gasped. 'He came naked, by night, alone and very hungry; yet he was not afraid! Look, he has pushed one of my babes to one side already. And that lame butcher would have killed him and would have run off to the Waingunga while the villagers here hunted through all our lairs in revenge! Keep him? Assuredly I will keep him. Lie still, little frog. O thou Mowgli — for Mowgli the Frog I will call thee — the time will come when thou wilt hunt Shere Khan as he has hunted thee.'

'But what will our Pack say?' said Father Wolf.

The Law of the Jungle lays down very clearly that any wolf may, when he marries, withdraw from the Pack he belongs to; but as soon as his cubs are old enough to stand on their feet he must bring them to the Pack Council, which is generally held once a month at full moon, in order that the other wolves may identify them. After that inspection the cubs are free to run where they please, and until they have killed their first buck no excuse is accepted if a grown wolf of the Pack kills one of them. The punishment is death where the murderer can be found; and if you think for a minute you will see that this must be so.

Father Wolf waited till his cubs could run a little, and then on the night of the Pack Meeting took them and Mowgli and Mother Wolf to the Council Rock — a hilltop covered with stones and boulders where a hundred wolves could hide. Akela, the great grey Lone Wolf, who led all the Pack by strength and cunning, lay out at full length on his rock, and below him sat forty or more wolves of every size and colour, from badger-coloured veterans who could handle a buck alone, to young black three-year-olds who thought they could. The Lone Wolf had led them for a year now. He had fallen twice into a wolf-trap in his youth, and once he had been beaten and left for dead; so he knew the manners and customs of men. There was very little talking at the Rock. The cubs tumbled over each other in the centre of the circle where their mothers and fathers sat, and now and again a senior wolf would go quietly up to a cub, look at him carefully, and return to his place on noiseless feet. Sometimes a mother would push her cub far out into the moonlight, to be sure that he had not been overlooked. Akela from his rock would cry: 'Ye know the Law — ye know the Law. Look well, O Wolves!' and the anxious mothers would take up the call: 'Look — look well, O Wolves!'

At last — and Mother Wolf's neck-bristles lifted as the time came — Father Wolf pushed 'Mowgli the Frog,' as they called him, into the centre, where he sat laughing and playing with some pebbles that glistened in the moonlight.

Akela never raised his head from his paws, but went on with the monotonous cry: 'Look well!' A muffled roar came up from behind the rocks — the voice of Shere Khan crying: 'The cub is mine. Give him to me. What have the Free People to do with a man's cub?' Akela never even twitched his ears: all he said was: 'Look well, O Wolves! What have the Free People to do with the orders of any save the Free People? Look well!'

There was a chorus of deep growls, and a young wolf in his fourth year flung back Shere Khan's question to Akela: 'What have the Free People to do with a man's cub?' Now, the Law of the Jungle lays down that if there is any dispute as to the right of a cub to be accepted by the Pack, he must be spoken for by at least two members of the Pack who are not his father and mother.

'Who speaks for this cub?' said Akela. 'Among the Free People who speaks?' There was no answer, and Mother Wolf got ready for what she knew would be her last fight, if things came to fighting.

Then the only other creature who is allowed at the Pack Council — Baloo, the sleepy brown bear who teaches the wolf-cubs the Law of the Jungle: old Baloo, who can come and go where he pleases because he eats only nuts and roots and honey — rose up on his hindquarters and grunted.

'The man's cub — the man's cub?' he said. '*I* speak for the man's cub. There is no harm in a man's cub. I have no gift of words, but I speak the truth. Let him run with the Pack, and be entered with the others. I myself will teach him.'

'We need yet another,' said Akela. 'Baloo has spoken, and he is our teacher for the young cubs. Who speaks besides Baloo?'

A black shadow dropped down into the circle. It was Bagheera the Black Panther, inky black all over, but with the panther markings showing up in certain lights like the pattern of watered silk. Everybody knew Bagheera, and nobody cared to cross his path; for he was as cunning as Tabaqui, as bold as the wild buffalo, and as reckless as the wounded elephant. But he had a voice as soft as wild honey dripping from a tree, and a skin softer than down.

'O Akela, and ye the Free People,' he purred, 'I have no right in your assembly; but the Law of the Jungle says that if there is a doubt which is not a killing matter in regard to a new cub, the life of that cub may be bought at a price. And the Law does not say who may or may not pay that price. Am I right?'

'Good! good!' said the young wolves, who are always hungry. 'Listen to Bagheera. The cub can be bought for a price. It is the Law.'

'Knowing that I have no right to speak here, I ask your leave.'

'Speak then,' cried twenty voices.

'To kill a naked cub is shame. Besides, he may make better sport for you when he is grown. Baloo has spoken in his behalf. Now to Baloo's word I will add one bull, and a fat one, newly killed, not half a mile from here, if ye will accept the man's cub according to the Law. Is it difficult?'

There was a clamour of scores of voices, saying: 'What matter? He will die in the winter rains. He will scorch in the sun. What harm can a naked frog do us? Let him run with the Pack. Where is the bull, Bagheera? Let him be accepted.' And then came Akela's deep bay, crying: 'Look well — look well, O Wolves!'

Mowgli was still deeply interested in the pebbles and he did not notice when the wolves came and looked at him one by one. At last they all went down the hill for the dead bull, and only Akela, Bagheera, Baloo, and Mowgli's own wolves were left. Shere Khan roared still in the night, for he was very angry that Mowgli had not been handed over to him.

'Ay, roar well,' said Bagheera, under his whiskers; 'for the time comes when this naked thing will make thee roar to another tune, or I know nothing of Man.'

'It was well done,' said Akela. 'Men and their cubs are very wise. He may be a help in time.'

'Truly, a help in time of need; for none can hope to lead the Pack for ever,' said Bagheera.

Akela said nothing. He was thinking of the time that comes to every leader of every pack when his strength goes from him and he gets feebler and feebler, till at last he is killed by the wolves and a new leader comes up — to be killed in his turn.

'Take him away,' he said to Father Wolf, 'and train him as befits one of the Free People.'

And that is how Mowgli was entered into the Seeonee Wolf-Pack at the price of a bull and on Baloo's good word.

Now you must be content to skip ten or eleven whole years, and only guess at all the wonderful life that Mowgli led among the wolves, because if it were written out it would fill ever so many books. He grew up with the cubs, though they, of course, were grown wolves almost before he was a child, and Father Wolf taught him his business, and the meaning of things in the Jungle, till every rustle in the grass, every breath of the warm night air, every note of the owls above his head, every scratch of a bat's claws as it roosted for a while in a tree, and every splash of every little fish jumping in a pool, meant just as much to him as the work of his office means to a business man. When he was not learning, he sat out in the sun and slept, and ate and went to sleep again; when he felt dirty or hot he swam in the forest pools; and when he wanted honey (Baloo told him that honey and nuts were just as pleasant to eat as raw meat) he climbed up for it, and that Bagheera showed him how to do. Bagheera would lie out on a branch and call, 'Come along, Little Brother,' and at first Mowgli would cling like the sloth, but afterwards he would fling himself through the branches almost as boldly as the grey ape. He took his place at the Council Rock, too, when the Pack met, and there he discovered that if he stared hard at any wolf, the wolf would be forced to drop his eyes, and so he used to stare for fun. At other times he would pick the long thorns out of the pads of his friends, for wolves suffer terribly from thorns and burrs in their coats. He would go down the hillside into the cultivated lands by night, and look very curiously at the villagers in their huts, but he had a mistrust of men because Bagheera showed him a square box with a drop-gate so cunningly hidden in the Jungle that he nearly walked into it, and told him that it was a trap. He loved better than anything else to go with Bagheera into the dark warm heart of the forest, to sleep all through the drowsy day, and at night to see how Bagheera did his killing. Bagheera killed right and left as he felt hungry, and so did Mowgli — with one exception. As soon as he was old enough to understand things, Bagheera told him that he must never touch cattle because he had been bought into the Pack at the price of a bull's life. 'All the Jungle is thine,' said Bagheera, 'and thou canst kill everything that thou art strong enough to kill; but for the sake of the bull that bought thee thou must never kill or eat any cattle young or old. That is the Law of the Jungle.' Mowgli obeyed faithfully.

And he grew and grew strong as a boy must grow who does not know that he is learning any lessons, and who has nothing in the world to think of except things to eat.

Mother Wolf told him once or twice that Shere Khan was not a creature to be trusted, and that some day he must kill Shere Khan; but though a young wolf would have remembered that advice every hour, Mowgli forgot it because he was only a boy — though he would have called himself a wolf if he had been able to speak in any human tongue.

Shere Khan was always crossing his path in the Jungle, for as Akela grew older and feebler the lame tiger had come to be great friends with the younger wolves of the Pack, who followed him for scraps, a thing that Akela would never have allowed if he had dared to push his authority to the proper bounds. Then Shere Khan would flatter them and wonder that such fine young hunters were content to be led by a dying wolf and a man's cub. 'They tell me,' Shere Khan would say, 'that at Council ye dare not look him between the eyes'; and the young wolves would growl and bristle.

Bagheera, who had eyes and ears everywhere, knew something of this, and once or twice he told Mowgli in so many words that Shere Khan would kill him some day; and Mowgli would laugh and answer: 'I have the Pack and I have thee; and Baloo, though he is so lazy, might strike a blow or two for my sake. Why should I be afraid?'

It was one very warm day that a new notion came to Bagheera — born of something that he had heard. Perhaps Ikki the Porcupine had told him; but he said to Mowgli when they were deep in the Jungle, as the boy lay with his head on Bagheera's beautiful black skin: 'Little Brother, how often have I told thee that Shere Khan is thy enemy?'

'As many times as there are nuts on that palm,' said Mowgli, who, naturally, could not count. 'What of it? I am sleepy, Bagheera, and Shere Khan is all long tail and loud talk — like Mao, the Peacock.'

'But this is no time for sleeping. Ballo knows it; I know it; the Pack know it; and even the foolish, foolish deer know. Tabaqui has told thee, too.'

'Ho! ho!' said Mowgli. 'Tabaqui came to me not long ago with some rude talk that I was a naked man's cub and not fit to dig pig-nuts; but I caught Tabaqui by the tail and swung him twice against a palm-tree to teach him better manners.'

'That was foolishness; for though Tabaqui is a mischief-maker, he would have told thee of something that concerned thee closely. Open those eyes, Little Brother. Shere Khan dare not kill thee in the Jungle; but remember, Akela is very old, and soon the day comes when he cannot kill his buck, and then he will be leader no more. Many of the wolves that looked thee over when thou wast brought to the Council first are old too, and the young wolves believe, as Shere Khan has taught them, that a man-cub has no place with the Pack. In a little time thou wilt be a man.'

'And what is a man that he should not run with his brothers?' said Mowgli. 'I was born in the Jungle. I have obeyed the Law of the Jungle and there is no wolf of ours from whose paws I have not pulled a thorn. Surely they are my brothers!'

Bagheera stretched himself at full length and half shut his eyes. 'Little Brother,' said he, 'feel under my jaw.'

Mowgli put up his strong brown hand, and just under Bagheera's silky chin, where the giant rolling muscles were all hid by the glossy hair, he came upon a little bald spot.

'There is no one in the Jungle that knows that I, Bagheera, carry that mark — the mark of the collar; and yet, Little Brother, I was born among men, and it was among men that my mother died — in the cages of the King's Palace of Oodeypore. It was because of this that I paid the price for thee at the Council when thou wast a little naked cub. Yes, I too was born among men. I had never seen the Jungle. They fed me behind bars from an iron pan till one night I felt that I was Bagheera — the Panther — and no man's plaything, and I broke the silly lock with one blow of my paw and came away; and because I had learned the ways of men, I became more terrible in the Jungle than Shere Khan. Is it not so?'

'Yes,' said Mowgli; 'all the Jungle fear Bagheera — all except Mowgli.'

'Oh, *thou* art a man's cub,' said the Black Panther, very tenderly; 'and even as I returned to my Jungle, so thou must go back to men at last, — to the men who are thy brothers, — if thou art not killed in the Council.'

'But why — but why should any wish to kill me?' said Mowgli.

'Look at me,' said Bagheera; and Mowgli looked at him steadily between the eyes. The big panther turned his head away in half a minute.

'*That* is why,' he said, shifting his paw on the leaves. 'Not even I can look thee between the eyes, and I was born among men, and I love thee, Little Brother. The others they hate thee because their eyes cannot meet thine — because thou art wise — because thou hast pulled out thorns from their feet — because thou art a man.'

'I did not know these things,' said Mowgli sullenly; and he frowned under his heavy black eyebrows.

'What is the Law of the Jungle? Strike first and then give tongue. By thy very carelessness they know that thou art a man. But be wise. It is in my heart that when Akela misses his next kill, — and at each hunt it costs him more to pin the buck, — the Pack will turn against him and against thee. They will hold a Jungle Council at the Rock, and then — and then — I have it!' said Bagheera, leaping up. 'Go thou down quickly to the men's huts in the valley, and take some of the Red Flower which they grow there, so that when the time comes thou mayest have even a stronger friend than I or Baloo or those of the Pack that love thee. Get the Red Flower.'

By Red Flower Bagheera meant fire, only no creature in the Jungle will call fire by its proper name. Every beast lives in deadly fear of it, and invents a hundred ways of describing it.

'The Red Flower?' said Mowgli. 'That grows outside their huts in the twilight. I will get some.'

'There speaks the man's cub,' said Bagheera proudly. 'Remember that it grows in little pots.

Get one swiftly, and keep it by thee for time of need.'

'Good!' said Mowgli. 'I go. But art thou sure, O my Bagheera' — he slipped his arm round the splendid neck, and looked deep into the big eyes — 'art thou sure that all this is Shere Khan's doing?'

'By the Broken Lock that freed me, I am sure, Little Brother.'

'Then, by the Bull that bought me, I will pay Shere Khan full tale for this, and it may be a little over,' said Mowgli; and he bounded away.

'That is a man. That is all a man,' said Bagheera to himself, lying down again. 'Oh, Shere Khan, never was a blacker hunting than that frog-hunt of thine ten years ago!'

Mowgli was far and far through the forest, running hard, and his heart was hot in him. He came to the cave as the evening mist rose, and drew breath, and looked down the valley. The cubs were out, but Mother Wolf, at the back of the cave, knew by his breathing that something was troubling her frog.

'What is it, Son?' she said.

'Some bat's chatter of Shere Khan,' he called back. 'I hunt among the ploughed fields to-night,' and he plunged downward through the bushes, to the stream at the bottom of the valley. There he checked, for he heard the yell of the Pack hunting, heard the bellow of a hunted sambhur, and the snort as the buck turned at bay. Then there were wicked, bitter howls from the young wolves: 'Akela! Akela! Let the Lone Wolf show his strength. Room for the leader of the Pack! Spring, Akela!'

The Lone Wolf must have sprung and missed his hold, for Mowgli heard the snap of his teeth and then a yelp as the sambhur knocked him over with his fore-foot.

He did not wait for anything more, but dashed on; and the yells grew fainter behind him as he ran into the crop-lands where the villagers lived.

'Bagheera spoke truth,' he panted, as he nestled down in some cattle-fodder by the window of a hut. 'To-morrow is one day both for Akela and for me.'

Then he pressed his face close to the window and watched the fire on the hearth. He saw the husbandman's wife get up and feed it in the night with black lumps; and when the morning came and the mists were all white and cold, he saw the man's child pick up a wicker pot plastered inside with earth, fill it with lumps of red-hot charcoal, put it under his blanket, and go out to tend the cows in the byre.

'Is that all?' said Mowgli. 'If a cub can do it, there is nothing to fear'; so he strode round the corner and met the boy, took the pot from his hand, and disappeared into the mist while the boy howled with fear.

'They are very like me,' said Mowgli, blowing into the pot, as he had seen the woman do. 'This thing will die if I do not give it things to eat'; and he dropped twigs and dried bark on the red stuff. Half-way up the hill he met Bagheera with the morning dew shining like moonstones on his coat.

'Akela has missed,' said the Panther. 'They would have killed him last night, but they needed thee also. They were looking for thee on the hill.'

'I was among the ploughed lands. I am ready. See!' Mowgli held up the fire-pot.

'Good! Now, I have seen men thrust a dry branch into that stuff, and presently the Red Flower blossomed at the end of it. Art thou not afraid?'

'No. Why should I fear? I remember now — if it is not a dream — how, before I was a Wolf, I lay beside the Red Flower, and it was warm and pleasant.'

All that day Mowgli sat in the cave tending his fire-pot and dipping dry branches into it to see how they looked. He found a branch that satisfied him, and in the evening when Tabaqui came to the cave and told him rudely enough that he was wanted at the Council Rock, he laughed till Tabaqui ran away. Then Mowgli went to the Council, still laughing.

Akela the Lone Wolf lay by the side of his rock as a sign that the leadership of the Pack was open, and Shere Khan with his following of scrap-fed wolves walked to and fro openly, being flattered. Bagheera lay close to Mowgli, and the fire-pot was between Mowgli's knees. When they were all gathered together, Shere Khan began to speak — a thing he would never have dared to do when Akela was in his prime.

'He has no right,' whispered Bagheera. 'Say so. He is a dog's son. He will be frightened.'

Mowgli sprang to his feet. 'Free People,' he cried, 'does Shere Khan lead the Pack? What has a tiger to do with our leadership?'

'Seeing that the leadership is yet open, and being asked to speak — ' Shere Khan began.

'By whom?' said Mowgli. 'Are we *all* jackals, to fawn on this cattle-butcher? The leadership of the Pack is with the Pack alone.'

There were yells of 'Silence, thou man's cub!' 'Let him speak. He has kept our Law'; and at last the seniors of the Pack thundered: 'Let the Dead Wolf speak.' When a leader of the Pack has missed his kill, he is called the Dead Wolf as long as he lives, which is not long, as a rule.

Akela raised his old head wearily: —

'Free People, and ye too, jackals of Shere Khan, for many seasons I have led ye to and from the kill, and in all my time not one has been trapped or maimed. Now I have missed my kill. Ye know how that plot was made. Ye know how ye brought me up to an untried buck to make my weakness known. It was cleverly done. Your right is to kill me here on the Council Rock now. Therefore, I ask, who comes to make an end of the Lone Wolf? For it is my right, by the Law of the Jungle, that ye come one by one.'

There was a long hush, for no single wolf cared to fight Akela to the death. Then Shere Khan roared: 'Bah! what have we to do with this toothless fool? He is doomed to die! It is the man-cub who has lived too long. Free People, he was my meat from the first. Give him to me. I am weary of this man-wolf folly. He has troubled the Jungle for ten seasons. Give me the man-cub, or I will hunt here always, and not give you one bone. He is a man, a man's child, and from the marrow of my bones I hate him!'

Then more than half the Pack yelled: 'A man! a man! What has a man to do with us? Let him go to his own place.'

'And turn all the people of the villages against us?' clamoured Shere Khan. 'No; give him to me. He is a man, and none of us can look him between the eyes.'

Akela lifted his head again, and said: 'He has eaten our food. He has slept with us. He has driven game for us. He has broken no word of the Law of the Jungle.'

'Also, I paid for him with a bull when he was accepted. The worth of a bull is little, but Bagheera's honour is something that he will perhaps fight for,' said Bagheera, in his gentlest voice.

'A bull paid ten years ago!' the Pack snarled. 'What do we care for bones ten years old?'

'Or for a pledge?' said Bagheera, his white teeth bared under his lip. 'Well are ye called the Free People!'

'No man's cub can run with the people of the Jungle,' howled Shere Khan. 'Give him to me!'

'He is our brother in all but blood,' Akela

went on; 'and ye would kill him here! In truth, I have lived too long. Some of ye are eaters of cattle, and of others I have heard that, under Shere Khan's teaching, ye go by dark night and snatch children from the villager's doorstep. Therefore I know ye to be cowards, and it is to cowards I speak. It is certain that I must die, and my life is of no worth, or I would offer that in the Man-cub's place. But for the sake of the Honour of the Pack, — a little matter that by being without a leader ye have forgotten, — I promise that if ye let the Man-cub go to his own place, I will not, when my time comes to die, bare one tooth against ye. I will die without fighting. That will at least save the Pack three lives. More I cannot do; but if ye will, I can save ye the shame that comes of killing a brother against whom there is no fault, — a brother spoken for and bought into the Pack according to the Law of the Jungle.'

'He is a man — a man — a man!' snarled the Pack; and most of the wolves began to gather round Shere Khan, whose tail was beginning to switch.

'Now the business is in thy hands,' said Bagheera to Mowgli. '*We* can do no more except fight.'

Mowgli stood upright — the fire-pot in his hands. Then he stretched out his arms, and yawned in the face of the Council; but he was furious with rage and sorrow, for, wolf-like, the wolves had never told him how they hated him.

'Listen, you!' he cried. 'There is no need for this dog's jabber. Ye have told me so often to-night that I am a man (and indeed I would have been a wolf with you to my life's end), that I feel your words are true. So I do not call ye my brothers any more, but *sag* [dogs], as a man should. What ye will do, and what ye will not do, is not yours to say. That matter is with *me;* and that we may see the matter more plainly, I, the man, have brought here a little of the Red Flower which ye, dogs, fear.'

He flung the fire-pot on the ground, and some of the red coals lit a tuft of dried moss that flared up, as all the Council drew back in terror before the leaping flames.

Mowgli thrust his dead branch into the fire till the twigs lit and crackled, and whirled it above his head among the cowering wolves.

'Thou art the master,' said Bagheera, in an undertone. 'Save Akela from the death. He was ever thy friend.'

Akela, the grim old wolf who had never asked for mercy in his life, gave one piteous look at Mowgli as the boy stood all naked, his long black hair tossing over his shoulders in the light of the blazing branch that made the shadows jump and quiver.

'Good!' said Mowgli, staring round slowly. 'I see that ye are dogs. I go from you to my own people — if they be my own people. The Jungle is shut to me, and I must forget your talk and your companionship; but I will be more merciful than ye are. Because I was all but your brother in blood, I promise that when I am a man among men I will not betray ye to men as you have betrayed me.' He kicked the fire with his foot, and the sparks flew up. 'There shall be no war between any of us and the Pack. But there is a debt to pay before I go.' He strode forward to where Shere Khan sat blinking stupidly at the flames, and caught him by the tuft on his chin. Bagheera followed in case of accidents. 'Up, dog!' Mowgli cried. 'Up, when a man speaks, or I will set that coat ablaze!'

Shere Khan's ears lay flat back on his head, and he shut his eyes, for the blazing branch was very near.

'This cattle-killer said he would kill me in the Council because he had not killed me when I was a cub. Thus and thus, then, do we beat dogs when we are men. Stir a whisker, Lungri, and I ram the Red Flower down thy gullet!' He beat Shere Khan over the head with the branch, and the tiger whimpered and whined in an agony of fear.

'Pah! Singed jungle-cat — go now! But remember when next I come to the Council Rock, as a man should come, it will be with Shere Khan's hide on my head. For the rest, Akela goes free to live as he pleases. Ye will *not* kill him, because that is not my will. Nor do I think that ye will sit here any longer, lolling out your tongues as though ye were somebodies, instead of dogs whom I drive out — thus! Go!'

The fire was burning furiously at the end of the branch, and Mowgli struck right and left round the circle, and the wolves ran howling with the sparks burning their fur. At last there were only Akela, Bagheera, and perhaps ten wolves that had taken Mowgli's part. Then something began to hurt Mowgli inside him, as he had never been hurt in his life before, and he caught his breath and sobbed, and the tears ran down his face.

'What is it? What is it?' he said. 'I do not wish to leave the Jungle, and I do not know what this is. Am I dying, Bagheera?'

'No, Little Brother. Those are only tears such as men use,' said Bagheera. 'Now I know thou art a man, and a man's cub no longer. The Jungle is shut indeed to thee henceforward. Let them fall, Mowgli. They are only tears.' So Mowgli sat and cried as though his heart would break; and he had never cried in all his life before.

'Now,' he said, 'I will go to men. But first I must say farewell to my mother'; and he went to the cave where she lived with Father Wolf, and he cried on her coat, while the four cubs howled miserably.

'Ye will not forget me?' said Mowgli.

'Never while we can follow a trail,' said the cubs. 'Come to the foot of the hill when thou art a man, and we will talk to thee; and we will come into the crop-lands to play with thee by night.'

'Come soon!' said Father Wolf. 'Oh, wise little

frog, come again soon; for we be old, thy mother and I.'

'Come soon,' said Mother Wolf, 'little naked son of mine; for, listen, child of man, I loved thee more than ever I loved my cubs.'

'I will surely come,' said Mowgli; 'and when I come it will be to lay out Shere Khan's hide upon the Council Rock. Do not forget me! Tell them in the Jungle never to forget me!'

The dawn was beginning to break when Mowgli went down the hillside alone, to meet those mysterious things that are called men.

'Rikki-Tikki-Tavi'

Rudyard Kipling

At the hole where he went in
Red-Eye called to Wrinkle-Skin
Hear what little Red-Eye saith: —
'Nag, come up and dance with
    death!'
Eye to eye and head to head
    (*Keep the measure, Nag*).
This shall end when one is dead
    (*At thy pleasure, Nag*).
Turn for turn and twist for twist
    (*Run and hide thee, Nag*).
Hah! The hooded Death has
    missed!
    (*Woe betide thee, Nag!*)

This is the story of the great war that Rikki-tikki-tavi fought single-handed, through the bath-rooms of the big bungalow in Segowlee canton-ment. Darzee, the tailor-bird, helped him, and Chuchundra, the musk-rat, who never comes out into the middle of the floor, but always creeps round by the wall, gave him advice; but Rikki-tikki did the real fighting.

He was a mongoose, rather like a little cat in

his fur and his tail, but quite like a weasel in his head and his habits. His eyes and the end of his restless nose were pink; he could scratch himself anywhere he pleased with any leg, front or back, that he chose to use; he could fluff up his tail till it looked like a bottle-brush, and his war-cry as he scuttled through the long grass was: *Rikk-tikk-tikki-tikki-tchk!*

One day, a high summer flood washed him out of the burrow where he lived with his father and mother, and carried him, kicking and clucking, down a roadside ditch. He found a little wisp of grass floating there, and clung to it till he lost his senses. When he revived, he was lying in the hot sun on the middle of a garden path, very draggled indeed, and a small boy was saying: 'Here's a dead mongoose. Let's have a funeral.'

'No,' said his mother; 'let's take him in and dry him. Perhaps he isn't really dead.'

They took him into the house, and a big man picked him up between his finger and thumb and said he was not dead but half choked; so they wrapped him in cotton-wool, and warmed him over a little fire, and he opened his eyes and sneezed.

'Now,' said the big man (he was an Englishman who had just moved into the bungalow); 'don't frighten him, and we'll see what he'll do.'

It is the hardest thing in the world to frighten a mongoose, because he is eaten up from nose to tail with curiosity. The motto of all the mongoose family is, 'Run and find out'; and Rikki-tikki was a true mongoose. He looked at the cotton-wool, decided that it was not good to eat, ran all round the table, sat up and put his fur in order, scratched himself, and jumped on the small boy's shoulder.

'Don't be frightened, Teddy,' said his father. 'That's his way of making friends.'

'Ouch! He's tickling under my chin,' said Teddy.

Rikki-tikki looked down between the boy's collar and neck, snuffed at his ear, and climbed down to the floor, where he sat rubbing his nose.

'Good gracious,' said Teddy's mother, 'and that's a wild creature! I suppose he's so tame because we've been kind to him.'

'All mongooses are like that,' said her husband. 'If Teddy doesn't pick him up by the tail, or try to put him in a cage, he'll run in and out of the house all day long. Let's give him something to eat.'

They gave him a little piece of raw meat. Rikki-tikki liked it immensely, and when it was finished he went out into the veranda and sat in the sunshine and fluffed up his fur to make it dry to the roots. Then he felt better.

'There are more things to find out about in this house,' he said to himself, 'than all my family could find out in all their lives. I shall certainly stay and find out.'

He spent all that day roaming over the house. He nearly drowned himself in the bath-tubs; put his nose into the ink on a writing-table, and burnt it on the end of the big man's cigar, for he climbed up in the big man's lap to see how writing was done. At nightfall he ran into Teddy's nursery to watch how kerosene lamps were lighted, and when Teddy went to bed Rikki-tikki climbed up too; but he was a restless companion, because he had to get up and attend to every noise all through the night, and find out what made it. Teddy's mother and father came in, the last thing, to look at their boy, and Rikki-tikki was awake on the pillow. 'I don't like that,' said Teddy's mother; 'he may bite the child.' 'He'll do no such thing,' said the father. 'Teddy's safer with that little beast than if he had a bloodhound to watch him. If a snake came into the nursery now ——'

But Teddy's mother wouldn't think of anything so awful.

Early in the morning Rikki-tikki came to early breakfast in the veranda riding on Teddy's shoulder, and they gave him banana and some boiled egg; and he sat on all their laps one after the other, because every well-brought-up mongoose always hopes to be a house-mongoose some day and have rooms to run about in; and Rikki-tikki's mother (she used to live in the General's house at Segowlee) had carefully told Rikki what to do if ever he came across white men.

Then Rikki-tikki went out into the garden to see what was to be seen. It was a large garden, only half cultivated, with bushes, as big as summer-houses, of Marshal Niel roses; lime and orange trees, clumps of bamboos, and thickets of high grass. Rikki-tikki licked his lips. 'This is a splendid hunting-ground,' he said, and his tail grew bottle-brushy at the thought of it, and he scuttled up and down the garden, snuffing here and there till he heard very sorrowful voices in a thorn-bush. It was Darzee, the tailor-bird, and his wife. They had made a beautiful nest by pulling two big leaves together and stitching them up the edges with fibres, and had filled the hollow with cotton and downy fluff. The nest swayed to and fro, as they sat on the rim and cried.

'What is the matter?' asked Rikki-tikki.

'We are very miserable,' said Darzee. 'One of our babies fell out of the nest yesterday and Nag ate him.'

'H'm!' said Rikki-tikki, 'that is very sad — but I am a stranger here. Who is Nag?'

Darzee and his wife only cowered down in the nest without answering, for from the thick grass at the foot of the bush there came a low hiss — a horrid cold sound that made Rikki-tikki jump back two clear feet. Then inch by inch out of the grass rose up the head and spread hood of Nag, the big black cobra, and he was five feet long from tongue to tail. When he had lifted one-third of himself clear of the ground, he stayed balancing to and fro exactly as a dandelion-tuft balances in the wind, and he looked at Rikki-tikki with the wicked snake's eyes that never change their expression, whatever the snake may be thinking of.

'Who is Nag,' said he. '*I* am Nag. The great God Brahm put his mark upon all our people, when the first cobra spread his hood to keep the sun off Brahm as he slept. Look, and be afraid!'

He spread out his hood more than ever, and Rikki-tikki saw the spectacle-mark on the back of it that looks exactly like the eye part of a hook-and-eye fastening. He was afraid for the minute; but it is impossible for a mongoose to stay frightened for any length of time, and though Rikki-tikki had never met a live cobra before, his mother had fed him on dead ones, and he knew that all a grown mongoose's business in life was to fight and eat snakes. Nag knew that too and, at the bottom of his cold heart, he was afraid.

'Well,' said Rikki-tikki, and his tail began to fluff up again, 'marks or no marks, do you think it is right for you to eat fledglings out of a nest?'

Nag was thinking to himself, and watching the least little movement in the grass behind Rikki-tikki. He knew that mongooses in the garden meant death sooner or later for him and his family; but he wanted to get Rikki-tikki off his guard. So he dropped his head a little, and put it on one side.

'Let us talk,' he said. 'You eat eggs. Why should not I eat birds?'

'Behind you! Look behind you!' sang Darzee.

Rikki-tikki knew better than to waste time in

staring. He jumped up in the air as high as he could go, and just under him whizzed by the head of Nagaina, Nag's wicked wife. She had crept up behind him as he was talking, to make an end of him; and he heard her savage hiss as the stroke missed. He came down almost across her back, and if he had been an old mongoose he would have known that then was the time to break her back with one bite; but he was afraid of the terrible lashing return-stroke of the cobra. He bit, indeed, but did not bite long enough, and he jumped clear of the whisking tail, leaving Nagaina torn and angry.

'Wicked, wicked Darzee!' said Nag, lashing up as high as he could reach toward the nest in the thorn-bush; but Darzee had built it out of reach of snakes, and it only swayed to and fro.

Rikki-tikki felt his eyes growing red and hot (when a mongoose's eyes grow red, he is angry), and he sat back on his tail and hind legs like a little kangaroo, and looked all round him, and chattered with rage. But Nag and Nagaina had disappeared into the grass. When a snake misses its stroke, it never says anything or gives any sign of what it means to do next. Rikki-tikki did not care to follow them, for he did not feel sure that he could manage two snakes at once. So he trotted off to the gravel path near the house, and sat down to think. It was a serious matter for him. If you read the old books of natural history, you will find they say that when the mongoose fights the snake and happens to get bitten, he runs off and eats some herb that cures him. That is not true. The victory is only a matter of quickness of eye and quickness of foot, — snake's blow against the mongoose's jump, — and as no eye can follow the motion of a snake's head when it strikes, this makes things much more wonderful than any magic herb. Rikki-tikki knew he was a young mongoose, and it made him all the more pleased to think that he had managed to escape a blow from behind. It gave him confidence in himself, and when Teddy came running down the path, Rikki-tikki was ready to be petted. But just as Teddy was stooping, something wriggled a little in the dust, and a tiny voice said: 'Be careful. I am Death?' It was Karait, the dusty brown snakeling that lies for choice on the dusty earth; and his bite is as dangerous as the cobra's. But he is so small that nobody thinks of him, and so he does the more harm to people.

Rikki-tikki's eyes grew red again, and he danced up to Karait with the peculiar rocking, swaying motion that he had inherited from his family. It looks very funny, but it is so perfectly balanced a gait that you can fly off from it at any angle you please; and in dealing with snakes this is an advantage. If Rikki-tikki had only known, he was doing a much more dangerous thing than fighting Nag, for Karait is so small, and can turn so quickly, that unless Rikki bit him close to the back of the head, he would get the return-stroke in his eye or his lip. But Rikki did not know: his eyes were all red, and he rocked back and forth, looking for a good place to hold. Karait struck out, Rikki jumped sideways and tried to run in, but the wicked little dusty gray head lashed within a fraction of his shoulder, and he had to jump over the body, and the head followed his heels close.

Teddy shouted to the house: 'Oh, look here! Our mongoose is killing a snake'; and Rikki-tikki heard a scream from Teddy's mother. His father ran out with a stick, but by the time he came up, Karait had lunged out once too far, and Rikki-tikki had sprung, jumped on the snake's back, dropped his head far between his fore-legs, bitten as high up the back as he could get hold, and rolled away. That bite paralysed Karait, and Rikki-tikki was just going to eat him up from the tail, after the custom of his family at dinner, when he remembered that a full meal makes a slow mongoose, and if he wanted all his strength and quickness ready, he must keep himself thin. He went away for a dust-bath under the castor-oil bushes, while Teddy's father beat the dead Karait. 'What is the use of that?' thought Rikki-tikki; 'I have settled it all'; and then Teddy's mother picked him up from the dust and hugged him, crying that he had saved Teddy from death, and Teddy's father said that he was a providence, and Teddy looked on with big scared eyes. Rikki-tikki was rather amused at all the fuss, which, of course, he did not understand. Teddy's mother might just as well have petted Teddy for playing in the dust. Rikki was thoroughly enjoying himself.

That night at dinner, walking to and fro among the wine-glasses on the table, he might have stuffed himself three times over with nice things; but he remembered Nag and Nagaina, and though it was very pleasant to be patted and petted by Teddy's mother, and to sit on Teddy's shoulder, his eyes would get red from time to time, and he would go off into his long war-cry of *Rikk-tikk-tikki-tikki-tchk!'*

Teddy carried him off to bed, and insisted on Rikki-tikki's sleeping under his chin. Rikki-tikki was too well bred to bite or scratch, but as soon as Teddy was asleep he went off for his nightly walk round the house, and in the dark he ran up against Chuchundra, the musk-rat, creeping round by the wall. Chuchundra is a broken-hearted little beast. He whimpers and cheeps all night, trying to make up his mind to run into the middle of the room; but he never gets there.

'Don't kill me,' said Chuchundra, almost weeping. 'Rikki-tikki, don't kill me!'

'Do you think a snake-killer kills musk-rats?' said Rikki-tikki scornfully.

'Those who kill snakes get killed by snakes,' said Chuchundra, more sorrowfully than ever. 'And how am I to be sure that Nag won't mistake me for you some dark night?'

'There's not the least danger,' said Rikki-tikki; 'but Nag is in the garden, and I know you don't go there.'

'My cousin Chua, the rat, told me —— ' said

Chuchundra, and then he stopped.

'Told you what?'

'H'sh! Nag is everywhere, Rikki-tikki. You should have talked to Chua in the garden.'

'I didn't — so you must tell me. Quick, Chuchundra, or I'll bite you!'

Chuchundra sat down and cried till the tears rolled off his whiskers. 'I am a very poor man,' he sobbed. 'I never had spirit enough to run out into the middle of the room. H'sh! I mustn't tell you anything. Can't you *hear*, Rikki-tikki?'

Rikki-tikki listened. The house was as still as still, but he thought he could just catch the faintest *scratch-scratch* in the world, — a noise as faint as that of a wasp walking on a window-pane, — the dry scratch of a snake's scales on brickwork.

'That's Nag or Nagaina,' he said to himself; 'and he is crawling into the bath-room sluice. You're right, Chuchundra; I should have talked to Chua.'

He stole off to Teddy's bath-room, but there was nothing there, and then to Teddy's mother's bath-room. At the bottom of the smooth plaster wall there was a brick pulled out to make a sluice for the bath-water, and as Rikki-tikki stole in by the masonry curb where the bath is put, he heard Nag and Nagaina whispering together outside in the moonlight.

'When the house is emptied of people,' said Nagaina to her husband, '*he* will have to go away, and then the garden will be our own again.

208

Go in quietly, and remember that the big man who killed Karait is the first one to bite. Then come out and tell me, and we will hunt for Rikki-tikki together.'

'But are you sure that there is anything to be gained by killing the people?' said Nag.

'Everything. When there were no people in the bungalow, did we have any mongoose in the garden? So long as the bungalow is empty, we are king and queen of the garden; and remember that as soon as our eggs in the melon-bed hatch (as they may to-morrow), our children will need room and quiet.'

'I had not thought of that,' said Nag. 'I will go, but there is no need that we should hunt for Rikki-tikki afterward. I will kill the big man and his wife, and the child if I can, and come away quietly. Then the bungalow will be empty, and Rikki-tikki will go.'

Rikki-tikki tingled all over with rage and hatred at this, and then Nag's head came through the sluice, and his five feet of cold body followed it. Angry as he was, Rikki-tikki was very frightened as he saw the size of the big cobra. Nag coiled himself up, raised his head, and looked into the bath-room in the dark, and Rikki could see his eyes glitter.

'Now, if I kill him here, Nagaina will know; and if I fight him on the open floor, the odds are in his favour. What am I to do?' said Rikki-tikki-tavi.

Nag waved to and fro, and then Rikki-tikki

heard him drinking from the biggest water-jar that was used to fill the bath. 'That is good,' said the snake. 'Now, when Karait was killed, the big man had a stick. He may have that stick still, but when he comes in to bathe in the morning he will not have a stick. I shall wait here till he comes. Nagaina — do you hear me? — I shall wait here in the cool till daytime.'

There was no answer from outside, so Rikki-tikki knew Nagaina had gone away. Nag coiled himself down, coil by coil, round the bulge at the bottom of the water-jar, and Rikki-tikki stayed still as death. After an hour he began to move, muscle by muscle, towards the jar. Nag was asleep, and Rikki-tikki looked at his big back, wondering which would be the best place for a good hold. 'If I don't break his back at the first jump,' said Rikki, 'he can still fight; and if he fights — O Rikki!' He looked at the thickness of the neck below the hood, but that was too much for him; and a bite near the tail would only make Nag savage.

'It must be the head,' he said at last; 'the head above the hood; and, when I am once there, I must not let go.'

Then he jumped. The head was lying a little clear of the water-jar, under the curve of it; and, as his teeth met, Rikki braced his back against the bulge of the red earthenware to hold down the head. This gave him just one second's purchase, and he made the most of it. Then he was battered to and fro as a rat is shaken by a dog — to and fro on the floor, up and down, and round in great circles, but his eyes were red and he held on as the body cartwhipped over the floor, upsetting the tin dipper and the soapdish and the flesh-brush, and banged against the tin side of the bath. As he held he closed his jaws tighter and tighter, for he made sure he would be banged to death, and, for the honour of his family, he preferred to be found with his teeth locked. He was dizzy, aching, and felt shaken to pieces when something went off like a thunderclap just behind him; a hot wind knocked him senseless and red fire singed his fur. The big man had been wakened by the noise, and had fired both barrels of a shot-gun into Nag just behind the hood.

Rikki-tikki held on with his eyes shut, for now he was quite sure he was dead; but the head did not move, and the big man picked him up and said: 'It's the mongoose again, Alice; the little chap has saved *our* lives now.' Then Teddy's mother came in with a very white face, and saw what was left of Nag, and Rikki-tikki dragged himself to Teddy's bedroom and spent half the rest of the night shaking himself tenderly to find out whether he really was broken into forty pieces, as he fancied.

When morning came he was very stiff, but well pleased with his doings. 'Now I have Nagaina to settle with, and she will be worse than five Nags, and there's no knowing when the eggs she spoke of will hatch. Goodness! I must go and see

Darzee,' he said.

Without waiting for breakfast, Rikki-tikki ran to the thorn-bush where Darzee was singing a song of triumph at the top of his voice. The news of Nag's death was all over the garden, for the sweeper had thrown the body on the rubbish-heap.

'Oh, you stupid tuft of feathers!' said Rikki-tikki angrily. 'Is this the time to sing?'

'Nag is dead — is dead — is dead!' sang Darzee. 'The valiant Rikki-tikki caught him by the head and held fast. The big man brought the bang-stick, and Nag fell in two pieces! He will never eat my babies again.'

'All that's true enough; but where's Nagaina?' said Rikki-tikki, looking carefully round him.

'Nagaina came to the bath-room sluice and called for Nag,' Darzee went on; 'and Nag came out on the end of a stick — the sweeper picked him up on the end of a stick and threw him upon the rubbish-heap. Let us sing about the great, the red-eyed Rikki-tikki!' and Darzee filled his throat and sang.

'If I could get up to your nest, I'd roll your babies out!' said Rikki-tikki. 'You don't know when to do the right thing at the right time. You're safe enough in your nest there, but it's war for me down here. Stop singing a minute, Darzee.'

'For the great, beautiful Rikki-tikki's sake I will stop,' said Darzee. 'What is it, O Killer of the terrible Nag?'

'Where is Nagaina, for the third time?'

'On the rubbish-heap by the stables, mourning for Nag. Great is Rikki-tikki with the white teeth.'

'Bother my white teeth! Have you ever heard where she keeps her eggs?'

'In the melon-bed, on the end nearest the wall, where the sun strikes nearly all day. She hid them there weeks ago.'

'And you never thought it worth while to tell me? The end nearest the wall, you said?'

'Rikki-tikki, you are not going to eat her eggs?'

'Not eat exactly; no. Darzee, if you have a grain of sense you will fly off to the stables and pretend that your wing is broken, and let Nagaina chase you away to this bush? I must get to the melon-bed, and if I went there now she'd see me.'

Darzee was a feather-brained little fellow who could never hold more than one idea at a time in his head; and just because he knew that Nagaina's children were born in eggs like his own, he didn't think at first that it was fair to kill them. But his wife was a sensible bird, and she knew that cobra's eggs meant young cobras later on; so she flew off from the nest, and left Darzee to keep the babies warm, and continue his song about the death of Nag. Darzee was very like a man in some ways.

She fluttered in front of Nagaina by the rubbish-heap, and cried out, 'Oh, my wing is broken! The boy in the house threw a stone at me and broke it.' Then she fluttered more desperately than ever.

Nagaina lifted up her head and hissed, 'You warned Rikki-tikki when I would have killed him. Indeed and truly, you've chosen a bad place to be lame in.' And she moved toward Darzee's wife, slipping along over the dust.

'The boy broke it with a stone!' shrieked Darzee's wife.

'Well! It may be some consolation to you when you're dead to know that I shall settle accounts with the boy. My husband lies on the rubbish-heap this morning, but before night the boy in the house will lie very still. What is the use of running away? I am sure to catch you. Little fool, look at me!'

Darzee's wife knew better than to do *that*, for a bird who looks at a snake's eyes gets so frightened that she cannot move. Darzee's wife fluttered on, piping sorrowfully, and never leaving the ground, and Nagaina quickened her pace.

Rikki-tikki heard them going up the path from the stables, and he raced for the end of the melon-patch near the wall. There, in the warm litter above the melons, very cunningly hidden, he found twenty-five eggs, about the size of a bantam's eggs, but with whitish skins instead of shells.

'I was not a day too soon,' he said; for he could see the baby cobras curled up inside the skin, and he knew that the minute they were hatched they could each kill a man or a mongoose.

He bit off the tops of the eggs as fast as he could, taking care to crush the young cobras, and turned over the litter from time to time to see whether he had missed any. At last there were only three eggs left, and Rikki-tikki began to chuckle to himself, when he heard Darzee's wife screaming:

'Rikki-tikki, I led Nagaina toward the house, and she has gone into the veranda, and — oh, come quickly — she means killing!'

Rikki-tikki smashed two eggs, and tumbled backward down the melon-bed with the third egg in his mouth, and scuttled to the veranda as hard as he could put foot to the ground. Teddy and his mother and father were there at early breakfast; but Rikki-tikki saw that they were not eating anything. They sat stone-still, and their faces were white. Nagaina was coiled up on the matting by Teddy's chair, within easy striking distance of Teddy's bare leg, and she was swaying to and fro, singing a song of triumph.

'Son of the big man that killed Nag,' she hissed, 'stay still. I am not ready yet. Wait a little. Keep very still, all you three! If you move I strike, and if you do not move I strike. Oh, foolish people, who killed my Nag!'

Teddy's eyes were fixed on his father, and all his father could do was to whisper, 'Sit still, Teddy. You mustn't move. Teddy, keep still.'

Then Rikki-tikki came up and cried: 'Turn round, Nagaina; turn and fight!'

'All in good time,' said she, without moving her eyes. 'I will settle my account with *you* presently. Look at your friends, Rikki-tikki. They are still and white. They are afraid. They dare not move, and if you come a step nearer I strike.'

'Look at your eggs,' said Rikki-tikki, 'in the melon-bed near the wall. Go and look, Nagaina!'

The big snake turned half round, and saw the egg on the veranda. 'Ah-h! Give it to me,' she said.

Rikki-tikki put his paws one on each side of the egg, and his eyes were blood-red. 'What price for a snake's egg? For a young cobra? For a young king-cobra? For the last — the very last of the brood? The ants are eating all the others down by the melon-bed.'

Nagaina spun clear round, forgetting everything for the sake of the one egg; and Rikki-tikki saw Teddy's father shoot out a big hand, catch Teddy by the shoulder, and drag him across the little table with the tea-cups, safe and out of reach of Nagaina.

'Tricked! Tricked! Tricked! *Rikk-tck-tck!*' chuckled Rikki-tikki. 'The boy is safe, and it was I — I — I — that caught Nag by the hood last night in the bath-room.' Then he began to jump up and down, all four feet together, his head close to the floor. 'He threw me to and fro, but he could not shake me off. He was dead before the big man blew him in two. I did it! *Rikki-tikki-tck-tck!* Come then, Nagaina. Come and fight with me. You shall not be a widow long.'

Nagaina saw that she had lost her chance of killing Teddy, and the egg lay between Rikki-tikki's paws. 'Give me the egg, Rikki-tikki. Give me the last of my eggs, and I will go away and never come back,' she said, lowering her hood.

'Yes, you will go away, and you will never come back; for you will go the rubbish-heap with Nag. Fight, widow! The big man has gone for his gun! Fight!'

Rikki-tikki was bounding all round Nagaina, keeping just out of reach of her stroke, his little eyes like hot coals. Nagaina gathered herself together, and flung out at him. Rikki-tikki jumped up and backwards. Again and again and again she struck, and each time her head came with a whack on the matting of the veranda and she gathered herself together like a watch-spring. Then Rikki-tikki danced in a circle to get behind her, and Nagaina spun round to keep her head to his head, so that the rustle of her tail on the matting sounded like dry leaves blown along by the wind.

He had forgotten the egg. It still lay on the veranda, and Nagaina came nearer and nearer to it, till at last, while Rikki-tikki was drawing breath, she caught it in her mouth, turned to the veranda steps, and flew like an arrow down the path, with Rikki-tikki behind her. When the cobra runs for her life, she goes like a whip-lash flicked across a horse's neck. Rikki-tikki knew that he must catch her, or all the trouble would begin again. She headed straight for the long grass by the thorn-bush, and as he was running, Rikki-tikki heard Darzee still singing his foolish little song of triumph. But Darzee's wife was wiser. She flew off her nest as Nagaina came along, and flapped her wings about Nagaina's head. If Darzee had helped they might have turned her; but Nagaina only lowered her hood and went on. Still, the instant's delay brought Rikki-tikki up to her, and as she plunged into the rat-hole where she and Nag used to live, his little white teeth were clenched on her tail, and he went down with her — and very few mongooses, however wise and old they may be, care to follow a cobra into its hole. It was dark in the hole; and Rikki-tikki never knew when it might open out and give Nagaina room to turn and strike at him. He held on savagely, and struck out his feet to act as brakes on the dark slope of the hot, moist earth. Then the grass by the mouth of the hole stopped waving, and Darzee said: 'It is all over with Rikki-tikki! We must sing his death-song. Valiant Rikki-tikki is dead! For Nagaina will surely kill him underground.'

So he sang a very mournful song that he made up on the spur of the minute, and just as he got to the most touching part the grass quivered again, and Rikki-tikki, covered with dirt, dragged himself out of the hole leg by leg, licking his whiskers. Darzee stopped with a little shout. Rikki-tikki shook some of the dust out of his fur and sneezed. 'It is all over,' he said. 'The widow will never come out again.' And the red ants that live between the grass stems heard him, and began to troop down one after another to see if he had spoken the truth.

Rikki-tikki curled himself up in the grass and slept where he was — slept and slept till it was late in the afternoon, for he had done a hard day's work.

'Now,' he said, when he awoke, 'I will go back to the house. Tell the Coppersmith, Darzee, and he will tell the garden that Nagaina is dead.'

The Coppersmith is a bird who makes a noise exactly like the beating of a little hammer on a copper pot; and the reason he is always making it is because he is the town-crier to every Indian garden, and tells all the news to everybody who cares to listen. As Rikki-tikki went up the path, he heard his 'attention' notes like a tiny dinner-gong; and then the steady *'Ding-dong-tock!* Nag is dead — *dong!* Nagaina is dead! *Ding-dong-tock!'* That set all the birds in the garden singing, and the frogs croaking; for Nag and Nagaina used to eat frogs as well as little birds.

When Rikki got to the house, Teddy and Teddy's mother (she looked very white still, for she had been fainting) and Teddy's father came out and almost cried over him; and that night he ate all that was given him till he could eat no more, and went to bed on Teddy's shoulder, where Teddy's mother saw him when she came to look late at night.

'He saved our lives and Teddy's life,' she said

219

to her husband. 'Just think, he saved all our lives.'

Rikki-tikki woke up with a jump, for the mongooses are light sleepers.

'Oh, it's you,' said he. 'What are you bothering for? All the cobras are dead; and if they weren't, I'm here.'

Rikki-tikki had a right to be proud of himself; but he did not grow too proud, and he kept that garden as a mongoose should keep it, with tooth and jump and spring and bite, till never a cobra dared show its head inside the walls.

Darzee's Chaunt
(SUNG IN HONOUR OF RIKKI-TIKKI-TAVI)

Singer and tailor am I —
    Doubled the joys that I know —
Proud of my lilt to the sky,
    Proud of the house that I sew.
Over and under, so weave I my music — so
    weave I the house that I sew.

Sing to your fledglings again,
    Mother, O lift up your head!
Evil that plagued us is slain,
    Death in the garden lies dead.
Terror that hid in the roses is impotent —
    flung on the dunghill and dead!

Who has delivered us, who?
    Tell me his nest and his name.
Rikki, the valiant, the true,

Tikki, with eyeballs of flame —
Rikk-tikki-tikki, the ivory-fanged, the hunter
   with eyeballs of flame!

Give him the Thanks of the Birds,
   Bowing with tail-feathers spread,
Praise him with nightingale words —
   Nay, I will praise him instead.
Hear! I will sing you the praise of the bottle-
   tailed Rikki with eyeballs of red!

(*Here Rikki-tikki interrupted, so the rest of the song
is lost.*)

Adolf

D. H. Lawrence

hen we were children our father often worked on the night shift. Once it was springtime, and he used to arrive home, black and tired, just as we were downstairs in our night-dresses. Then night met morning face to face, and the contact was not always happy. Perhaps it was painful to my father to see us gaily entering upon the day into which he dragged himself soiled and weary. He didn't like going to bed in the spring morning sunshine.

But sometimes he was happy, because of his long walk through the dewy fields in the first daybreak. He loved the open morning, the crystal and the space, after a night down pit. He watched every bird, every stir in the trembling grass, answered the whinnying of the pewits and tweeted to the wrens. If he could, he also would have whinnied and tweeted and whistled in a native language that was not human. He liked non-human things best.

One sunny morning we were all sitting at table when we heard his heavy slurring walk up the entry. We became uneasy. His was always a disturbing presence, trammelling. He passed the window darkly, and we heard him go into the scullery and put down his tin bottle. But directly he came into the kitchen. We felt at once that he had something to communicate. No one spoke. We watched his black face for a second.

"Give me a drink," he said.

My mother hastily poured out his tea. He went to pour it out into his saucer. But instead of drinking he suddenly put something on the table among the teacups. A tiny brown rabbit! A small rabbit, a mere morsel, sitting against the bread as still as if it were a made thing.

"A rabbit! A young one! Who gave it you, Father?"

But he laughed enigmatically, with a sliding motion of his yellow-grey eyes, and went to take off his coat. We pounced on the rabbit.

"Is it alive? Can you feel its heart beat?"

My father came back and sat down heavily in his armchair. He dragged his saucer to him, and blew his tea, pushing out his red lips under his black moustache.

"Where did you get it, Father?"

"I picked it up," he said, wiping his naked forearm over his mouth and beard.

"Where?"

"It is a wild one!" came my mother's quick voice.

"Yes, it is."

"Then why did you bring it?" cried my mother.

"Oh, we wanted it," came our cry.

"Yes, I've no doubt you did —" retorted my mother. But she was drowned in our clamour of questions.

On the field path my father had found a dead mother rabbit and three dead little ones — this one alive, but unmoving.

"But what had killed them, Daddy?"

"I couldn't say, my child. I s'd think she'd aten something."

"Why did you bring it!" — again my mother's voice of condemnation. "You know what it will be."

My father made no answer, but we were loud in protest.

"He must bring it. It's not big enough to live by itself. It would die," we shouted.

"Yes, and it will die now. And then there'll be *another* outcry."

My mother set her face against the tragedy of dead pets. Our hearts sank.

"It won't die, Father, will it? Why will it? It won't."

"I s'd think not," said my father.

"You know well enough it will. Haven't we had it all before!" said my mother.

"They dunna always pine," replied my father testily.

But my mother reminded him of other little wild animals he had brought, which had sulked and refused to live, and brought storms of tears and trouble in our house of lunatics.

Trouble fell on us. The little rabbit sat on our

lap, unmoving, its eye wide and dark. We brought it milk, warm milk, and held it to its nose. It sat as still as if it was far away, retreated down some deep burrow, hidden, oblivious. We wetted its mouth and whiskers with drops of milk. It gave no sign, did not even shake off the wet white drops. Somebody began to shed a few secret tears.

"What did I say?" cried my mother. "Take it and put it down in the field."

Her command was in vain. We were driven to get dressed for school. There sat the rabbit. It was like a tiny obscure cloud. Watching it, the emotions died out of our breast. Useless to love it, to yearn over it. Its little feelings were all ambushed. They must be circumvented. Love and affection were a trespass upon it. A little wild thing, it became more mute and asphyxiated still in its own arrest, when we approached with love. We must not love it. We must circumvent it for its own existence.

So I passed the order to my sister and my mother. The rabbit was not to be spoken to, nor even looked at. Wrapping it in a piece of flannel, I put it in an obscure corner of the cold parlour, and put a saucer of milk before its nose. My mother was forbidden to enter the parlour while we were at school.

"As if I should take any notice of your nonsense," she cried, affronted. Yet I doubt if she ventured into the parlour.

At midday, after school, creeping into the

front room, there we saw the rabbit still and unmoving in the piece of flannel. Strange greybrown neutralization of life, still living! It was a sore problem to us.

"Why won't it drink its milk, Mother?" we whispered. Our father was asleep.

"It prefers to sulk its life away, silly little thing." A profound problem. Prefers to sulk its life away! We put young dandelion leaves to its nose. The sphinx was not more oblivious. Yet its eye was bright.

At tea time, however, it had hopped a few inches, out of its flannel, and there it sat again, uncovered, a little solid cloud of muteness, brown, with unmoving whiskers. Only its side palpitated slightly with life.

Darkness came; my father set off to work. The rabbit was still unmoving. Dumb despair was coming over the sisters, a threat of tears before bedtime. Clouds of my mother's anger gathered as she muttered against my father's wantonness.

Once more the rabbit was wrapped in the old pit singlet. But now it was carried into the scullery and put under the copper fire-place, that it might imagine itself inside a burrow. The saucers were placed about, four or five, here and there on the floor, so that if the little creature *should* chance to hop abroad it could not fail to come upon some food. After this my mother was allowed to take from the scullery what she wanted and then she was forbidden to open the door.

When morning came and it was light, I went

downstairs. Opening the scullery door, I heard a slight scuffle. Then I saw dabbles of milk all over the floor and tiny rabbit droppings in the saucers. And there was the miscreant, the tips of his ears showing behind a pair of boots. I peeped at him. He sat bright-eyed and askance, twitching his nose and looking at me while not looking at me.

He was alive — very much alive. But still we were afraid to trespass much on his confidence.

"Father!" My father was arrested at the door. "Father the rabbit's alive."

"Back your life it is," said my father.

"Mind how you go in."

By evening, however, the little creature was tame, quite tame. He was christened Adolf. We were enchanted by him. We couldn't really love him, because he was wild and loveless to the end. But he was an unmixed delight.

We decided he was too small to live in a hutch — he must live at large in the house. My mother protested, but in vain. He was so tiny. So we had him upstairs, and he dropped his tiny pills on the bed and we were enchanted.

Adolf made himself instantly at home. He had the run of the house, and was perfectly happy, with his tunnels and his holes behind the furniture.

We loved him to take meals with us. He would sit on the table humping his back, sipping his milk, shaking his whiskers and his tender ears, hopping off and hobbling back to his saucer, with an air of supreme unconcern. Suddenly he was alert. He hobbled a few tiny paces, and reared himself up inquisitively at the sugar basin. He fluttered his tiny fore-paws, and then reached and laid them on the edge of the basin, while he craned his thin neck and peeped in. He trembled his whiskers at the sugar, then did his best to lift down a lump.

"*Do* you think I will have it? Animals in the sugar pot!" cried my mother, with a rap of her hand on the table.

Which so delighted the electric Adolf that he flung his hindquarters and knocked over a cup.

"It's your own fault, Mother. If you left him alone —"

He continued to take tea with us. He rather liked warm tea. And he loved sugar. Having nibled a lump, he would turn to the butter. There he was shooed off by our parent. He soon learned to treat her shooing with indifference. Still, she hated him to put his nose in the food. And he loved to do it. And one day between them they overturned the cream-jub. Adolf deluged his little chest, bounced back in terror, was seized by his little ears by my mother and bounced down on the hearth-rug. There he shivered in momentary discomfort, and suddenly set off in a wild flight to the parlour.

This last was his happy hunting-ground. He had cultivated the bad habit of pensively nibbling certain bits of cloth in the hearth-rug. When chased from this pasture he would retreat under the sofa. There he would twinkle in Buddhist meditation until suddenly, no one knew why, he would go off like an alarm clock. With a sudden bumping scuffle he would whirl out of the room, going through the doorway with his little ears flying. Then we would hear his thunderbolt hurtling in the parlour, but before we could follow, the wild streak of Adolf would flash past us, on an electric wind that swept him round the scullery and carried him back, a little mad thing, flying possessed like a ball round the parlour. After which ebullition he would sit in a corner composed and distant, twitching his whiskers in abstract meditation. And it was in vain we questioned him about his outbursts. He just went off like a gun, and was as calm after it as a gun that smokes placidly.

Alas, he grew up rapidly. It was almost impossible to keep him from the outer door.

One day, as we were playing by the stile, I saw his brown shadow loiter across the road and pass into the field that faced the houses. Instantly a cry of "Adolf!" — a cry he knew full well. And instantly a wind swept him away down the sloping meadow, his tail twinkling and zigzagging through the grass. After him we pelted. It was a strange sight to see him, ears back, his little loins so powerful, flinging the world behind him. We ran ourselves out of breath, but could not catch him. Then somebody headed him off, and he sat with sudden unconcern, twitching his nose under a bunch of nettles.

His wanderings cost him a shock. One Sunday morning my father had just been quarrelling with a peddler and we were hearing the aftermath indoors, when there came a sudden unearthly scream from the yard. We flew out. There sat Adolf cowering under a bench, while a great black-and-white cat glowered intently at him, a few yards away. Sight not to be forgotten. Adolf rolling back his eyes and parting his strange muzzle in another scream, the cat stretching forward in a slow elongation.

Ha, how we hated that cat! How we pursued him over the chapel wall and across the neighbours' gardens!

Adolf was still only half grown.

"Cats!" said my mother. "Hideous detestable animals, why do people harbour them?"

But Adolf was becoming too much for her. He dropped too many pills. And suddenly to hear him clumping downstairs when she was alone in the house was startling. And to keep him from the door was impossible. Cats prowled outside. It was worse than having a child to look after.

Yet we would not have him shut up. He became more lusty, more callous than ever. He was a strong kicker, and many a scratch on face and arms did we owe to him. But he brought his own doom on himself. The lace curtains in the parlour — my mother was rather proud of them — fell on the floor very full. One of Adolf's joys was to scuffle wildly through them as though through some foamy undergrowth. He had already torn rents in them.

One day he entangled himself altogether. He kicked, he whirled round in a mad, nebulous inferno. He screamed — and brought down the curtain-rod with a smash, right on the best-beloved pelargonium, just as my mother rushed in. She extricated him, but she never forgave him. And he never forgave either. A heartless wildness had come over him.

Even we understood that he must go. It was decided, after a long deliberation, that my father should carry him back to the wildwoods. Once again he was stowed into the great pocket of the pit jacket.

"Best pop him i' th' pot," said my father, who enjoyed raising the wind of indignation.

And so, next day, our father said that Adolf, set down on the edge of the coppice, had hopped away with utmost indifference, neither elated nor moved. We heard it and believed. But many, many were the heart-searchings. How would the other rabbits receive him? Would they smell his tameness, his humanized degradation, and rend him? My mother pooh-poohed the extravagant idea.

However, he was gone, and we were rather relieved. My father kept an eye open for him. He declared that several times passing the coppice in the early morning, he had seen Adolf peeping through the nettle-stalks. He had called him, in an odd, high-voiced, cajoling fashion. But Adolf had not responded. Wildness gains so soon upon its creatures. And they become so contemptuous then of our tame presence. So it seemed to me. I myself would go to the edge of the coppice, and call softly. I myself would imagine bright eyes between the nettle-stalks, flash of a white, scornful tail past the bracken. That insolent white tail, as Adolf turned his flank on us!

Particularly Cats*

Doris Lessing

The little black cat, for a variety of sad reasons, was homeless and joined our household. It would have been better for harmony if she had been a male cat. As it was, the two she-cats met as enemies, crouched watching each other for hours.

Grey cat, half her side still stubbly from the razor, refusing to sleep on my bed, refusing to eat until coaxed, unhappy and unsure of herself, was determined about one thing: that the black cat was not going to take her place.

Black cat, on her side, knew she was going to live here, and would not be chased away. She did not fight: grey cat was bigger and stronger. She got into the corner of a seat, her back protected by a wall, and never took her eyes off grey cat.

When her enemy went to sleep, black cat ate and drank. Then she surveyed the garden with which she had already become acquainted from the end of a smart leash and collar, examined it

*This is the seventh chapter of Doris Lessing's memoir about cats, *Particularly Cats*.

233

carefully. Then she examined the house, floor by floor. My bed, she decided, was the place for her. At which grey cat leaped up, spitting, and chased the black cat away, took her place on my bed. Black cat then took up a position on the sofa.

Black cat's character is altogether different from grey cat's. She is a steady, obstinate, modest little beast. She knew no coquetry until she saw grey cat's: did not pose, flirt, roll, scamper, or show off.

She knew she was not the first cat of the household; grey cat was boss cat. But as second cat she had rights, and insisted on them. The two cats never fought, physically. They fought great duels with their eyes. On either side of the kitchen they sat: green eyes, yellow eyes staring. If black cat did something over the edge of what grey cat thought was tolerable, grey cat gave a faint growl, and made subtle threatening movements with her muscles. Black cat desisted. Grey cat slept on my bed; black cat must not. Grey cat could sit on the table; but not black cat. When visitors came, grey cat was first at the door. And grey cat would not eat, unless separately, out of a newly washed saucer, with newly cut food, and in a fresh place in the kitchen. For black cat, the old food corner would do.

Black cat submitted to all this, and with the humans in the house was modestly affectionate, wreathed our legs, purred, talked — she is half-

Siamese too; but always with an eye on grey cat.

This behaviour did not accord with her appearance. Grey cat's looks and her behaviour have always gone together: her looks have dictated her character.

But black cat is ambiguous. For instance, her size. She is a small slender cat. When she has kittens, it seems incredible there could be room for them. But pick her up: she is solid, heavy; a strong, close-packed little beast. She does not look at all modest, domestic; and as maternal as she later turned out to be.

She is elegant. She has a curved noble profile, like a cat on a tomb. When she sits straight, paws side by side, staring, or crouches, eyes half-masked, she is still, remote, withdrawn to some distant place inside herself. At such times she is sombre, inspires awe. And she is black, black, black. Black glossy whiskers, black lashes, not a white hair anywhere. If grey cat's designer was a master of subtlety, of loving detail, then black cat's said: I shall create a black cat, the quintessence of black cat, a cat from the Underworld.

It took about two weeks for these antagonists to establish rules of precedence. They never touched, or played, or licked each other: they created a balance where they were always conscious of each other, in watchful hostility. And that was sad, remembering how grey cat and her grown child had played and cleaned each other and wound about each other. Perhaps, we thought, these two might learn affection in time.

But then black cat got sick, and poor grey cat's hard-fought-for position was lost completely.

Black cat had a cold, I thought. Her bowels were out of order: she made frequent trips to the garden. She was sick several times.

If I had taken her to the doctor then, she would not have been so very ill. She had enteritis; but I did not know how bad that is, and that very few cats get over it, not, at least, while they are still half-kitten. On the second night of her illness I woke and saw her crouched in a corner — coughing, I thought at first. But she was trying to be sick — with nothing left to be sick with. Her jaws and mouth were covered with white froth, a sticky foam which would not easily wipe off. I washed it off. She went back to the corner, crouching, looking in front of her. The way she sat was ominous: immobile, patient, and she was not asleep. She was waiting.

In the morning I took her to the cat hospital around the corner, by now bitten by remorse because I had not taken her earlier. She was very ill, they said; and from the way they said it, I knew she was not expected to live. She was badly dehydrated and had a roaring temperature. They gave her an injection for the fever, and said she must be made to take liquid — if possible. She would not drink, I said. No, they would not, they said, past a certain stage in the illness, which was characterized by another symptom: cats decide to die. They creep into a cool place somewhere, because of the heat of their blood, crouch down, and wait to die.

When I took black cat home, she stalked gauntly into the garden. It was early autumn and cold. She crouched against the chill of the garden wall, cold earth under her, in the patient waiting position of the night before.

I carried her in, and put her on a blanket, not too close to a radiator. She went back to the garden: same position, same deadly, patient position.

I took her back and shut her in. She crept to the door, and settled down there, nose towards it, waiting to die.

I tempted her with water, water and glucose, meat juices. It wasn't that she refused them: she had gone beyond them; food was something that she had left behind. She did not want to come back; she would not.

Next day the people at the hospital said her temperature was still very high. It had not come down. And she *must* drink.

I brought her home and thought it out. Clearly, keeping black cat alive would be a full-time job. And I was busy. And, as people in the house were pointing out, she was only a cat.

But she was *not* just a cat. For a variety of reasons, all of them human and irrelevant to her, she must not be allowed to die.

I mixed a nasty but useful solution of glucose, blood and water, and fought black cat.

She would not open her jaws to take it. A

small feverish creature, shadow-light, having lost all her healthy solidity of flesh, she sat, or rather, collapsed, in my lap, and shut her teeth against the spoon. It was the strength of weakness: no, no, no.

I forced her teeth open, using her canines as levers. The liquid was in her throat, but she would not swallow. I held her jaws up, and the liquid ran out of the sides of her mouth. But some of it must have got down, because after the third, fourth, fifth spoonful, she made a faint swallowing movement.

So that was it. Every half hour. I took the poor creature from her corner, and forced liquid down her. I was afraid of hurting her jaw, because of using so much pressure on her projecting teeth. Her jaw was probably very painful.

That night I put her by me on the bed, and woke her every hour. Though she was not really asleep. She crouched, the heat from the fever sending waves all around her, eyes half-open, suffering the end of her life.

Next day the fever had still not gone down. But the day after it had; and now the clinic gave her glucose injections. Each injection left a large soft bulge under her stiff hide. But she did not care; she cared about nothing at all.

Now that the fever was gone, she was very cold. I wrapped her in an old towel, and put her near the radiator. Every half hour, black cat and I fought. Or rather, black cat's intention to die fought with my intention that she should not.

At night, she crouched by me on the bed, trembling with the sad faint inner trembling of extreme weakness, a towel over her. Wherever I put her she stayed; she did not have the strength to move. But she would *not* open her jaws to take liquid. She would not. All her remaining strength went into saying *no*.

Ten days went by. I took her to the cat hospital every day. It is a place where young vets are trained, a teaching hospital. The people of the neighbourhood take dogs and cats every morning, between nine and twelve. We sat on rows of benches in a large bare waiting room, with the sick animals fretting, whining, barking. All kinds of friendships were struck up on account of the illnesses of these animals.

And all kinds of small sad incidents stay in my mind. For instance, there was a woman, middle-aged, her hair dyed light blonde, over a haggard face. She had the most beautiful large dog which was sleek with food and attention. There could not have been much wrong with the dog, which was lively, and barked and was proud of itself. But the woman stood in a light suit, always the same suit, without a coat. It was a little cold, not very, and the rest of us wore light dresses or sweaters. But she shivered uncontrollably; the flesh on her arms and legs was not there. It was clear that she did not have enough to eat, and that her money and time went on the dog. To feed a dog of that size costs a lot of money. A cat costs, I reckon, ten shillings a week, even if it isn't a spoiled beast, as ours both are. That woman lived through her dog. I think everyone felt it. The people in this area are mostly poor: the way they looked at her, shivering there with her pampered beast, and then invited her to jump the queue to get out of the cold into the building while we waited for the doors to open, said that they understood her situation and were sorry for her.

And an incident at the other extreme — or apparently so. A fat bulldog — but very fat, rolls of flesh all over it — was brought in by a fat boy of about twelve. The doctors had the dog on the examination table, and explained to the boy that a dog must eat just so much, and only once a day: there was nothing wrong with it but overfeeding. And it must not be fed bits of cake and bread and sweets and . . . The fat boy repeated, over and over again, that he would go back and tell his mother, he would tell his mother, he said; but what *she* wanted to know was, why did the dog wheeze and pant, after all, it was only two years old, and it would not run and play and bark as other dogs did. Well, said the doctors patiently, it was as easy to overfeed an animal as to underfeed it. If you overfeed a dog, you see . . .

Extraordinarily patient they are; and very kind. And tactful. The things that must be done to animals which would upset their owners take place behind closed doors. Poor black cat was taken off for her injections and was gone twenty minutes, half an hour, before being returned to me with the subcutaneous water lumping her stiff dirty fur.

She had not licked herself, cleaned herself, for days. She could not move. She was not getting better. If all my attention, if all the skills of the clinic made no difference, well, perhaps after all she should be allowed to die, since that was what she wanted. There she sat, day after day, under the radiator. Her fur was already like a dead cat's, with dust and fluff in it; her eyes were gummy; the fur around her mouth was solid with the glucose I tried to pour into her.

I thought of what it was like being sick in bed, the feeling of irritable disgust, of self-hatred that sets in, until it seems to be the illness itself. One's hair needs washing; one can smell the sourness of illness on one's breath, one's skin. One seems shut inside a shell of sickness, a miasma of illness. Then along comes the nurse, washes one's face, brushes one's hair, and whisks away sour-smelling sheets.

No, of course cats are not human; humans are not cats; but all the same, I couldn't believe that such a fastidious little beast as black cat was not suffering from the knowledge of how dirty and smelly she was.

But you can't wash a cat. First I took a light towel wrung out in hot water, and rubbed her with it, gently, all over, to get rid of the dirt and fluff and stickiness. This took a long time. She remained passive, suffered probably, because by now her skin was punctured by so many injections. Then, when she was clean, fur and ears and eyes, I dried her with a warmed towel.

And then — and I think it was this that made the difference — I made my hands warm by heating them in hot water, and I rubbed her, very slowly, all over. I tried to rub some life into her cold body. I did this for some time, about half an hour.

When it was finished, I covered her with a clean warm towel. And then, very stiff and slow, she got up and walked across the kitchen. She soon crouched down again, where the impulse to move had ebbed out. But she *had* moved, of her own accord.

Next day I asked the doctors if rubbing the cat might have made some difference. They said, probably not, they thought it was the injections. However that may be, there is no doubt the point where there was a possibility of her living came when she was cleaned and rubbed. For another ten days she was given glucose by the clinic; forced to take the nasty mixtures of meat juices, water and glucose by me; and rubbed and brushed twice a day.

And all this time, poor grey cat was pushed on one side. First things first. Black cat needed too much attention for grey cat to be given much. But grey cat was not going to accept handouts, no secondbest for her. She simply removed herself, physically and emotionally, and watched.

Sometimes she came cautiously to black cat, to all intents and purposes already dead, sniffed at her, and backed away. Sometimes her hair lifted as she sniffed at black cat. Once or twice, during the time black cat was creeping out into the cold garden to die, grey cat went too, and sat a few paces away, watching her. But she did not seem to be hostile; she did not try to hurt black cat.

During all that time, grey cat never played, or did her tricks, or made special demands over her food. She was not petted, and she slept in the corner of the bedroom on the floor, not rolled up into a luxurious ball, but crouching to watch the bed where black cat was being nursed.

Then black cat began to recover, and the worst period started — that is, from the human point of view. And perhaps for black cat too, who had been bullied back into life against her will. She was like a kitten who had to do everything new, or like a very old person. She had no control of her bowels: had forgotten, it seemed, the function of dirt boxes. She ate painfully, clumsily, and made messes as she ate. And wherever she was, she might suddenly collapse, and sit crouching and staring in front of her. Very upsetting it was: the small sick aloof beast, always sitting in a stiff crouch, never rolled up, or stretched out. And staring — a deathlike cat she looked, with her staring distant eyes. For a while I thought she might have gone a little crazy.

But she got better. She stopped messing floors. She ate. And one day, instead of settling into her usual waiting crouch, she remembered that one could lie curled. It did not come easily or at once. She made two or three attempts, as if her muscles could not remember how the thing was done. Then, she curled herself up, nose to tail, and slept. She was a cat again.

But she still had not licked herself. I tried to remind her by taking a forepaw and rubbing it over her cheek, but she let it drop. It was too soon.

I had to go away for a six-week trip, and the cats were left with a friend to look after them.

When I came back into the kitchen, grey cat was sitting on the table, boss cat again. And on the floor was black cat, glossy, sleek, clean and purring.

The balance of power had been restored. And black cat had forgotten she had been ill. But not quite. Her muscles had never quite recovered. There is a stiffness in her haunches: she can't jump cleanly, though well enough. On her back above her tail is a thin patch in the fur. And somewhere in her brain is held a memory of that time. Over a year later I took her to the clinic because she had a minor ear infection. She did not mind being carried there in the basket. She did not mind the waiting room. But when she was carried into the diagnosing room, she began to tremble and to salivate. They took her into the inside room, where she had had so many injections, to clean her ears, and when she was brought back, she was rigid with fright, her mouth streaming, and she trembled for hours afterwards. But she is a normal cat, with normal instincts.

For the Love of a Man*

Jack London

When John Thornton froze his feet in the previous December, his partners had made him comfortable and left him to get well, going on themselves up the river to get out a raft of sawlogs for Dawson. He was still limping slightly at the time he rescued Buck, but with the continued warm weather even the slight limp left him. And here, lying by the river bank through the long spring days, watching the running water, listening lazily to the songs of birds and the hum of nature, Buck slowly won back his strength.

A rest comes very good after one has traveled three thousand miles, and it must be confessed that Buck waxed lazy as his wounds healed, his muscles swelled out, and the flesh came back to cover his bones. For that matter, they were all loafing, — Buck, John Thornton, and Skeet and Nig, — waiting for the raft to come that was to carry them down to Dawson. Skeet was a little Irish setter who early made friends with Buck, who, in a dying condition, was unable to resent

*From *The Call of the Wild*.

her first advances. She had the doctor trait which some dogs possess; and as a mother cat washes her kittens, so she washed and cleansed Buck's wounds. Regularly, each morning after he had finished his breakfast, she performed her self-appointed task, till he came to look for her ministrations as much as he did for Thornton's. Nig, equally friendly, though less demonstrative, was a huge black dog, half bloodhound and half deerhound, with eyes that laughed and a boundless good nature. To Buck's surprise these dogs manifested no jealousy toward him. They seemed to share the kindliness and largeness of John Thornton. As Buck grew stronger they enticed him into all sorts of ridiculous games, in which Thornton himself could not forbear to join; and in this fashion Buck romped through his convalescence and into a new existence. Love, genuine passionate love, was his for the first time. This he had never experienced at Judge Miller's down in the sun-kissed Santa Clara Valley. With the Judge's sons, hunting and tramping, it had been a working partnership; with the Judge's grandsons, a sort of pompous guardianship; and with the Judge himself, a stately and dignified friendship. But love that was feverish and burning, that was adoration, that was madness, it had taken John Thornton to arouse.

This man had saved his life, which was something; but, further, he was the ideal master. Other men saw to the welfare of their dogs from a sense of duty and business expediency; he saw to the welfare of his as if they were his own children, because he could not help it. And he saw further. He never forgot a kindly greeting or a cheering word, and to sit down for a long talk with them ("gas" he called it) was as much his delight as theirs. He had a way of taking Buck's head roughly between his hands, and resting his own head upon Buck's, of shaking him back and forth, the while calling him ill names that to Buck were love names. Buck knew no greater joy than that rough embrace and the sound of murmured oaths, and at each jerk back and forth it seemed that his heart would be shaken out of his body, so great was its ecstasy. And when, released, he sprang to his feet, his mouth laughing, his eyes eloquent, his throat vibrant with unuttered sound, and in that fashion remained without movement, John Thornton would reverently exclaim, "God! you can all but speak!"

Buck had a trick of love expression that was akin to hurt. He would often seize Thornton's hand in his mouth and close so fiercely that the flesh bore the impress of his teeth for some time afterward. And as Buck understood the oaths to be love words, so the man understood this feigned bite for a caress.

For the most part, however, Buck's love was expressed in adoration. While he went wild with happiness when Thornton touched him or spoke to him, he did not seek these tokens. Unlike Skeet, who was wont to shove her nose under

Thornton's hand and nudge and nudge till petted, or Nig, who would stalk up and rest his great head on Thornton's knee, Buck was content to adore at a distance. He would lie by the hour, eager, alert, at Thornton's feet, looking up into his face, dwelling upon it, studying it, following with keenest interest each fleeting expression, every movement or change of feature. Or, as chance might have it, he would lie farther away, to the side or rear, watching the outlines of the man and the occasional movements of his body. And often, such was the communion in which they lived, the strength of Buck's gaze would draw John Thornton's head around, and he would return the gaze, without speech, his heart shining out of his eyes as Buck's heart shone out.

For a long time after his rescue, Buck did not like Thornton to get out of his sight. From the moment he left the tent to when he entered it again, Buck would follow at his heels. His transient masters since he had come into the Northland had bred in him a fear that no master could be permanent. He was afraid that Thornton would pass out of his life as Perrault and François and the Scotch half-breed had passed out. Even in the night, in his dreams, he was haunted by this fear. At such times he would shake off sleep and creep through the chill to the flap of the tent, where he would stand and listen to the sound of his master's breathing.

But in spite of this great love he bore John Thornton, which seemed to bespeak the soft civilizing influence, the strain of the primitive, which the Northland had aroused in him, remained alive and active. Faithfulness and devotion, things born of fire and roof, were his; yet he retained his wildness and wiliness. He was a thing of the wild, come in from the wild to sit by John Thornton's fire, rather than a dog of the soft Southland stamped with the marks of generations of civilization. Because of his very great love, he could not steal from this man, but from any other man, in any other camp, he did not hesitate an instant; while the cunning with which he stole enabled him to escape detection.

His face and body were scored by the teeth of many dogs, and he fought as fiercely as ever and more shrewdly. Skeet and Nig were too good-natured for quarreling, — besides, they belonged to John Thornton; but the strange dog, no matter what the breed or valor, swiftly acknowledged Buck's supremacy or found himself struggling for life with a terrible antagonist. And Buck was merciless. He had learned well the law of club and fang, and he never forewent an advantage or drew back from a foe he had started on the way to Death. He had lessoned from Spitz, and from the chief fighting dogs of the police and mail, and knew there was no middle course. He must master or be mastered; while to show mercy was a weakness. Mercy did not exist in the primordial life. It was misunderstood for fear, and such misunderstandings made for death. Kill or be killed, eat or be eaten, was the law; and this mandate, down out of the depths of Time, he obeyed.

He was older than the days he had seen and the breaths he had drawn. He linked the past with the present, and the eternity behind him throbbed through him in a mighty rhythm to which he swayed as the tides and seasons swayed. He sat by John Thornton's fire, a broad-breasted dog, white-fanged and long-furred; but behind him were the shades of all manner of dogs, half-wolves and wild wolves, urgent and prompting, tasting the savor of the meat he ate, thirsting for the water he drank, scenting the wind with him, listening with him and telling him the sounds made by the wild life in the forest, dictating his moods, directing his actions, lying down to sleep with him when he lay down, and dreaming with him and beyond him and becoming themselves the stuff of his dreams.

So peremptorily did these shades beckon him, that each day mankind and the claims of mankind slipped farther from him. Deep in the forest a call was sounding, and as often as he heard this call, mysteriously thrilling and luring, he felt compelled to turn his back upon the fire and the beaten earth around it, and to plunge into the forest, and on and on, he knew not where or why; nor did he wonder where or why, the call sounding imperiously, deep in the forest. But as often as he gained the soft unbroken earth and the green shade, the love for John Thornton drew him back to the fire again.

Thornton alone held him. The rest of mankind was as nothing. Chance travelers might praise or pet him; but he was cold under it all, and from a too demonstrative man he would get up and walk away. When Thornton's partners, Hans and Pete, arrived on the long-expected raft, Buck refused to notice them till he learned they were close to Thornton; after that he tolerated them in a passive sort of way, accepting favors from them as though he favored them by accepting. They were of the same large type as Thornton, living close to the earth, thinking simply and seeing clearly; and ere they swung the raft into the big eddy by the sawmill at Dawson, they understood Buck and his ways, and did not insist upon an intimacy such as obtained with Skeet and Nig.

For Thornton, however, his love seemed to grow and grow. He, alone among men, could put a pack upon Buck's back in the summer traveling. Nothing was too great for Buck to do, when Thornton commanded. One day (they had grub-staked themselves from the proceeds of the raft and left Dawson for the head-waters of the Tanana) the men and dogs were sitting on the crest of a cliff which fell away, straight down, to naked bed-rock three hundred feet below. John Thornton was sitting near the edge, Buck at his shoulder. A thoughtless whim seized Thornton, and he drew the attention of Hans and Pete to the experiment he had in mind. "Jump, Buck!" he commanded, sweeping his arm out and over the chasm. The next instant he was grappling with Buck on the exreme edge, while Hans and Pete were dragging them back into safety.

"It's uncanny," Pete said, after it was over and they had caught their speech.

Thornton shook his head. "No, it is splendid, and it is terrible, too. Do you know, it sometimes makes me afraid."

"I'm not hankering to be the man that lays hands on you while he's around," Pete announced conclusively, nodding his head toward Buck.

"Py Jingo!" was Han's contribution, "not mineself either."

It was at Circle City, ere the year was out, that Pete's apprehensions were realized. "Black" Burton, a man evil-tempered and malicious, had been picking a quarrel with a tenderfoot at the bar, when Thornton stepped good-naturedly between. Buck, as was his custom, was lying in a corner, head on paws, watching his master's every action. Burton struck out, without warning, straight from the shoulder. Thornton was sent spinning, and saved himself from falling only by clutching the rail of the bar.

Those who were looking on heard what was neither bark nor yelp, but a something which is best described as a roar, and they saw Buck's body rise up in the air as he left the floor for Burton's throat. The man saved his life by instinctively throwing out his arm, but was hurled backward to the floor with Buck on top of him. Buck loosed his teeth from the flesh of the arm and drove in again for the throat. This time the man succeeded only in partly blocking, and his throat was torn open. Then the crowd was upon Buck, and he was driven off; but while a surgeon checked the bleeding, he prowled up and down, growling furiously, attempting to rush in, and being forced back by an array of hostile clubs. A "miners' meeting," called on the spot, decided that the dog had sufficient provocation, and Buck was discharged. But his reputation was made, and from that day his name spread through every camp in Alaska.

Later on, in the fall of the year, he saved John Thornton's life in quite another fashion. The three partners were lining a long and narrow poling-boat down a bad stretch of rapids on the Forty-Mile Creek. Hans and Pete moved along the bank, snubbing with a thin Manila rope from tree to tree, while Thornton remained in the boat, helping its descent by means of a pole, and shouting directions to the shore. Buck on the bank, worried and anxious, kept abreast of the boat, his eyes never off his master.

At a particularly bad spot, where a ledge of barely submerged rocks jutted out into the river, Hans cast off the rope, and, while Thornton poled the boat out into the stream, ran down the bank with the end in his hand to snub the boat when it had cleared the ledge. This it did, and was flying down-stream in a current as swift as a mill-race, when Hans checked it with the rope and checked too suddenly. The boat flirted over and snubbed in to the bank bottom up, while Thornton, flung sheer out of it, was carried downstream toward the worst part of the rapids, a stretch of wild water in which no swimmer could live.

Buck had sprung in on the instant; and at the end of three hundred yards, amid a mad swirl of water, he overhauled Thornton. When he felt him grasp his tail, Buck headed for the bank, swimming with all his splendid strength. But the progress shoreward was slow; the progress down-stream amazingly rapid. From below came the fatal roaring where the wild current went wilder and was rent in shreds and spray by the rocks which thrust through like the teeth of an enormous comb. The suck of the water as it took the beginning of the last steep pitch was frightful, and Thornton knew that the shore was impossible. He scraped furiously over a rock, bruised across a second, and struck a third with crushing force. He clutched its slippery top with both hands, releasing Buck, and above the roar of the churning water shouted: "Go, Buck! Go!"

Buck could not hold his own, and swept on down-stream, struggling desperately, but unable to win back. When he heard Thornton's command repeated, he partly reared out of the water, throwing his head high, as though for a last look, then turned obediently toward the bank. He swam powerfully and was dragged ashore by Pete and Hans at the very point where swimming ceased to be possible and destruction began.

They knew that the time a man could cling to a slippery rock in the face of that driving current was a matter of minutes, and they ran as fast as they could up the bank to a point far above where Thornton was hanging on. They attached the line with which they had been snubbing the boat to Buck's neck and shoulders, being careful that it should neither strangle him nor impede his swimming, and launched him into the stream. He struck out boldly, but not straight enough into the stream. He discovered the mistake too late, when Thornton was abreast of him and a bare half-dozen strokes away while he was being carried helplessly past.

Hans promptly snubbed with the rope, as though Buck were a boat. The rope thus tightening on him in the sweep of the current, he was jerked under the surface, and under the surface he remained till his body struck against the bank and he was hauled out. He was half drowned, and Hans and Pete threw themselves upon him, pounding the breath into him and the water out of him. He staggered to his feet and fell down. The faint sound of Thornton's voice came to them, and though they could not make out the words of it, they knew that he was in his extremity. His master's voice acted on Buck like an electric shock. He sprang to his feet and ran up the bank ahead of the men to the point of his previous departure.

Again the rope was attached and he was launched, and again he struck out, but this time straight into the stream. He had miscalculated once, but he would not be guilty of it a second time. Hans paid out the rope, permitting no slack, while Pete kept it clear of coils. Buck held on till he was on a line straight above Thornton; then he turned, and with the speed of an express train headed down upon him. Thornton saw him coming, and, as Buck struck him like a battering ram, with the whole force of the current behind him, he reached up and closed with both arms around the shaggy neck. Hans snubbed the rope around the tree, and Buck and Thornton were jerked under the water. Strangling, suffocating, sometimes one uppermost and sometimes the other, dragging over the jagged bottom, smashing against rocks and snags, they veered in to the bank.

Thornton came to, belly downward and being violently propelled back and forth across a drift log by Hans and Pete. His first glance was for Buck, over whose limp and apparently lifeless body Nig was setting up a howl, while Skeet was licking the wet face and closed eyes. Thornton was himself bruised and battered, and he went carefully over Buck's body, when he had been brought around, finding three broken ribs.

"That settles it," he announced. "We camp right here." And camp they did, till Buck's ribs knitted and he was able to travel.

That winter, at Dawson, Buck performed another exploit, not so heroic, perhaps, but one that put his name many notches higher on the totem-pole of Alaskan fame. This exploit was particularly gratifying to the three men; for they stood in need of the outfit which it furnished, and were enabled to make a long-desired trip into the virgin East, where miners had not yet appeared. It was brought about by a conversation in the Eldorado Saloon, in which men waxed boastful of their favorite dogs. Buck, because of his record, was the target for these men, and Thornton was driven stoutly to defend him. At the end of half an hour one man stated that his dog could start a sled with five hundred pounds and walk off with it; a second bragged six hundred for his dog; and a third, seven hundred.

"Pooh! pooh!" said John Thornton; "Buck can start a thousand pounds."

"And break it out? and walk off with it for a hundred yards?" demanded Matthewson, a Bonanza King, he of the seven hundred vaunt.

"And break it out, and walk off with it for a hundred yards," John Thornton said cooly.

"Well," Matthewson said, slowly and deliberately, so that all could hear, "I've got a thousand dollars that says he can't. And there it is." So saying, he slammed a sack of gold dust the size of a bologna sausage down upon the bar.

Nobody spoke. Thornton's bluff, if bluff it was, had been called. He could feel a flush of warm blood creeping up his face. His tongue had tricked him. He did not know whether Buck could start a thousand pounds. Half a ton! The enormousness of it appalled him. He had great faith in Buck's strength and had often thought him capable of starting such a load; but never, as now, had he faced the possibility of it, the eyes of a dozen men fixed upon him, silent and waiting. Further, he had no thousand dollars; nor had Hans or Pete.

"I've got a sled standing outside now, with twenty fifty-pound sacks of flour on it," Matthewson went on with brutal directness; "so don't let that hinder you."

Thornton did not reply. He did not know what to say. He glanced from face to face in the absent way of a man who has lost the power of thought and is seeking somewhere to find the thing that will start it going again. The face of Jim O'Brien, a Mastodon King and old-time comrade, caught his eyes. It was as a cue to him, seeming to rouse him to do what he would never have dreamed of doing.

"Can you lend me a thousand?" he asked, almost in a whisper.

"Sure," answered O'Brien, thumping down a plethoric sack by the side of Matthewson's. "Though it's little faith I'm having, John, that the beast can do the trick."

The Eldorado emptied its occupants into the street to see the test. The tables were deserted, and the dealers and gamekeepers came forth to see the outcome of the wager and to lay odds. Several hundred men, furred and mittened, banked around the sled within easy distance. Matthewson's sled, loaded with a thousand pounds of flour, had been standing for a couple of hours, and in the intense cold (it was sixty below zero) the runners had frozen fast to the hard-packed snow. Men offered odds of two to one that Buck could not budge the sled. A quibble arose concerning the phrase "break out." O'Brien contended it was Thornton's privilege to knock the runners loose, leaving Buck to "break it out" from a dead standstill. Matthewson insisted that the phrase included breaking the runners from the frozen grip of the snow. A majority of the men who had witnessed the making of the bet decided in his favor, whereat the odds went up to three to one against Buck.

There were no takers. Not a man believed him capable of the feat. Thornton had been hurried into the wager, heavy with doubt; and now that he looked at the sled itself, the concrete fact, with the regular team of ten dogs curled up in the snow before it, the more impossible the task appeared. Matthewson waxed jubilant.

"Three to one!" he proclaimed. "I'll lay you another thousand at that figure, Thornton. What d'ye say?"

Thornton's doubt was strong in his face, but his fighting spirit was aroused — the fighting spirit that soars above odds, fails to recognize the impossible, and is deaf to all save the clamor for battle. He called Hans and Pete to him. Their sacks were slim, and with his own the three partners could rake together only two hundred dollars. In the ebb of their fortunes, this sum was their total capital; yet they laid it unhesitatingly against Matthewson's six hundred.

The team of ten dogs was unhitched, and Buck, with his own harness, was put into the sled. He had caught the contagion of the excitement, and he felt that in some way he must do a great thing for John Thornton. Murmurs of admiration at his splendid appearance went up. He was in perfect condition, without an ounce of superfluous flesh, and the one hundred and fifty pounds that he weighed were so many pounds of grit and virility. His furry coat shone with the sheen of silk. Down the neck and across the shoulders, his mane, in repose as it was, half bristled and seemed to lift with every movement, as though excess of vigor made each particular hair alive and active. The great beast and heavy forelegs were no more than in proportion with the rest of the body, where the muscles showed in tight rolls underneath the skin. Men felt these muscles and proclaimed them hard as iron, and the odds went down to two to one.

"Gad, sir! Gad, sir!" spluttered a member of the latest dynasty, a king of the Skookum Benches. "I offer you eight hundred for him, sir, before the test, sir; eight hundred just as he stands."

Thornton shook his head and stepped to Buck's side.

"You must stand off from him," Matthewson protested. "Free play and plenty of room."

The crowd fell silent; only could be heard the

voices of the gamblers vainly offering two to one. Everybody acknowledged Buck a magnificent animal, but twenty fifty-pound sacks of flour bulked too large in their eyes for them to loosen their pouch-strings.

Thornton knelt down by Buck's side. He took his head in his two hands and rested cheek on cheek. He did not playfully shake him, as was his wont, or murmur soft love curses; but he whispered in his ear. "As you love me, Buck. As you love me," was what he whispered. Buck whined with suppressed eagerness.

The crowd was watching curiously. The affair was growing mysterious. It seemed like a conjuration. As Thornton got to his feet, Buck seized his mittened hand between his jaws, pressing in with his teeth and releasing slowly, half-reluctantly. It was the answer, in terms, not of speech, but of love. Thornton stepped well back.

"Now, Buck," he said.

Buck tightened his traces, then slackened them for a matter of several inches. It was the way he had learned.

"Gee!" Thornton's voice rang out, sharp in the tense silence.

Buck swung to his right, ending the movement in a plunge that took up the slack and with a sudden jerk arrested his one hundred and fifty pounds. The load quivered, and from under the runners arose a crisp crackling.

"Haw!" Thornton commanded.

Buck duplicated the manœuvre, this time to the left. The crackling turned into a snapping, the sled pivoting and the runners slipping and grating several inches to the side. The sled was broken out. Men were holding their breaths, although they were intensely unconscious of the fact.

"Now, MUSH!"

Thornton's command cracked out like a pistol-shot. Buck threw himself forward, tightening the traces with a jarring lunge. His whole body was gathered compactly together in the tremendous effort, the muscles writhing and knotting like live things under the silky fur. His great chest was low to the ground, his head forward and down, while his feet were flying like mad, the claws scarring the hard-packed snow in parallel grooves. The sled swayed and trembled, half-started forward. One of his feet slipped, and one man groaned aloud. Then the sled lurched ahead in what appeared a rapid succession of jerks, though it never really came to a dead stop again . . . half an inch . . . an inch . . . two inches. . . . The jerks perceptibly diminished; as the sled gained momentum, he caught them up, till it was moving steadily along.

Men gasped and began to breathe again, unaware that for a moment they had ceased to breathe. Thornton was running behind, encouraging Buck with short, cheery words. The distance had been measured off, and as he neared the pile of firewood which marked the end of the hundred yards, a cheer began to grow and grow, which burst into a roar as he passed the firewood and halted at command. Every man was tearing himself loose, even Matthewson. Hats and mittens were flying in the air. Men were shaking hands, it did not matter with whom, and bubbling over in a general incoherent babel.

But Thornton fell on his knees beside Buck. Head was against head, and he was shaking him back and forth. Those who hurried up heard him cursing Buck, and he cursed him long and fervently, and softly and lovingly.

"Gad, sir! Gad, sir!" spluttered the Skookum Bench king. "I'll give you a thousand for him, sir, a thousand, sir — twelve hundred, sir."

Thornton rose to his feet. His eyes were wet. The tears were streaming frankly down his cheeks. "Sir," he said to the Skookum Bench king, "no, sir. You can go to hell, sir. It's the best I can do for you, sir."

Buck seized Thornton's hand in his teeth. Thornton shook him back and forth. As though animated by a common impulse, the onlookers drew back to a respectful distance; nor were they again indiscreet enough to interrupt.

Never Cry Wolf*

Farley Mowat

As I was a newcomer to the barrens, it behooved me to familiarize myself with the country in a cautious manner. Hence, on my first expedition afield I contented myself with making a circular tour on a radius of about three hundred yards from the cabin.

This expedition revealed little except the presence of four or five hundred caribou skeletons; indeed, the entire area surrounding the cabin seemed to be carpeted in caribou bones. Since I knew from my researches in Churchill that trappers never shot caribou, I could only assume that these animals had been killed by wolves. This was a sobering conclusion. Assuming that the density of the caribou kill was uniform over the whole country, the sample I had seen indicated that wolves must kill, on the average, about twenty million caribou a year in Keewatin alone.

After this dismaying tour of the boneyard it

*From Farley Mowat's longer work by the same title, which recounts the author's sojourn in the Arctic regions to study wolves.

was three days before I found time for another trip afield. Carrying a rifle and wearing my revolver, I went a quarter-mile on this second expedition — but saw no wolves. However, to my surprise I observed that the density of caribou remains decreased in an almost geometric ratio to the distance from the cabin.

Meantime spring had come to the Barrens with volcanic violence. The snows melted so fast that the frozen rivers could not carry the melted water, which flowed six feet deep on top of the ice. Finally the ice let go, with a thunderous explosion; then it promptly jammed, and in short order the river beside which I was living had entered into the cabin, bringing with it the accumulated refuse left by Mike's fourteen Huskies during a long winter.

Eventually the jam broke and the waters subsided; but the cabin had lost its charm, for the debris on the floor was a foot thick and somewhat repellent. I decided to pitch my tent on a gravel ridge above the cabin; and here I was vainly trying to go to sleep that evening when I became aware of unfamiliar sounds. Sitting bolt upright, I listened intently.

The sounds were coming from just across the river, to the north, and they were a weird medley of whines, whimpers, and small howls. My grip on the rifle slowly relaxed. If there is one thing at which scientists are adept, it is learning from experience; I was not to be fooled twice. The cries were obviously those of a Husky, probably a young one, and I deduced that it must be one of Mike's dogs (he owned three half-grown pups not yet trained to harness which ran loose after the team) that had got lost, retraced its way to the cabin, and was now begging for someone to come and be nice to it.

I was delighted. If that pup needed a friend, a chum, I was its man! I climbed hastily into my clothes, ran down to the riverbank, launched the canoe, and paddled lustily for the far bank.

The pup had never ceased its mournful plaint, and I was about to call out reassuringly when it occurred to me that an unfamiliar human voice might frighten it. I decided to stalk it instead, and to betray my presence only when I was close enough for soothing murmurs.

From the nature of the sounds I had assumed the dog was only a few yards away from the far bank, but as I made my way in the dim half-light, over broken boulders and across gravel ridges, the sounds seemed to remain at the same volume while I appeared to be getting no closer. I assumed the pup was retreating, perhaps out of shyness. In my anxiety not to startle it away entirely, I still kept quiet, even when the whimpering wail stopped, leaving me uncertain about the right direction to pursue. However, I saw a steep ridge looming ahead of me and I suspected that, once I gained its summit, I would have a clear enough view to enable me to locate the lost animal. As I neared the crest of the ridge

I got down on my stomach (practicing the fieldcraft I had learned in the Boy Scouts) and cautiously inched my way the last few feet.

My head came slowly over the crest — and there was my quarry. He was lying down, evidently resting after his mournful singsong, and his nose was about six feet from mine. We stared at one another in silence. I do not know what went on in his massive skull, but my head was full of the most disturbing thoughts. I was peering straight into the amber gaze of a fully grown Arctic wolf, who probably weighed more than I did, and who was certainly a lot better versed in close-combat techniques than I would ever be.

For some seconds neither of us moved but continued to stare hypnotically into one another's eyes. The wolf was the first to break the spell. With a spring which would have done justice to a Russian dancer, he leaped about a yard straight into the air and came down running. The textbooks say a wolf can run twenty-five miles an hour, but this one did not appear to be running, so much as flying low. Within seconds he had vanished from my sight.

My own reaction was not so dramatic, although I may very well have set some sort of a record for a cross-country traverse myself. My return over the river was accomplished with such verve that I paddled the canoe almost her full length up on the beach on the other side. Then, remembering my responsibilities to my scientific supplies, I entered the cabin, barred the door, and regardless of the discomfort caused by the stench of the debris on the floor made myself as comfortable as I could on top of the table for the balance of the short-lived night.

It had been a strenuous interlude, but I could congratulate myself that I had, at last, established contact — no matter how briefly — with the study species.

The next morning I undertook to clean up the Stygian mess in the cabin, and in the process I uncovered my compass. I set it on the windowsill while I continued with my work, but the sun caught its brass surface and it glittered at me so accusingly that I resigned myself to making another effort to restore the lost contact between me and the wolves.

My progress on this second safari was even slower, since I was carrying my rifle, shotgun, pistol and pistol belt, a small hatchet, and my hunting knife, together with a flask of wolf-juice in case I fell into one of the icy streams.

It was a hot day, and spring days in the subarctic can be nearly as hot as in the tropics. The first mosquitoes were already heralding the approach of the sky-filling swarms which would soon make travel on the Barrens a veritable trip through hell. I located the wolf tracks and resolutely set out upon the trail.

It led directly across the muskeg for several miles; but although the wolf had sunk in only three or four inches, my steps sank in until I reached solid ice a foot beneath the surface. It was with great relief that I finally breasted another gravel ridge and lost all trace of the wolf tracks.

My attempts to find them again were perfunctory. As I gazed around me at the morose world of rolling muskeg and frost-shattered stone that stretched uninterruptedly to a horizon so distant it might as well have been the horizon of the sea, I felt lonelier than I had ever felt in all my life. No friendly sound of aircraft engines broke the silence of that empty sky. No distant rumble of traffic set the ground beneath my feet to shaking. Only the disembodied whistling of an unseen plover gave any indication that life existed anywhere in all this lunar land where no tree grew.

I found a niche amongst some lichen-covered rocks and, having firmly jammed myself into it, ate and drank my lunch. Then I picked up the binoculars and began to scan the barren landscape for some signs of life.

Directly in front of me was the ice-covered bay of a great lake, and on the far side of this bay was something which at least relieved the somber monochrome of the muskeg colorings. It was a yellow sand esker, rising to a height of fifty or sixty feet and winding sinuously away into the distance like a gigantic snake.

These Barrenland eskers are the inverted beds of long-vanished rivers which once flowed through and over the glaciers that, ten thousand years ago, covered the Keewatin Barrens to a depth of several thousand feet. When the ice melted, sandy riverbeds were deposited on the land below, where they now provide almost the sole visual relief in the bleak monotony of the tundra plains.

I gazed at this one with affection, studying it closely; and as I swept it with my glasses I saw something move at last. The distance was great, but the impression I had was of someone, just the other side of the esker crest, waving his arm above his head. Much excited, I stumbled to my feet and trotted along the ridge to its termination on the shore of the bay. I was then not more than three hundred yards from the esker and when I got my breath back I took another look through the glasses.

The object I had previously glimpsed was still in view, but now it looked like a white feather boa being vehemently waved by persons or person unseen. It was a most inexplicable object, and nothing I had ever heard of in my study of natural history seemed to fit it. As I stared in perplexity, the first boa was joined by a second one, also waving furiously, and both boas began to move slowly along, parallel to the crest of the esker.

I began to feel somewhat uneasy, for here was a phenomenon which did not seem to be subject to scientific explanation. In fact I was on the point of abandoning my interest in the spectacle until some expert in psychic research happened along — when, without warning, both boas turned toward me, began rising higher and higher, and finally revealed themselves as the tails of two wolves proceeding to top the esker.

The esker overlooked my position on the bay's shore, and I felt as nakedly exposed as the lady in the famous brassiére advertisement. Hunkering down to make myself as small as possible, I wormed my way into the rocks and did my best to be unobtrusvie. I need not have worried. The wolves paid no attention to me, if indeed they even saw me. They were far too engrossed in their own affairs, which, as I slowly and incredulously began to realize, were at that moment centered around the playing of a game of tag.

It was difficult to believe my eyes. They were romping like a pair of month-old pups! The smaller wolf (who soon gave concrete evidence that she was a female) took the initiative. Putting her head down on her forepaws and elevating her posterior in a most undignified manner, she suddenly pounced toward the much larger male whom I now recognized as my acquaintance of two days earlier. He, in his attempt to evade her, tripped and went sprawling. Instantly she was upon him, nipping him smartly in the backside, before leaping away to run around him in frenzied circles. The male scrambled to his feet and gave chase, but only by the most strenuous efforts was he able to close the gap until he, in his turn, was able to nip *her* backside. Thereupon the roles were again reversed, and the female began to pursue the male, who led her on a wild scrabble up, over, down, and back across the esker until finally both wolves lost their footing on the steep slope and went skidding down it inextricably locked together.

When they reached the bottom they separated, shook the sand out of their hair, and stood panting heavily, almost nose to nose. Then the female reared up and quite literally embraced the male with both forepaws while she proceeded to smother him in long-tongued kisses.

The male appeared to be enduring this overt display of affection, rather than enjoying it. He kept trying to avert his head, to no avail. Involuntarily I felt my sympathy warming toward him, for, in truth, it was a disgusting exhibition of wanton passion. Nevertheless he bore it with what stoicism he could muster until the female tired. Turning from him, she climbed halfway up the esker slope and . . . disappeared.

She seemed to have vanished off the face of the earth without leaving a trace behind her. Not until I swung the glasses back toward a dark shadow in a fold of the esker near where I had last seen her did I understand. The dark shadow was the mouth of a cave, or den, and the female wolf had almost certainly gone into it.

I was so elated by the realization that I had not only located a pair of wolves, but by an incredible stroke of fortune had found their den as well, that I forgot all caution and ran to a nearby knoll in order to gain a better view of the den mouth.

The male wolf, who had been loafing about the foot of the esker after the departure of his wife, instantly saw me. In three or four bounds he reached the ridge of the esker, where he stood facing me in an attitude of tense and threatening vigilance. As I looked up at him my sense of exhilaration waned rapidly. He no longer seemed like a playful pup, but had metamorphosed into a magnificent engine of destruction which impressed me so much that the neck of my flask positively rattled against my teeth.

I decided I had better not disturb the wolf family any more that day, for fear of upsetting them and perhaps forcing them to move away. So I withdrew. It was not an easy withdrawal, for one of the most difficult things I know of is to walk backward up a broken rocky slope for three quarters of a mile encumbered, as I was, by the complex hardware of a scientist's trade.

When I reached the ridge from which I had first seen the wolves I took a last quick look through the binoculars. The female was still invisible, and the male had so far relaxed his attitude of vigilance as to lie down on the crest of the esker. While I watched he turned around two or three times, as a dog will, and then settled himself, nose under tail, with the evident intention of having a nap.

I was much relieved to see he was no longer interested in me, for it would have been a tragedy if my accidental intrusion had unduly disturbed these wolves, thereby prejudicing what promised to be a unique opportunity to study the beasts I had come so far to find.

I went completely to the wolves. To begin with I set up a den of my own as near to the wolves as I could conveniently get without disturbing the even tenor of their lives too much. After all, I *was* a stranger, and an unwolflike one, so I did not feel I should go too far too fast.

Abandoning Mike's cabin (with considerable relief, since as the days warmed up so did the smell), I took a tiny tent and set it up on the shore of the bay immediately opposite to the den esker. I kept my camping gear to the barest minimum — a small primus stove, a stew pot, a teakettle, and a sleeping bag were the essentials. I took no weapons of any kind, although there were times when I regretted this omission, even if only fleetingly. The big telescope was set up in the mouth of the tent in such a way that I could observe the den by day or night without even getting out of my sleeping bag.

During the first few days of my sojourn with the wolves I stayed inside the tent except for brief and necessary visits to the out-of-doors which I always undertook when the wolves were not in sight. The point of this personal concealment was to allow the animals to get used to the tent and to accept it as only another bump on a very bumpy piece of terrain. Later, when the mosquito population reached full flowering, I stayed in the tent practically all of the time unless there was a strong wind blowing, for the most bloodthirsty beasts in the Arctic are not wolves, but the insatiable mosquitoes.

My precautions against disturbing the wolves were superfluous. It had required a week for me to get their measure, but they must have taken mine at our first meeting; and, while there was nothing overtly disdainful in their evident assessment of me, they managed to ignore my presence, and indeed my very existence, with a thoroughness which was somehow disconcerting.

Quite by accident I had pitched my tent within ten yards of one of the major paths used by the wolves when they were going to, or coming from, their hunting grounds to the westward; and only a few hours after I had taken up residence one of the wolves came back from a trip and discovered me and my tent. He was at the end of a hard night's work and was clearly tired and anxious to go home to bed. He came over a small rise fifty yards from me with his head down, his eyes half-closed, and a preoccupied air about him. Far from being the preternaturally alert and suspicious beast of fiction, this wolf was so self-engrossed that he came straight on to within fifteen yards of me, and might have gone right past the tent without seeing it at all, had I not banged my elbow against the teakettle, making a resounding clank. The wolf's head came up and his eyes opened wide, but he did not stop or falter in his pace. One brief, sidelong glance was all he vouchsafed to me as he continued on his way.

It was true that I wanted to be inconspicuous, but I felt uncomfortable at being so totally ignored. Nevertheless, during the two weeks which followed, one or more wolves used the track past my tent almost every night — and never, except on one memorable occasion, did they evince the slightest interest in me.

By the time this happened I had learned a good deal about my wolfish neighbors, and one of the facts which had emerged was that they were not nomadic roamers, as is almost universally believed, but were settled beasts and the possessors of a large permanent estate with very definite boundaries.

The territory owned by my wolf family comprised more than a hundred square miles, bounded on one side by a river but otherwise not delimited by geographical features. Nevertheless there *were* boundaries, clearly indicated in wolfish fashion.

Anyone who has observed a dog doing his neighborhood rounds anad leaving his personal mark on each convenient post will have already guessed how the wolves marked out *their* property. Once a week, more or less, the clan made the rounds of the family lands and freshened up the boundary markers — a sort of lupine beating of the bounds. This careful attention to property rights was perhaps made necessary by the presence of two other wolf families whose lands abutted on ours, although I never discovered any evidence of bickering or disagreements between the owners of the various adjoining estates. I suspect, therefore, that it was more of a ritual activity.

In any event, once I had become aware of the strong feeling of property rights which existed amongst the wolves, I decided to use this knowledge to make them at least recognize my existence. One evening, after they had gone off for their regular nightly hunt, I staked out a property claim of my own, embracing perhaps three acres, with the tent at the middle, and *including a hundred-yard long section of the wolves' path.*

Staking the land turned out to be rather more difficult than I had anticipated. In order to ensure that my claim would not be overlooked, I felt obliged to make a property mark on stones, clumps of moss, and patches of vegetation at intervals of not more than fifteen feet around the circumference of my claim. This took most of the night and required frequent returns to the tent to consume copious quantities of tea; but before dawn brought the hunters home the task was done, and I retired, somewhat exhausted, to observe results.

I had not long to wait. At 0814 hours, according to my wolf log, the leading male of the clan appeared over the ridge behind me, padding homeward with his usual air of preoccupation. As usual he did not deign to glance at the tent;

but when he reached the point where my property line intersected the trail, he stopped as abruptly as if he had run into an invisible wall. He was only fifty yards from me and with my binoculars I could see his expression very clearly.

His attitude of fatigue vanished and was replaced by a look of bewilderment. Cautiously he extended his nose and sniffed at one of my marked bushes. He did not seem to know what to make of it or what to do about it. After a minute of complete indecision he backed away a few yards and sat down. And then, finally, he looked directly at the tent and at me. It was a long, thoughtful, considering sort of look.

Having achieved my object — that of forcing at least one of the wolves to take cognizance of my existence — I now began to wonder if, in my ignorance, I had transgressed some unknown wolf law of major importance and would have to pay for my temerity. I found myself regretting the absence of a weapon as the look I was getting became longer, yet more thoughtful, and still more intent.

I began to grow decidedly fidgety, for I dislike staring matches, and in this particular case I was up against a master, whose yellow glare seemed to become more baleful as I attempted to stare him down.

The situation was becoming intolerable. In an effort to break the impasse I loudly cleared my throat and turned my back on the wolf (for a tenth of a second) to indicate as clearly as possible that I found his continued scrutiny impolite, if not actually offensive.

He appeared to take the hint. Getting to his feet he had another sniff at my marker, and then he seemed to make up his mind. Briskly, and with an air of decision, he turned his attention away from me and began a systematic tour of the area I had staked out as my own. As he came to each boundary marker he sniffed it once or twice, then carefully placed *his* mark on the outside of each clump of grass or stone. As I watched I saw where I, in my ignorance, had erred. He made his mark with such economy that he was able to complete the entire circuit without having to reload once, or, to change the simile slightly, he did it all on one tank of fuel.

The task completed — and it had taken him no longer than fifteen minutes — he rejoined the path at the point where it left my property and trotted off towards his home — leaving me with a good deal to occupy my thoughts.

The realization that the wolves' summer diet consisted chiefly of mice did not conclude my work in the field of dietetics. I knew that the mouse-wolf relationship was a revolutionary one to science and would be treated with suspicion, and possibly with ridicule, unless it could be so thoroughly substantiated that there would be no room to doubt its validity.

I had already established two major points:
1. That wolves caught and ate mice.

2. That the small rodents were sufficiently numerous to support the wolf population.

There remained, however, a third point vital to the proof of my contention. This concerned the nutritional value of mice. It was imperative for me to prove that a diet of small rodents would suffice to maintain a large carnivore in good condition.

I recognized that this was not going to be an easy task. Only a controlled experiment would do, and since I could not exert the necessary control over the wolves, I was at a loss how to proceed. Had Mike still been in the vicinity I might have borrowed two of his Huskies and, by feeding one of them on mice alone and the other on caribou meat (if and when this became obtainable), and then subjecting both dogs to similar tests, I would have been able to adduce the proof for or against the validity of the mouse-wolf concept. But Mike was gone, and I had no idea when he might return.

For some days I pondered the problem, and then one morning, while I was preparing some lemmings and meadow mice as specimens, inspiration struck me. Despite the fact that man is not wholly carnivorous, I could see no valid reason why I should not use myself as a test subject. It was true that there was only one of me; but the difficulty this posed could be met by setting up two timed intervals, during one of which I would confine myself to a mouse diet while during a second period of equal length I would eat canned meat and fresh fish. At the end of each period I would run a series of physiological tests upon myself and finally compare the two sets of results. While not absolutely conclusive as far as wolves were concerned, evidence that *my* metabolic functions remained unimpaired under a mouse regimen would strongly indicate that wolves, too, could survive and function normally on the same diet.

There being no time like the present, I resolved to begin the experiment at once. Having cleaned the basinful of small corpses which remained from my morning session of mouse skinning, I placed them in a pot and hung it over my primus stove. The pot gave off a most delicate and delicious odor as the water boiled, and I was in excellent appetite by the time the stew was done.

Eating these small mammals presented something of a problem at first because of the numerous minute bones; however, I found that the bones could be chewed and swallowed without much difficulty. The taste of the mice — a purely subjective factor and not in the least relevant to the experiment — was pleasing, if rather bland. As the experiment progressed, this blandness led to a degree of boredom and a consequent loss of appetite and I was forced to seek variety in my methods of preparation.

Of the several recipes which I developed, the finest by far was Creamed Mouse, and in the event that any of my readers may be interested in personally exploiting this hitherto overlooked source of excellent animal protein, I give the recipe in full.

SOURIS À LA CRÊME

INGREDIENTS:

One dozen fat mice	Salt and pepper
One cup white flour	Cloves
One piece sowbelly	Ethyl alcohol

[I should perhaps note that sowbelly is normally only available in the Arctic, but ordinary salt pork can be substituted.]

Skin and gut the mice, but do not remove the heads; wash, then place in a pot with enough alcohol to cover the carcasses. Allow to marinate for about two hours. Cut sowbelly into small cubes and fry slowly until most of the fat has been rendered. Now remove the carcasses from the alcohol and roll them in a mixture of salt, pepper, and flour; then place in frying pan and sauté for about five minutes (being careful not to allow the pan to get too hot, or the delicate meat will dry out and become tough and stringy). Now add a cup of alcohol and six or eight cloves. Cover the pan and allow to simmer slowly for fifteen minutes. The cream sauce can be made according to any standard recipe. When the sauce is ready, drench the carcasses with it, cover, and allow to rest in a warm place for ten minutes before serving.

During the first week of the mouse diet I found that my vigor remained unimpaired, and that I suffered no apparent ill effects. However, I did begin to develop a craving for fats. It was this which made me realize that my experiment, up to this point, had been rendered partly invalid by an oversight — and one, moreover, which did my scientific training no credit. The wolves, as I should have remembered, *ate the whole mouse;* and my dissections had shown that these small rodents stored most of their fat in the abdominal cavity, adhering to the intestinal mesenteries, rather than subcutaneously or in the muscular tissue. It was an inexcusable error I had made, and I hastened to rectify it. From this time to the end of the experimental period I too ate the whole mouse, without the skin of course, and I found that my fat craving was considerably eased.

It was during the final stages of my mouse diet that Mike returned to his cabin. He brought with him a cousin of his, the young Eskimo, Ootek, who was to become my boon companion and who was to prove invaluable to me in my wolf researches. However, on my first encounter with Ootek I found him almost as reserved and difficult of approach as Mike had been, and in fact still remained.

I had made a trip back to the cabin to fetch some additional supplies and the sight of smoke rising from the chimney cheered me greatly, for, to tell the truth, there had been times when I

would have enjoyed a little human companionship. When I entered the cabin Mike was frying
a panful of venison steak, while Ootek looked
on. They had been lucky enough to kill a stray
animal some sixty miles to the north. After a
somewhat awkward few minutes, during which
Mike seemed to be hopefully trying to ignore my
existence, I managed to break the ice and achieve
an introduction to Ootek, who responded by
sidling around to the other side of the table and
putting as much distance between us as possible.
These two then sat down to their dinner, and
Mike eventually offered me a plate of fried steak
too.

I would have enjoyed eating it, but I was still
conducting my experiment, and so I had to
refuse, after having first explained my reasons to
Mike. He accepted my excuses with the inscru-
table silence of his Eskimo ancestors, but he
evidently passed on my explanation to Ootek,
who, whatever he may have thought about it and
me, reacted in a typical Eskomoan way. Late
that evening when I was about to return to my
observation tent, Ootek waylaid me outside the
cabin. With a shy but charming smile he held
out a small parcel wrapped in deerskin. Graciously
I undid the sinew binding and examined the
present; for such it was. It consisted of a clutch
of five small blue eggs, undoubtedly belonging
to one of the thrush species, though I could not
be certain of the identification.

Grateful, but at a loss to understand the

implications of the gift, I returned to the cabin and asked Mike.

"Eskimo thinks if man eat mice his parts get small like mice," he explained reluctantly. "But if man eat eggs everything comes out all right. Ootek scared for you."

Ootek's acceptance of me had an ameliorating effect upon Mike's attitude. Although Mike continued to harbor a deep-rooted suspicion that I was not quite right in the head and might yet prove dangerous unless closely watched, he loosened up as much as his taciturn nature would permit and tried to be cooperative. This was a great boon to me, for I was able to enlist his aid as an interpreter between Ootek and myself.

Ootek had a great deal to add to my knowledge of wolves' food habits. Having confirmed what I had already discovered about the role mice played in their diet, he told me that wolves also ate great numbers of ground squirrels and at times even seemed to prefer them to caribou.

These ground squirrels are abundant throughout most of the Arctic, although Wolf House Bay lies just south of their range. They are close relatives of the common gopher of the western plains, but unlike the gopher they have a very poor sense of self-preservation. Consquently they fall easy prey to wolves and foxes. In summer, when they are well fed and fat, they may weigh as much as two pounds, so that a wolf can often kill enough of them to make a good meal with only a fraction of the energy expenditure involved in hunting caribou.

I had assumed that fishes could hardly enter largely into the wolves' diet, but Ootek assured me I was wrong. He told me he had several times watched wolves fishing for jackfish or Northern pike. At spawning time in the spring these big fish, which sometimes weigh as much as forty pounds, invade the intricate network of narrow channels in boggy marshes along the lake shores.

When a wolf decides to go after them he jumps into one of the larger channels and wades upstream, splashing mightily as he goes, and driving the pike ahead of him into progressively narrower and shallower channels. Eventually the fish realizes its danger and turns to make a dash for open water; but the wolf stands in its way and one quick chop of those great jaws is enough to break the back of even the largest pike. Ootek told me he once watched a wolf catch seven large pike in less than an hour.

Wolves also caught suckers when these sluggish fish were making their spawning runs up the tundra streams, he said; but the wolf's technique in this case was to crouch on a rock in a shallow section of the stream and snatch up the suckers as they passed — a method rather similar to that employed by bears when they are catching salmon.

Another although minor source of food consisted of Arctic sculpins; small fishes which lurk under rocks in shoal water. The wolves caught these by wading along the shore and turning over the rocks with paws or nose, snapping up the exposed sculpins before they could escape.

Later in the summer I was able to confirm Ootek's account of the sculpin fishery when I watched Uncle Albert spend part of the afternoon engaged in it. Unfortunately, I never did see wolves catch pike; but, having heard how they did it from Ootek, I tried it myself with considerable success, imitating the reported actions of the wolves in all respects, except that I used a short spear, instead of my teeth, with which to administer the *coup de grâce*.

These sidelights on the lupine character were fascinating, but it was when we came to a discussion of the role played by caribou in the life of the wolf that Ootek really opened my eyes.

The wolf and the caribou were so closely linked, he told me, that they were almost a single entity. He explained what he meant by telling me a story which sounded a little like something out of the Old Testament; but which, so Mike assured me, was a part of the semi-religious folklore of the inland Eskimos, who, alas for their immortal souls, were still happily heathen.

Here, paraphrased, is Ootek's tale.

"In the beginning there was a Woman and a Man, and nothing else walked or swam or flew in the world until one day the Woman dug a great hole in the ground and began fishing in it. One by one she pulled out all the animals, and the last one she pulled out of the hole was the caribou. Then Kaila, who is the God of the Sky, told the Woman the caribou was the greatest gift of all, for the caribou would be the sustenance of man.

"The Woman set the caribou free and ordered it to go out over the land and multiply, and the caribou did as the Woman said; and in time the land was filled with caribou, so the sons of the Woman hunted well, and they were fed and clothed and had good skin tents to live in, all from the caribou.

"The sons of the Woman hunted only the big, fat caribou, for they had no wish to kill the weak and the small and the sick, since these were no good to eat, nor were their skins much good. And, after a time, it happened that the sick and the weak came to outnumber the fat and the strong, and when the sons saw this they were dismayed and they complained to the Woman.

"Then the Woman made magic and spoke to Kaila and said: 'Your work is no good, for the caribou grow weak and sick, and if we eat them we must grow weak and sick also.'

"Kaila heard, and he said 'My work is good. I shall tell Amorak [the spirit of the Wolf], and he shall tell his children, and they will eat the sick and the weak and the small caribou, so that the land will be left for the fat and the good ones.'

"And this is what happended, and this is why the caribou and the wolf are one; for the caribou feeds the wolf, but it is the wolf who keeps the caribou strong."

I was slightly stunned by this story, for I was not prepared to have an unlettered and untutored Eskimo give me a lecture, even in parable form, illustrating the theory of survival of the fittest through the agency of natural selection. In any event, I was skeptical about the happy relationship which Ootek postulated as existing between caribou and wolf. Although I had already been disabused of the truth of a good many scientifically established beliefs about wolves by my own recent experiences, I could hardly believe that the all-powerful and intelligent wolf would limit his predation on the caribou herds to culling the sick and the infirm when he could, presumably, take his choice of the fattest and most succulent individuals. Furthermore, I had what I thought was excellent ammunition with which to demolish Ootek's thesis.

"Ask him then," I told Mike, "how come there are so many skeletons of big and evidently healthy caribou scattered around the cabin and all over the tundra for miles to the north of here."

"Don't need to ask him that," Mike replied with unabashed candor. "It was me killed those deer. I got fourteen dogs to feed and it takes maybe two, three caribou a week for that. I got to feed myself too. And then, I got to kill lots of deer everywhere all over the trapping country. I set four, five traps around each deer like that and get plenty foxes when they come to feed. It is no use for me to shoot skinny caribou. What I got to have is the big fat ones."

I was staggered. "How many do you think you kill in a year?" I asked.

Mike grinned proudly. "I'm pretty damn good shot. Kill maybe two, three hundred, maybe more."

When I had partially recovered from that one, I asked him if this was the usual thing for trappers.

"Every trapper got to do the same," he said. "Indians, white men, all the way down south far as caribou go in the wintertime, they got to kill lots of them or they can't trap no good. Of course they not all the time lucky to get *enough* caribou; then they got to feed the dogs on fish. But dogs can't work good on fish — get weak and sick and can't haul no loads. Caribou is better."

I knew from having studied the files at Ottawa that there were eighteen hundred trappers in those portions of Saskatchewan, Manitoba, and southern Keewatin which composed the winter range of the Keewatin caribou herd. I also knew that many of these trappers had been polled by Ottawa, through the agency of the fur trading companies, for information which might help explain the rapid decline in the size of the Keewatin caribou herd. I had read the results of this poll. To a man, the trappers and traders denied that they killed more than one or two caribou a year; and to a man they had insisted that wolves slaughtered the deer in untold thousands.

Although mathematics have never been my strong point, I tried to work out some totals from the information at hand. Being a naturally conservative fellow, I cut the number of trappers in half, and then cut Mike's annual caribou kill in half, before multiplying the two. No matter how many times I multiplied, I kept coming up with the fantastic figure of 112,000 animals killed by trappers in this area every year.

I realized it was not a figure I could use in my reports — not unless I wished to be posted to the Galapagos Islands to conduct a ten-year study on tortoise ticks.

In any event, what Mike and Ootek had told me was largely heresay evidence, and this was not what I was employed to gather. Resolutely I put these disturbing revelations out of mind, and went back to learning the truth the hard way.

Rascal*
Sterling North

ascal had one virtue, rare in human beings, the capacity for gratitude. Feed him a favorite food, say a kind word, and he was your friend.

This simple approach to the heart of a raccoon produced some odd friendships in our neighborhood. Rascal's circle included Joe Hanks, the dim-witted janitor of the Methodist Church, who was convinced that the German Lutherans were planning to poison the water supply of Brailsford Junction.

"Stands to reason, don't it?" Joe said. "They got the water tower right up there on German Hill behind the Lutheran Church. All they got to do is drop a couple of little poison pills down the air vent and next morning we'll all wake up dead."

Joe was otherwise harmless. He pumped the pipe organ when sober, and let me pump it when he started getting drunk. His secret for winning Rascal's affection came in his lunchbox. He

*This is the third chapter of Sterling North's *Rascal: A Memoir of a Better Era*. Rascal is a tame raccoon.

always gave my raccoon half of one of his jelly sandwiches. Rascal thought Joe was one of the nicest people he had ever met.

Another friend was Bumblebee Jim Vandevander, the bald, three-hundred-pound son of our equally large washerwoman. Jim arrived every Monday morning pulling a little coaster wagon behind him to pick up our washing, and brought it back on Friday, clean, fresh-smelling, and beautifully ironed. On each arrival he gave Rascal a peppermint candy. What more could one ask of a friend?

Rascal couldn't, of course, read the calendar or the clock, but he knew almost to the minute when Bumblebee Jim was arriving and always became eager and talkative, anticipating his piece of candy. I finally concluded that raccoons, who do most of their hunting at night, have an extremely acute sense of hearing. Apparently Rascal was aware of the first faint rattle of the coaster wagon far down the street.

From all the sounds of summer — the whirr of distant lawn mowers, the singing of the cicadas, the clip-clop of horses' hoofs, and the orchestration of the birds, Rascal could distinguish and identify, long before I could, the distant approach of the coaster wagon.

Not all of Rascal's motives were ulterior. He loved music for its own sake and had definite preferences among the records I played for him on the wind-up Victrola. Wagnerian sopranos hurt his ears. But he would sit, dreamy-eyed, listening to his favorite popular song: "There's a Long, Long Trail A-winding." In that ballad nightingales are mentioned.

I asked my father one morning if we have nightingales in America, or any other bird that sings at night.

"Not nightingales," he said, "but we do have whippoorwills, of course."

"I've never heard a whippoorwill."

"Can that be possible? Why, when I was a boy . . ."

And he was off on a pilgrimage into the past when Wisconsin was still half wilderness, when panthers sometimes looked in through the windows, and the whippoorwills called all night long.

Thure Ludwig Theodor Kumlien (1819–88) always came into these reminiscences somewhere. He was a great pioneer naturalist, for whom the Kumlien gull, aster, and anemone were named. A contemporary of Thoreau and Audubon and Agassiz, he had been trained at Upsala in Sweden, and had come to southern Wisconsin in the 1840's, buying eighty acres adjoining the North homestead.

"Kumlien could start the whippoorwills any night by playing his flute," my father said. "Far across the fields we heard them, the old man with his flute, his son playing the violin, the hundreds of whippoorwills calling — that's music to remember."

It made me sad that I could not have known Kumlien, and walked the woods with him, learning every bird and flower and insect. I had been born too late, it seemed, even to hear a whippoorwill.

My father looked at me for a moment as though he were really seeing me.

"Let's take the day off," he said. "There must be a pair of whippoorwills somewhere around here."

Those were rare and gala days when my father took me rambling. While I slapped together a few cheese sandwiches, and packed half a dozen bottles of cold root beer and pop in the lunch basket, my father drove downtown to hang a sign on the office door:

Gone For The Day

He came back with the windshield down, the top back, and his white curls blowing in the wind. He was wearing a pair of motor goggles and looked very handsome and dashing, I thought. I put on my goggles too. Rascal, of course, wore his permanently. He perched between us on the back of the seat, gazing rapturously ahead.

We had sold the old Model T, and now were driving a huge seven-passenger Oldsmobile which my father had accepted in one of his numerous real estate swaps. It was rather large for the two of us, but we needed that big back seat for the occasions when we took Wowser with us. The Saint Bernard would never lie down in the car.

He lumbered from one side to the other, peering forward with worried face and furrowed brow, occasionally woofing a deep-throated warning. But Wowser couldn't go today. He would frighten too many birds. The three of us were leaving him behind.

We were a happy trio as my father pulled down the gas lever and roared from low into second, and from second into high. We took the Newville road which led toward Lake Koshkonong, one of the largest lakes in Wisconsin, which is formed by a widening in Rock River, and deepened by the dam at Indian Ford. In former years it had been covered in the shallows by hundreds of acres of wild rice which had attracted thousands of waterfowl and migrating bands of Indians. There were still many flocks of wild ducks and geese each spring and fall, and big pickerel and wall-eyed pike for which we sometimes trolled from a rowboat.

We swung upstream from Newville toward Taylor's point where an old resort hotel called the Lake House then stood. There were few cottages on Koshkonong in those days, merely groves and meadows, and miles of sand beaches. Several creeks entered shallow bays where great blue herons waded stealthily, striking as swiftly as a water snake to seize and swallow small fish and frogs.

We took the Lake House road, and followed a grassy lane to the limestone cliff jutting into the lake, a promontory crowned with white clover and shaded by magnificent old trees. My father set the emergency brake, and I chocked the wheels with large stones to be sure that the Oldsmobile would not bounce from that seventy-five-foot precipice into the lake.

Then all three of us went running out to the very tip of the point as though we were a little mad with happiness — as indeed we were. This was our very own lake, filling our life to the brim. We had each been born almost within the sound of its waves. Here we had spent our separate boyhoods. Here we fished and swam and canoed and searched for arrowheads.

The view from the point was superb. We could see the outlet of the lake into Rock River, downstream to our right, and ten miles away to our left the inlet in the blue haze.

My father's memories and mine differed, of course, for he had known these shores when they were heavily forested and he had visited the Indian wigwams on Crab Apple point, Thibault's point, and Charlie's bluff. At the age of twelve he had fallen slightly in love with a pretty Indian girl, so light-skinned and delicate of feature that my father was sure she was more than half French. The Indians had moved on, like the waterfowl they hunted, and with them went the girl, whom he never saw again.

Most prominent of all the points was a dark, lush projection which was the delta made by Koshkonong Creek — perhaps the wildest bit of woods and water in the entire region.

I had been careless in supervising Rascal, and I looked just in time to see him disappearing down a crooked ravine that angled through the limestone toward the lake. It was a moist and pleasant cleft in the rock with wild columbine blooming from every crevice, and it led by a devious and dangerous route to a little cave named for the Indian chief, Black Hawk. Rascal was only exploring, but I feared the small raccoon might take a dangerous tumble at the edge of the precipice.

"I'm going after him," I shouted to my father.

"Well, be careful, son," he said.

He was a casual parent who never tried to stop me from risking any hazard, even when I swam through the floodgates at Indian Ford. He knew I could climb like a squirrel and swim like an otter. So he had no worries about me now.

The little ravine, nicked into the cliff, was steep and slippery. But the chase was swift, for there, well ahead of me, was that ringed tail, disappearing around one turn after another.

"Come back here, Rascal," I shouted sternly. But the raccoon paid no attention. I pulled a sugar lump from my pocket, usually a successful recourse. But Rascal was having none of it. He did not hesitate a moment until he reached the sheer cliff with a twenty-foot drop to the cave's entrance, toward which he peered down eagerly.

I trilled in our mutual language and he responded. But over he went, scrambling backward down that wall of rock. I reached the edge a moment too late to stop him; and I could only hold my breath until he arrived safely at the cave.

There was nothing for it now but to inch my own way down that last twenty feet, catching a toe hold or finger hold wherever possible between the strata of limestone. In a few minutes, however, I too was safely at the entrance, which offered crawl space to the inner room.

It wasn't a large cave. But, by tradition, it had furnished Black Hawk a hiding place while he was being pursued by Abraham Lincoln, Jefferson Davis, and other young soldiers during the Black Hawk War. The episode was probably a myth, but the boys of that area who scrambled down to the small cavern believed every word of the story, and shuddered to think that the ghost of Black Hawk might be lurking there in the gloom.

The sandy floor of this cool hideaway was large enough for a small campfire and two or three campers. And there was a convenient ledge four feet above the floor, which furnished sleeping space for an uncomfortable night wrapped in blankets.

When my eyes grew accustomed to the dim light, I saw Rascal. He was prowling along the shelf of rock trying to reach the tiny, gleaming stalactites which hung from the low roof of the cave. He was reaching up with his eager little hands when I caught him.

I had no desire to punish him. I merely held him close. And Rascal told me in every way he could that I was completely forgiven for having cornered and captured him.

My father greeted us as we came safely up the cliff. He had been certain that I would rescue the raccoon, and then would survive the climb. Living much in the past, and never in the worrisome future, his outlook was so tranquil that he drifted pleasantly from 1862 to 1962 — seven months short of a full century — with very little sense of personal or international tragedy. Curiously enough, this lifelong detachment accompanied an excellent university education, a vast store of disorganized knowledge, and a certain amount of charm.

"Whippoorwills," he explained, "are seldom seen in the daylight. They crouch on fence rails or the limbs of trees. If they flutter up for a moment they resemble giant Cecropia moths. We won't find them until after dusk, and that gives us many hours."

With the whole day ahead of us, we took our swimming trunks and the lunch basket and started down the long sloping path to the beach. My father was the acknowledged expert on the Indian trails of southern Wisconsin.

"This was a Fox-Winnebago-Sac trail," my father said. "It was used by Black Hawk and his warriors and by their pursuers. These large burial mounds were probably made by much earlier tribes."

Along these trails were to be found bird-points,

hunting arrows, skinning knives, and scrapers, mostly of flint. In my father's fine collection there were also black and gleaming obsidian spear points, some of them eight inches long, red calumets transported from Minnesota, and copper ornaments from the Lake Superior region.

As we progressed downward toward the beach, Rascal trundled along obediently, panting in the manner of dogs and raccoons when they are hot. The sight of glistening water ahead, cool and inviting, increased his gait to a gallop.

I paused to examine his tracks which made a design like beadwork on an Indian quiver. The handprints and footprints resembled those of a very small human baby. Where Rascal had been *walking*, the imprint of the retreating left hand was paired with that of the advancing right foot, and vice versa. But where he had broken into a *gallop*, all four tracks tended to bunch.

For all his intelligent adaptability, my small friend was aided in every act by intricate and inborn patterns of raccoon behavior.

On this curve of the shore a very cold, spring-fed rivulet rushed down from the hills, twisting among glacial boulders and the roots of oak trees to fan across the white sand to the lake. In a pool of this stream I placed the bottles of root beer and pop, awaiting our picnic.

My father and I donned swimming trunks, and soon all three of us were in the lake. Sandpipers tipped and scurried along the beach, darting in and out as the waves advanced or retreated. Rails slithered through the reeds, and somewhere, safely hidden, an American bittern began to "pump" his odd, deep note, like the sound of a sledge hammer driving a fencepost into marshy soil.

My father was a strong swimmer, using the old-fashioned breast stroke. I was very proud of the fact that I had learned the fast, effective Australian crawl. But Rascal could only dog-paddle.

He came along bravely, however, keeping his nose out of water, indicating again that raccoons probably can't dive. For a three-month-old he was doing excellently. But soon he was panting from the exertion and looking to me as his natural protector. We were in deep water now, and the best I could do for him was to roll over on my back in a floating position, arch my chest, and offer him a good platform. He scrambled gratefully aboard, whimpering slightly in self-pity. But soon he had regained his courage and his breath, and in he plunged again.

I had thought that Rascal had demonstrated his top speed, but as we came around a grassy point I learned my error. There, to her surprise and ours, was the modest mate of the glamorous mallard drake — garbed in becoming brown, and leading a late nesting of downy ducklings. This mallard mother had eleven beautiful babies, light as thistledown, following her for dear life in a straight-line flotilla.

Rascal accelerated by at least ten percent upon

seeing the tempting sight ahead. He obviously had visions of a juicy duckling dinner. I wanted to forestall this slaughter, but my father said quietly, "Wait a minute, son, and watch what happens."

The ducklings performed a marvelous maneuver around the mother duck while she turned back to face the intruder. Putting herself between her endangered brood and Rascal, she swam directly toward the raccoon with no more fear than as though he had been a muskrat. On came my crazy pet. On came the determined mother duck. It seemed a duel to the death, or at least a head-on collision.

At the last possible moment the mallard used her wings and was partially airborne. She aimed one strong and accurate blow of her bill between Rascal's avid eyes, flew over his head, and wheeled to join her ducklings.

Rascal wasn't actually hurt, but his pride was wounded. He swam back to me talking about it sorrowfully, and I gave him another rest after his shattering experience. In a few minutes he began to pretend he had forgotten all about that duckling dinner; and soon we went ashore for other food.

Raccoons have a passion for turtle eggs, and search for them on every beach. The turtles bury their eggs in the sand to let them be hatched by the warmth of the sun. But many a nest of eggs becomes a banquet for a raccoon.

Rascal had never been told about turtle eggs. But his keen nostrils informed him that somewhere in this sand was a gastronomic delight he had never sampled.

For at least three seconds he froze in the manner of a bird dog coming to a point. Then he began digging more furiously than he had ever dug before. Success! Up they came, all thirty-four of them, almost as big as golf balls, meaning that they were the eggs of a big snapping turtle. For the next half hour Rascal was with us physically, but elsewhere in spirit, obviously in some realm where gourmet raccoons feast for eternity, their eyes on the stars while their swift hands and sharp little teeth tear open turtle eggs to gorge upon them.

While we ate our picnic lunch, Rascal was busy slightly depleting the next generation of snapping turtles. He was so completely satiated that he even refused the last few sips of my strawberry pop.

The sun was past the meridian, but there were many summer hours to squander before we might hear the first evening whippoorwill.

My father, who owned farms in this region, decided we might as well visit them to see how the tobacco was leafing out, and how the wheat harvest was progressing.

It should be said in passing that "ownership" of a piece of property was never that simple with my father. Although he never touched a card, he was a born gambler, particularly in real estate. When he took title to a farm, he immediately loaded it with a first mortgage and usually a second mortgage. With the money thus liberated he would buy another farm and repeat the process. It was very much like buying securities on a margin. When the market was rising, he pyramided his paper profits. But in every farm recession he came close to disaster.

I didn't understand his complex bookkeeping, and perhaps he didn't either. But at this moment he felt he was fairly wealthy, with a wheat ranch in Montana, and some eight or ten other pieces of endangered property.

My mother hadn't lived to see much of this new prosperity. A delicate, highly intelligent woman, she had entered college at the age of fourteen and graduated at the head of her class. She had accepted and married my father, for better or for worse, sharing more years of poverty than of comfort. She did the worrying for the family; and it was largely worry that killed her at forty-seven. My father, who lived in an insulated dream world, took all of his losses philosophically, even the loss of my mother.

On this summer day in 1918 he had no worries whatsoever, unless he briefly remembered that Herschel was fighting in the front lines in France. The price of leaf tobacco was soaring as were the prices of other farm products, and land was selling at an all-time high. His corn fields were green and thriving and his wheat and oats were promising a record yield to the acre. In lush pastures through which small brooks wandered, his herds of Holstein and Guernsey cattle grazed contentedly in knee-deep grass and clover.

I always enjoyed these farm excursions, particularly the opportunity to watch colts and calves high-tailing through the pastures. The young of almost every species, it seemed, were glad to be alive, Rascal included.

Just now, however, my little raccoon was happily exhausted, sleeping off his overindulgence in turtle eggs. He lay on the back seat, his ringed tail coiled neatly over his face. He continued to sleep until "first lamp light" when we were nearing our destination in search of whippoor-wills.

We had no time to visit the site of the cabin where my father had been born or the big brick house on the same homestead where he had spent his boyhood. If we were to reach the Kumlien property, we must leave the car at this point and walk through meadowland along the old Milwaukee trail, long since abandoned. Up this trail from Galena, Illinois had once moved heavy oxcarts pulled by six or eight yoke of oxen. These "toad-crushers," bringing pigs of lead from the mines to the lake port, had wheels made of the cross sections of giant white oak trees. The screaming of these wheels on their wooden axles could be heard for miles.

Down this same trail from Milwaukee had come such early settlers as Thure Kumlien from Sweden and my ancestors from England.

The ruts were now overgrown with grass, and

healed by the passage of time, but we could see them clearly as my father, Rascal, and I walked through the gathering dusk accompanied only by the shadows of pioneers long dead, moving through fields and forests of memory.

Above us circled the nighthawks searching insects, their aerial acrobatics graceful and erratic.

"Notice the ovals of white under each wing," my father said. "That is one of the few ways you can tell nighthawks from whippoorwills."

"What other ways?"

"The whippoorwill's call, of course, and his whiskers."

"How can you get near enough to see a whippoorwill's whiskers?"

"You seldom can," my father admitted, "but on those which Kumlien mounted, they were obvious enough: stiff bristles on either side of the wide mouth, probably for sensing the flying insects he scoops up for food."

We walked on in silence approaching the forty acres of virgin forest which Kumlien had protected from the ax. It is gone now, but it was there when I was a boy, a sanctuary and a memorial, haunted by the spirit of the gentle Swede who played his flute for the whippoorwills.

We came at last to the flowing well which the old naturalist had dug, ringed with heavy limestone slabs, its cold water gushing up from below and winding off in a little stream through marshy pastures to the lake.

I was thirsty and went down on my knees to

drink from the clear deep pool. But my father said, "Wait a minute, Sterling. Try this."

From mint that Kumlien had once planted my father plucked a few leaves, asked me to rub them between my fingers and then taste them thoroughly. They were delightful and tangy. And when I drank from the well, I tasted water more cool and refreshing than any I had ever known. In the amber afterlight around that woodland spring we all three drank; then amid the ferns we waited for my first whippoorwill.

Very slowly the full moon edged above the horizon until we could see its entire circumference. Rascal roamed a bit, and caught and ate a cricket. But he was still too well fed to be restless. He came back to me, chirring comfortably, and to his chirr were added other night sounds, the wings of big moths soft upon the air, the rustling of small creatures in the grass, meadow mice perhaps, and the chorus of the frogs in the marsh.

Then, then it came! Three pure syllables, three times repeated:

Whip-poor-will, whip-poor-will, whip-poor-will.

A soloist against the symphony of the night making me feel weightless, airborne, and eerie — happy, but also immeasurably sad.

Again the whippoorwill called. And on this second invitation another whippoorwill answered courteously. For nearly half an hour they carried on their spirited duet.

My small raccoon sat listening intently, well aware of the exact direction from which each call was coming. Having had his afternoon nap, he was now ready to make a night of it.

The concert ended as abruptly as it had begun, and we awoke as from a dream. We scrambled up from the ferns, and by the light of the rising moon, turned westward down the old trail which had brought my people to this land of lakes and rivers.

His First Flight

Liam O'Flaherty

The young seagull was alone on his ledge. His two brothers and his sister had already flown away the day before. He had been afraid to fly with them. Somehow when he had taken a little run forward to the brink of the ledge and attempted to flap his wings he became afraid. The great expanse of sea stretched down beneath, and it was such a long way down — miles down. He felt certain that his wings would never support him, so he bent his head and ran away back to the little hold under the ledge where he slept at night. Even when each of his brothers and his little sister, whose wings were far shorter than his own, ran to the brink, flapped their wings, and flew away he failed to muster up courage to take that plunge which appeared to him so desperate. His father and mother had come around calling to him shrilly, upbraiding him, threatening to let him starve on his ledge unless he flew away. But for the life of him he could not move.

That was twenty-four hours ago. Since then nobody had come near him. The day before, all day long, he had watched his parents flying about with his brothers and sister, perfecting them in the art of flight, teaching them how to skim the waves and how to dive for fish. He had, in fact, seen his older brother catch his first herring and devour it, standing on a rock, while his parents circled around raising a proud cackle. And all the morning the whole family had walked about on the big plateau midway down the opposite cliff, taunting him with his cowardice.

The sun was now ascending the sky, blazing warmly on his ledge that faced the south. He felt the heat because he had not eaten since the previous nightfall. Then he had found a dried piece of mackerel's tail at the far end of his ledge. Now there was not a single scrap of food left. He had searched every inch, rooting among the rough, dirt-caked straw nest where he and his brothers and sister had been hatched. He even gnawed at the dried pieces of spotted eggshell. It was like eating part of himself. He had then trotted back and forth from one end of the ledge to the other, his grey body the colour of the cliff, his long grey legs stepping daintily, trying to find some means of reaching his parents without having to fly. But on each side of him the ledge ended in a sheer fall of precipice, with the sea beneath. And between him and his parents there was a deep, wide chasm. Surely he could reach them without flying if he could only move northwards along the cliff face? But then on what could he walk? There was no ledge, and he was not a fly. And above him he could see nothing.

The precipice was sheer, and the top of it was perhaps farther away than the sea beneath him.

He stepped slowly out to the brink of the ledge, and, standing on one leg with the other leg hidden under his wing, he closed one eye, then the other, and pretended to be falling asleep. Still they took no notice of him. He saw his two brothers and his sister lying on the plateau dozing, with their heads sunk into their necks. His father was preening the feathers on his white back. Only his mother was looking at him. She was standing on a little high hump on the plateau, her white breast thrust forward. Now and again she tore at a piece of fish that lay at her feet, and then scraped each side of her beak on the rock. The sight of the food maddened him. How he loved to tear food that way, scraping his beak now and again to whet it! He uttered a low cackle. His mother cackled too, and looked over at him.

"Ga, ga, ga," he cried, begging her to bring him over some food. "Gaw-ool-ah," she screamed back derisively. But he kept calling plaintively, and after a minute or so he uttered a joyful scream. His mother had picked up a piece of the fish and was flying across to him with it. He leaned out eagerly, tapping the rock with his feet, trying to get nearer to her as she flew across. But when she was just opposite to him, abreast of the ledge, she halted, her legs hanging limp, her wings motionless, the piece of fish in her beak almost within reach of his beak. He waited a moment in surprise, wondering why she did not come nearer, and then, maddened by hunger, he dived at the fish. With a loud scream he fell outwards and downwards into space. His mother had swooped upwards. As he passed beneath her he heard the swish of her wings. Then a monstrous terror seized him and his heart stood still. He could hear nothing. But it only lasted a moment. The next moment he felt his wings spread outwards. The wind rushed against his breast feathers, then under his stomach and against his wings. He could feel the tips of his wings cutting through the air. He was not falling headlong now. He was soaring gradually downwards and outwards. He was no longer afraid. He just felt a bit dizzy. Then he flapped his wings once and he soared upwards. He uttered a joyous scream and flapped them again. He soared higher. He raised his breast and banked against the wind. "Ga, ga, ga. Ga, ga, ga. Gaw-ool-ah." His mother swooped past him, her wings making a loud noise. He answered her with another scream. Then his father flew over him screaming. Then he saw his two brothers and his sister flying around him curveting and banking and soaring and diving.

Then he completely forgot that he had not always been able to fly, and commenced himself to dive and soar and curvet, shrieking shrilly.

He was near the sea now, flying straight over it, facing straight out over the ocean. He saw a vast green sea beneath him, with little ridges moving over it, and he turned his beak sideways and crowed amusedly. His parents and his brothers and sister had landed on this green floor in front of him. They were beckoning to him, calling shrilly. He dropped his legs to stand on the green sea. His legs sank into it. He screamed with fright and attempted to rise again, flapping his wings. But he was tired and weak with hunger and he could not rise, exhausted by the strange exercise. His feet sank into the green sea, and then his belly touched it and he sank no farther. He was floating on it. And around him his family was screaming, praising him, and their beaks were offering him scraps of dog-fish.

He had made his first flight.

Puss in Boots

Charles Perrault

Once upon a time there was a miller who left no more riches to the three sons he had than his mill, his ass, and his cat. The division was soon made. Neither the lawyer nor the attorney was sent for. They would soon have eaten up all the poor property. The eldest had the mill, the second the ass, and the youngest nothing but the cat.

The youngest, as we can understand, was quite unhappy at having so poor a share.

"My brothers," said he, "may get their living handsomely enough by joining their stocks together; but, for my part, when I have eaten up my cat, and made me a muff of his skin, I must die of hunger."

The Cat, who heard all this, without appearing to take any notice, said to him with a grave and serious air: —

"Do not thus afflict yourself, my master; you have nothing else to do but to give me a bag, and get a pair of boots made for me, that I may scamper through the brambles, and you shall see that you have not so poor a portion in me as you think."

Though the Cat's master did not think much of what he said, he had seen him play such cunning tricks to catch rats and mice — hanging himself by the heels, or hiding himself in the meal, to make believe he was dead — that he did not altogether despair of his helping him in his misery. When the Cat had what he asked for, he booted himself very gallantly, and putting his bag about his neck, he held the strings of it in his two forepaws, and went into a warren where was a great number of rabbits. He put bran and sow-thistle into his bag, and, stretching out at length, as if he were dead, he waited for some young rabbits, not yet acquainted with the deceits of the world, to come and rummage his bag for what he had put into it.

Scarcely was he settled but he had what he wanted. A rash and foolish young rabbit jumped into his bag, and Monsieur Puss, immediately drawing close the strings, took him and killed him at once. Proud of his prey, he went with it to the palace, and asked to speak with the King. He was shown upstairs into his Majesty's apartment, and, making a low bow to the King, he said: —

"I have brought you, sire, a rabbit which my noble Lord, the Master of Carabas" (for that was the title which Puss was pleased to give his master) "has commanded me to present to your Majesty from him."

"Tell thy master," said the King, "that I thank him, and that I am pleased with his gift."

Another time he went and hid himself among some standing corn, still holding his bag open; and when a brace of partridges ran into it, he drew the strings, and so caught them both. He then went and made a present of these to the King, as he had done before of the rabbit which he took in the warren. The King, in like manner, received the partridges with great pleasure, and ordered his servants to reward him.

The Cat continued for two or three months thus to carry his Majesty, from time to time, some of his master's game. One day when he knew that the King was to take the air along the riverside, with his daughter, the most beautiful princess in the world, he said to his master: —

"If you will follow my advice, your fortune is made. You have nothing else to do but go and bathe in the river, just at the spot I shall show you, and leave the rest to me."

The Marquis of Carabas did what the Cat advised him to, without knowing what could be the use of doing it. While he was bathing, the King passed by, and the Cat cried out with all his might: —

"Help, help! My Lord the Marquis of Carabas is drowning!"

At this noise the King put his head out of the coach window, and seeing the Cat who had so often brought him game, he commanded his guards to run immediately to the assistance of his Lordship the Marquis of Carabas.

While they were drawing the poor Marquis

out of the river, the Cat came up to the coach and told the King that, while his master was bathing, there came by some rogues, who ran off with his clothes, though he had cried out, "Thieves! thieves!" several times, as loud as he could. The cunning Cat had hidden the clothes under a great stone. The King immediately commanded the officers of his wardrobe to run and fetch one of his best suits for the Lord Marquis of Carabas.

The King was extremely polite to him, and as the fine clothes he had given him set off his good looks (for he was well made and handsome), the King's daughter found him very much to her liking, and the Marquis of Carabas had no sooner cast two or three respectful and somewhat tender glances than she fell in love with him to distraction. The King would have him come into the coach and take part in the airing. The Cat, overjoyed to see his plan begin to succeed, marched on before, and, meeting with some countrymen, who were mowing a meadow, he said to them: —

"Good people, you who are mowing, if you do not tell the King that the meadow you mow belongs to my Lord Marquis of Carabas, you shall be chopped as small as herbs for the pot."

The King did not fail to ask the mowers to whom the meadow they were mowing belonged.

"To my Lord Marquis of Carabas," answered they all together, for the Cat's threat had made them afraid.

"You have a good property there," said the King to the Marquis of Carabas.

"You see, sire," said the Marquis, "this is a meadow which never fails to yield a plentiful harvest every year."

The Master Cat, who went still on before, met with some reapers, and said to them: —

"Good people, you who are reaping, if you do not say that all this corn belongs to the Marquis of Carabas, you shall be chopped as small as herbs for the pot."

The King, who passed by a moment after, wished to know to whom belonged all that corn, which he then saw.

"To my Lord Marquis of Carabas," replied the reapers, and the King was very well pleased with it, as well as the Marquis, whom he congratulated thereupon. The Master Cat, who went always before, said the same thing to all he met, and the King was astonished at the vast estates of my Lord Marquis of Carabas.

Monsieur Puss came at last to a stately castle, the master of which was on Ogre, the richest ever known; for all the lands which the King had then passed through belonged to his castle. The Cat, who had taken care to inform himself who this Ogre was and what he could do, asked to speak with him, saying he could not pass so near his castle without having the honor of paying his respects to him.

The Ogre received him as civilly as an Ogre could do, and made him sit down.

"I have been assured," said the Cat, "that you have the gift of being able to change yourself into all sorts of creatures you have a mind to; that you can, for example, transform yourself into a lion, or elephant, and the like."

"That is true," answered the Ogre, roughly; "and to convince you, you shall see me now become a lion."

Puss was so terrified at the sight of a lion so near him that he immediately climbed into the gutter, not without much trouble and danger, because of his boots, which were of no use at all to him for walking upon the tiles. A little while after, when Puss saw that the Ogre had resumed his natural form, he came down, and owned he had been very much frightened.

"I have, moreover, been informed," said the Cat, "but I know not how to believe it, that you have also the power to take on you the shape of the smallest animals; for example, to change yourself into a rat or mouse, but I must own to you I take this to be impossible."

"Impossible!" cried the Ogre; "you shall see." And at the same time he changed himself into a mouse, and began to run about the floor. Puss no sooner perceived this than he fell upon him and ate him up.

Meanwhile, the King, who saw, as he passed, this fine castle of the Ogre's, had a mind to go into it. Puss, who heard the noise of his Majesty's coach coming over the drawbridge, ran out, and said to the King, "Your Majesty is welcome to this castle of my Lord Marquis of Carabas."

"What! my Lord Marquis," cried the King, "and does this castle also belong to you? There can be nothing finer than this courtyard and all the stately buildings which surround it; let us see the interior, if you please."

The Marquis gave his hand to the young Princess, and followed the King, who went first. They passed into the great hall, where they found a magnificent collation, which the Ogre had prepared for his friends, who were that very day to visit him, but dared not to enter, knowing the King was there. His Majesty, charmed with the good qualities of my Lord of Carabas, as was also his daughter, who had fallen violently in love with him, and seeing the vast estate he possessed, said to him: —

"It will be owing to yourself only, my Lord Marquis, if you are not my son-in-law."

The Marguis, with low bows, accepted the honor which his Majesty conferred upon him, and forthwith that very same day married the Princess.

Puss became a great lord, and never ran after mice any more except for his diversion.

The Yearling*

Marjorie Kinnan Rawlings

here was not a field of
sweet potatoes, but an endless sea. Jody looked
behind him at the rows he had finished hoeing.
They were beginning to make a respectable
showing, but the rows unfinished seemed to
stretch to the horizon. The July heat simmered
on the earth. The sand was scalding to his bare
feet. The leaves of the sweet potato vines curled
upward, as though the dry soil, and not the sun,
were burning them. He pushed back his palmetto
hat and wiped his face with his sleeve. By the
sun, it must be nearly ten o'clock. His father
had said that if the sweet potatoes were hoed by
noon, he might go in the afternoon to see Fodder-
wing, and get a name for the fawn.

The fawn lay in the hedge-row in the shade of
an elderberry bush. It had been almost a nuisance
when he began his work. It had galloped up and
down the sweet potato beds, trampling the vines,
and knocking down the edges of the beds. It had

*This is the seventeenth chapter of Marjorie Kinnan
Rawlings' famous novel about a boy's coming of age
and his love of a fawn.

323

come and stood in front of him in the direct path of his hoeing, refusing to move, to force him to play with it. The wide-eyed, wondering expression of its first weeks with him had given way to an alert awareness. It had as wise a look as old Julia. Jody had almost decided that he would have to lead it back and shut it up in the shed, when of its own accord it sought the shade and lay down.

It lay watching him from the corner of one big eye, its head in its favorite position, twisted back against its own shoulder. Its small white tail flicked now and then and its spotted hide rippled, shaking off flies. If it would stay quiet, he could make better time at the hoeing. He liked to work with it near. It gave him a comfortable feeling that he had never had before in the company of a hoe. He attacked the weeds again lustily, and was pleased with himself to see his own progress. The rows fell away behind him. He whistled tunelessly.

He had thought of many names for the fawn, had called it by each in turn, but not one pleased him. All the names by which the dogs of his acquaintance had been called, Joe and Grab, Rover and Rob, on down the line, all were inadequate. It had such a light way of walking, "tippy-toed" as Penny put it, that he would have named it Twinkle-toes and called it "Twink" for short, but that reminded him of Twink Weatherby and spoiled the name. "Tip" itself would not do, because Penny had once had an ugly and vicious bull-dog by the name. Fodder-wing would not fail him. He had a great gift for naming his own pets. He had Racket the raccoon, Push the 'possum, Squeak the squirrel, and Preacher, the lame red-bird, who sang from his perch, "Preacher, preacher, preacher!" Fodder-wing said the other red-birds came to him from the forest to be married, but Jody had heard other red-birds sing the same words. At any rate, it was a good name.

He had done a great deal of work in the two weeks since Buck had gone home. Penny's strength was returning, but every now and then he became faint and dizzy and his heart pounded. Penny was sure it was the lingering effect of the rattlesnake venom, but Ma Baxter believed it was the fever, and dosed him with lemon-leaf tea. It was good to have him up and about again, with the cold fear gone. Jody tried to remember to spare him. It was so good to have the fawn, to be relieved of the dull lonely ache that had overtaken him so often, that he was filled with gratitude for his mother's tolerance of its presence. There was no question but that it did require a great deal of milk. It undoubtedly got in her way. It came into the house one day and discovered a pan of cornbread stirred up, ready for baking. It had cleaned the pan. Since then it had eaten — green leaves, cornmeal mixed with water, bits of biscuit, almost anything. It had to be shut in the shed when the Baxters ate. It butted and bleated and knocked dishes out of their hands. When Jody and Penny laughed at it, it tossed its head knowingly. The dogs at first had baited it, but they were now tolerant. Ma Baxter was tolerant, but she was never amused. Jody pointed out its charms.

"Ain't his eyes purty, Ma?"

"They see a pan o' cornbread too fur."

"Well, ain't he got a cute, foolish tail, Ma?"

"All deer's flags looks the same."

"But Ma, ain't it cute and foolish?"

"Hit's foolish, a'right."

The sun crept toward its zenith. The fawn came into the sweet potatoes and nibbled a few tender vines, then returned to the hedge-row and found a new place of shade under a wild cherry tree. Jody checked his work. He had a row and a half yet undone. He would have liked to go to the house for a drink of water, but that would cut down his remaining time too sharply. Perhaps dinner would be late. He pulled the hoe as fast as he dared without cutting the vines. When the sun stood over-head, he had finished the half-row, and the full row stretched mockingly before him. In a moment now his mother would beat on the iron ring by the kitchen door and he would have to stop. Penny had made it plain that there would be no quarter as to time. If the hoeing was not finished by dinner time, there would be no visit to Fodder-wing. He heard steps on the other side of the fence. Penny was standing there, watching him.

"A heap o' taters, ain't it, son?"

"Hit's a mort of 'em."

"Hard to think, this time next year, there'll not be one left. That baby o' yours there, under the cherry tree, he'll be wantin' his share of 'em. Remember the time we had, two year gone, keepin' the deer out?"

"Pa, I cain't make it. I ain't scarcely stopped all mornin', and I've yet got a row."

"Well now, I tell you. I ain't fixin' to let you off, for I said I'd not. But I'll strike a bargain. You go fetch fresh water for your Ma from the sink-hole, and I'll finish the 'taters this evenin'. Climbin' the walls o' that sink-hole purely beats me. Now that's a fair deal."

Jody dropped the hoe and started on a run for the house to get the water-buckets.

Penny called after him, "Don't try to tote 'em plumb full. A yearling ain't got a buck's strength."

The buckets alone were heavy. They were of hand-hewn cypress, and the ox-yoke from which they hung was of white oak. Jody hung the yoke over his shoulders and trotted down the road. The fawn loped after him. The sink-hole was dark and still. There was more sunlight in the early morning and at evening, than at noon, for the thick leaves of the trees cut off the overhead sun. The birds were still. Around the sandy rim of the sink-hole they were nooning and dusting themselves. In late afternoon they would fly down for water. The doves would come, and the jorees, the red-birds and the bee-martins, the mocking-birds and the quail. He could not be too hurried to run down the steep slope to the bottom of the great green bowl. The fawn followed and they splashed together across the pool. The fawn bent its head to drink. He had dreamed of this.

He said to it, "Some day I'll build me a house here. And I'll git you a doe, and we'll all live here by the pool."

A frog leaped and the fawn backed away. Jody laughed at it and ran up the slope to the drinking trough. He leaned over it to drink. The fawn, following, drank with him, sucking up the water and moving its mouth up and down the length of the trough. At one moment its head was against Jody's cheek and he sucked in the water with the same sound as the fawn, for the sake of companionship. He lifted his head and shook it and wiped his mouth. The fawn lifted its head, too, and the water dropped from its muzzle.

Jody filled the buckets with the gourd dipper that hung on the rim of the trough. Against his father's warning, he filled them nearly full. He would like to walk into the yard with them. He crouched and bent his shoulders under the yoke. When he straightened, he could not rise against the weight. He dipped out part of the water and was able to stand and pull his way up the remainder of the slope. The wooden yoke cut into his thin shoulders. His back ached. Halfway home, he was obliged to stop and set down the buckets and pour out more of the water. The fawn dipped its nose inquisitively into one of the buckets. Fortunately, his mother need not know.

She could not understand how clean the fawn was, and would not admit how sweet it smelled.

They were at dinner when he reached the house. He lited the buckets to the water shelf and shut up the fawn. He filled the water pitcher from the fresh buckets and took it in to the table. He had worked so hard and was so hot and tired that he was not particularly hungry. He was glad of this and was able to set aside a large portion of his own dinner for the fawn. The meat was a pot-roast from the bear's haunch, pickled in brine for keeping. It was a trifle coarse, with long fibers, but the flavor, he thought, was better than beef and almost as good as venison. He made his meal on the meat, with a helping of collard greens, and saved all his cornpone and his milk for the fawn.

Penny said, "We was mighty lucky 'twas a young bear like this un come scaperin' under our noses. Had it of been a big ol' male, we couldn't of et the meat this time o' year. The bears mates in July, Jody, and allus remember the meat o' the males ain't fitten when they're matin'. Don't never shoot one then unless it's botherin' you."

"Why ain't the meat fitten?"

"Now I don't know. But when they're courtin', they're mean and hateful —"

"Like Lem and Oliver?"

"— like Lem and Oliver. Their gorge rises, or their spleen, and seems like the hatefulness gits right into their flesh."

Ma Baxter said, "A boar hog's the same. Only

he's that-a-way the year around."

"Well Pa, do the male bears fight?"

"They'll fight turrible. The female'll stand off and watch the fightin' —"

"Like Twink Weatherby."

"— like Twink Weatherby, and then she'll go off with the one wins the fight. They'll stay in pairs all through July, mebbe into August. Then the males goes off and the cubs is borned in February. And don't you think a male, like ol' Slewfoot, won't eat them cubs do he come on 'em. That's another reason I hate bears. They ain't natural in their affections."

Ma Baxter said to Jody, "You look out, now, walkin' to Forresters' today. A matin' bear's a thing to shun."

Penny said, "Jest keep your eyes open. You're all right as long as you see a creetur first and don't take him by surprise. Even that rattlesnake that got me, why, I takened him by surprise and he wasn't no more'n lookin' out for hisself."

Ma Baxter said, "You'd stick up for the devil hisself."

"I reckon I would. The devil gits blamed for a heap o' things is nothin' but human cussedness."

She asked suspiciously, "Jody finish his hoein' like he belonged to?"

Penny said blandly, "He finished his contract."

He winked at Jody and Jody winked back. There was no use in trying to explain the difference to her. She was outside the good male understanding.

He said, "Ma, kin I go now?"

"Let's see. I'll need a mite o' wood toted in
—"

"Please don't think up nothin' long to do, Ma.
You wouldn't want I should be so late gittin'
home tonight the bears'd git me."

"You be later'n dark gittin' home and you'll
wish 'twas a bear had you, 'stid o' me."

He filled the wood-box and was ready to go.
His mother made him change his shirt and comb
his hair. He fretted at the delay.

She said, "I jest want then dirty Forresters to
know there's folks does live decent."

He said, "They ain't dirty. They jest live nice
and natural and enjoy theirselves."

She sniffed. He let out the fawn from the shed,
fed it from his hand, held the pan of milk mixed
with water for it to drink, and the two set off.
The fawn ran sometimes behind him, sometimes
ahead, making short forays into the brush,
bounding back to him in an alarm that Jody was
sure was only pretended. Sometimes it walked
beside him, and this was best. He laid his hand,
then, lightly on its neck, and fitted the rhythm
of his two legs to its four. He imagined that he
was another fawn. He bent his legs at the knees,
imitating its walk. He threw his head up, alertly.
A rabbit-pea vine was in blossom beside the road.
He pulled a length of it and twined it around the
fawn's neck for a halter. The rosy blooms made
the fawn so pretty that it seemed to him even his
mother would admire it. If it faded before he

331

returned, he would make a fresh halter on the way home.

At the cross-roads near the abandoned clearing, the fawn halted and lifted its nostrils into the wind. It pricked up its ears. It turned its head this way and that, savoring the air. He turned his own nose in the direction on which it seemed to settle. A strong odor came to him, pungent and rank. He felt the hair prickle on the back of his neck. He thought he heard a low rumbling sound and then a snapping that might be of teeth. He was tempted to turn tail and head for home. Yet he would always wonder what the sounds had been. He moved one step at a time around the turn in the road. The fawn stayed motionless behind him. He stopped short.

Two males bears were moving slowly ahead down the road, a hundred yards distant. They were on their hind legs, walking like men, shoulder to shoulder. Their walk seemed almost a dance, as when couples in the square dance moved side by side to do a figure. Suddenly they jostled each other, like wrestlers, and lifted their forepaws, and turned, snarling, each trying for the other's throat. One raked his claws across the other's head and the snarls grew to a roar. The fighting was violent for a few moments, then the pair walked on, boxing, jostling, parrying. The wind was in Jody's favor. They could never smell him. He crept down the road after them, keeping his distance. He could not bear to lose sight of them. He hoped they would fight to a finish, yet he should be terrorized if one should end the fight and turn his way. He decided that they had been fighting for a long time and were exhausted. There was blood in the sand. Each attack seemed less violent than the others. Each shoulder-to-shoulder walking was slower paced. As he stared, a female walked out of the bushes ahead with three males following her. They turned silently into the road and walked on in single file. The fighting pair swung their heads a moment, then fell in behind. Jody stood until the procession passed from sight, solemn and ludicrous and exciting.

He turned and ran back to the cross-roads. The fawn was nowhere to be seen. He called and it emerged from the scrub growth at the side of the road. He took the Forresters' road and ran down it. Now that it was over, he shook at his own boldness. But it was done now, and he would follow again, for all men were not privileged to see the creatures in their private moments.

He thought, "I've seen a thing."

It was good to become old and see the sights and hear the sounds that men saw and heard, like Buck and his father. That was why he liked to lie flat on his belly on the floor, or on the earth before the camp-fire, while men talked. They had seen marvels, and the older they were, the more marvels they had seen. He felt himself moving into a mystic company. He had a tale now of his own to tell on winter evenings.

His father would say, "Jody, tell about the

time you seed the two male bears fightin' down the road."

Above all, he could tell Fodder-wing. He ran again, for pleasure in his hurry to tell his friend his story. He would surprise him. He would walk up to Fodder-wing in the woods, or back of the house among his pets, or to his bed, if he were still ailing. The fawn would walk beside him. Fodder-wing's face would shine with its strange brightness. He would hunch his twisted body close and put out his gentle and crooked hand and touch the fawn. He would smile, to know that he, Jody, was content. After a long time Fodder-wing would speak, and what he said would be perhaps peculiar, but it would be beautiful.

Jody reached the Forrester land and hurried under the live oaks into the open yard. The house was somnolent. There was no curl of smoke from the chimney. There were no dogs in sight, but a hound was howling from the dog-pen at the rear. The Forresters were probably all sleeping through the heat of the early afternoon. But when they slept in the day-time, they over-flowed the house, out to the veranda, under the trees. He stopped and called.

"Fodder-wing! Hit's Jody!"

The hound whined. A chair scraped on the board floor inside the house. Buck came to the door. He looked down at Jody and passed his hand over his mouth. His eyes were unseeing. It seemed to Jody that he must be drunk.

Jody faltered, "I come to see Fodder-wing. I come to show him my fawn."

Buck shook his head as though he would shake away a bee that annoyed him, or his thoughts. He wiped his mouth again.

Jody said, "I come special."

Buck said, "He's dead."

The words had no meaning. They were only two brown leaves that blew past him into the air. But a coldness followed their passing, and a numbness took him. He was confused.

He repeated, "I come to see him."

"You come too late. I'd of fotched you, if there'd been time. There wasn't time to fotch ol' Doc. One minute he was breathin'. The next minute he jest wa'n't. Like as if you blowed out a candle."

Jody stared at Buck and Buck stared back at him. The numbness grew into a paralysis. He felt no sorrow, only a coldness and a faintness. Fodder-wing was neither dead nor alive. He was, simply, nowhere at all.

Buck said hoarsely, "You kin come look at him."

First Buck said that Fodder-wing was gone, like candlelight, and then he said that he was here. None of it made sense. Buck turned into the house. He looked back, compelling Jody with his dull eyes. Jody lifted one leg after the other and mounted the steps. He followed Buck into the house. The Forrester men sat all together. There was a oneness about them, sitting so, motionless and heavy. They were pieces of one great dark rock, broken into separate men. Pa Forrester turned his head and looked at Jody as though he were a stranger. Then he turned it away again. Lem and Mill-wheel looked at him. The others did not stir. It seemed to Jody that they saw him from over a wall they had built against him. They were unwilling to hold the sight of him. Buck groped for his hand. He led him toward the large bedroom. He started to speak. His voice broke. He stopped and gripped Jody's shoulder.

He said, "Bear up."

Fodder-wing lay with closed eyes, small and lost in the center of the great bed. He was smaller than when he had lain sleeping on his pallet. He was covered with a sheet, turned back beneath his chin. His arms were outside the sheet, folded across his chest, the palms of the hands falling outward, twisted and clumsy, as in life. Jody was frightened. Ma Forrester sat by the side of the bed. She held her apron over her head and rocked herself back and forth. She flung down the apron.

She said, "I've lost my boy. My pore crookedy boy."

She covered herself again and swayed from side to side.

She moaned, "The Lord's hard. Oh, the Lord's hard."

Jody wanted to run away. The bony face on the pillow terrified him. It was Fodder-wing and

336

it was not Fodder-wing. Buck drew him to the edge of the bed.

"He'll not hear, but speak to him."

Jody's throat worked. No words came. Fodder-wing seemed made of tallow, like a candle. Suddenly he was familiar.

Jody whispered, "Hey."

The paralysis broke, having spoken. His throat tightened as though a rope choked it. Fodder-wing's silence was intolerable. Now he understood. This was death. Death was a silence that gave back no answer. Fodder-wing would never speak to him again. He turned and buried his face against Buck's chest. The big arms gripped him. He stood a long time.

Buck said, "I knowed you'd hate it fearful."

They left the room. Pa Forrester beckoned to him. He went to his side. The old man stroked his arm. He waved at the circle of brooding men.

He said, "Ain't it quare now? We could of spared nigh ary one o' them fellers. The one we cain't spare was the one was takened." He added brightly, "And him a swivveled, no-account thing, too."

He sank back in his rocking chair, pondering the paradox.

Jody bruised them all with his presence. He wandered outside into the yard. He roamed to the back of the house. Fodder-wing's pets were here, caged and forgotten. A five-month's bear cub, brought no doubt to amuse him in his illness, was chained to a stake. It had walked its dusty circle, around and around, until its chain was tangled and it was help tight against the stake. Its water-pan was over-turned and empty. At sight of Jody, it rolled on its back and cried with a sound like a human baby. Squeak the squirrel ran his endless treadle. His cage had neither food nor water. The 'possum was asleep in its box. Preacher the red-bird hopped on his one good leg and pecked at the bare floor of his cage. The raccoon was not in sight.

Jody knew where Fodder-wing kept sacks of peanuts and corn for his creatures. His brothers had made him a little feed-box and kept it filled for him. Jody fed the small things first and watered them. He approached the bear cub cautiously. It was small and roly-poly, but he was not too certain what use it might make of its sharp claws. It whimpered and he reached out one arm to it. It wrapped all four legs around it and clung desperately. It rubbed its black nose against his shoulder. He untangled it and pulled away from it and straightened its chain and brought it a pan of water. It drank again and again, then took the pan from him with its paws like the hands, he thought, of a baby, and turned the last few cool drops on its stomach. He could have laughed aloud if he were not so heavy with sadness. But it relieved him to care for the animals, to give them, for the time, the comfort that their master could never offer them again. He wondered sorrowfully what would become of them.

He played abstractedly with them. The sharp joy that he had once felt when Fodder-wing shared them was muted. When Racket, the raccoon, came in from the forest with its queer, uneven gait, and recognized him, and climbed up his leg to his shoulder, and made its plaintive, chirring cry, and parted his hair with its thin, restless fingers, he longed so painfully for Fodder-wing that he had to lie on his belly and beat his feet in the sand.

The ache turned into a longing for the fawn. He got up and brought a handful of peanuts for the 'coon, to keep it occupied. He went in search of the fawn. He found it behind a myrtle bush, where it had been able to watch unobserved. He thought it might be thirsty, too, and he offered it water in the bear cub's pan. The fawn sniffed and would not drink. He was tempted to feed it a handful of corn from the Forrester's abundance, but decided it would not be honest to do so. Probably its teeth were still too tender to chew the hard kernels in any case. He sat down under a live oak and held the fawn close to him. There was a comfort in it not to be found in the hairy arms of Buck Forrester. He wondered if his pleasure in Fodder-wing's creatures had been dissipated because Fodder-wing was gone, or because the fawn now held all he needed of delight.

He said to it, "I'd not trade you for all of 'em, and the cub to boot."

A gratifying feeling of faithfulness came over

him, that the enchantment of the creatures he had so long coveted could not deflect his affections from the fawn.

The afternoon was endless. It came to him that something was unfinished. The Forresters ignored him, yet, somehow, he knew they expected him to stay. Buck would have said goodby to him if he were supposed to go. The sun dropped behind the live oaks. His mother would be angry. Yet he was waiting for something, if only dismissal by a sign. He was bound to Fodder-wing, tallow-white in the bed, and a thing waited that would set him free. At dusk the Forresters filed out of the house and went in silence about their chores. Smoke drifted from the chimney. The smell of fat pine blended with frying meat. He trailed after Buck, driving the cows to water.

He offered, "I done fed and watered the bear cub and the squirrel and them."

Buck touched a switch to a heifer.

He said, "I remembered them oncet today, and then my mind went black agin."

Jody said, "Kim I he'p?"

"They's a plenty of us here, to do. You could wait on Ma like Fodder-wing done. Keep up her fire and sich as that."

He went reluctantly into the house. He avoided the sight of the bedroom door. It was drawn almost closed. Ma Forrester was at the hearth. Her eyes were red. She stopped every few moments to touch them with the corner of her apron. Her straggly hair had been wet and brushed back smooth and neat, as though in honor of a guest.

He said, "I come to he'p."

She turned with a spoon in her hand.

She said, "I been standin' here thinkin' about your Ma. She's burrit as many as I got."

He fed the fire unhappily. He was increasingly uneasy. Yet he could not go. The meal was as meager as the Baxters' own. Ma Forrester set the table indifferently.

She said, "Now I forgot to make coffee. They'd drink coffee when they'd not eat."

She filled the pot and set it on the coals. The Forrester men came one by one to the back porch and washed their hands and faces and combed their hair and beards. There was no talk, no joking and jostling, no noisy stamping. They trooped in to the table like men in a dream. Pa Forrester came in from the bedroom. He looked about him wonderingly.

He said, "Ain't is quare —"

Jody sat down next to Ma Forrester. She served the plates with meat, then began to cry.

She said, "I counted him in, same as always. Oh my Lord, I counted him in."

Buck said, "Well now, Ma, Jody'll eat his portion and mebbe grow up big as me. Eh, boy?"

The family rallied. For a few minutes they ate hungrily. Then a nauseating fullness came over them and they pushed away their plates.

Ma Forrester said, "I got no heart to clean up

tonight, nor you neither. Jest stack the plates 'til tomorrer mornin'.''

Release, then, would come in the morning. She looked at Jody's plate.

She said, "You ain't et your biscuit nor drinked your milk, boy. What ailded 'em?"

"That's for my fawn. I allus save him some o' my dinner."

She said, "You pore lamb." She began to cry again. "Wouldn't my boy of loved to seed your fawn. He talked about it and he talked about it. He said, 'Jody's got him a brother.' "

Jody felt the hateful thickening of his throat. He swallowed.

He said, "That's how come me to be here. I came for Fodder-wing to name my fawn."

"Why," she said, "he named it. Last time he talked about it, he give it a name. He said, 'A fawn carries its flag so merry. A fawn's tail's a leetle white merry flag. If I had me a fawn, I'd name him "Flag." "Flag the fawn," is what I'd call him.' "

Jody repeated, "Flag."

He thought he would burst. Fodder-wing had talked of him and had named the fawn. There was happiness tangled with his grief that was both comforting and unbearable.

He said, "I reckon I best go feed him. I best go feed Flag."

He slid from his chair and went outside with the cup of milk and the biscuits. Fodder-wing seemed close and living.

He called, "Here, Flag!"

The fawn came to him and it seemed to him that it knew the name, and had perhaps always known it. He soaked the biscuits in the milk and fed them to it. Its muzzle was soft and wet in his hand. He went back into the house and the fawn followed.

He said, "Kin Flag come in?"

"Bring him right in and welcome."

He sat down stiffly on Fodder-wing's three-legged stool in the corner.

Pa Forrester said, "Hit'd pleasure him, you comin' to set up with him tonight."

That, then, was the thing expected of him.

"And 'twouldn't scarcely be decent, buryin' him in the mornin' without you was here. He didn't have no friend but you."

Jody cast off his anxiety over his mother and father like a too-ragged shirt. It was of no importance, in the face of matters so grave. Ma Forrester went into the bedroom to take the early vigil. The fawn nosed about the room, smelling of one man after the other, then came and lay down beside Jody. Darkness came tangibly into the house, adding its heaviness to theirs. They sat smothered under the thick air of sorrow that only the winds of time could blow away.

At nine o'clock Buck stirred and lit a candle. At ten o'clock a horse and rider clattered into the yard. It was Penny on old Caesar. He dropped the reins over its head and came into the house. Pa Forrester, as head of the house, rose and greeted him. Penny looked about at the dark faces. The old man pointed to the half-open bedroom door.

Penny said, "The boy?"

Pa Forrester nodded.

"Gone — or goin'?"

"Gone."

"I feared it. Hit come over me, that was what was keepin' Jody away."

He laid one hand on the old man's shoulder.

"I feel for you."

He spoke to one man after the other. He looked directly at Lem.

"Howdy, Lem."

Lem hesitated.

"Howdy, Penny."

Mill-wheel gave him his chair.

Penny asked, "When did it happen?"

"Jest at dawn today."

"Ma goed in to see would he eat a bite o' breakfast."

"He'd been layin' punishin' a day-two, and we'd had ol' Doc, but he seemed to be mendin'."

The talk broke over Penny in a torrent. The relief of words washed and cleansed a hurt that had been in-growing. He listened gravely, nodding his head from time to time. He was a small staunch rock against which their grief might beat. When they finished and fell quiet, he talked of his own losses. It was a reminder that no man was spared. What all had borne, each could bear. He shared their sorrow, and they became a part of his, and the sharing spread their grief a little, by thinning it.

Buck said, "Likely Jody'd like to set up with him alone a whiles."

Jody was in a panic when they took him into the room and turned away to close the door. Something sat in a far dark corner of the room and it was the same thing that had prowled the scrub the night his father had been bitten.

He said, "Would it be all right, did Flag come, too?"

They agreed that it was seemly and the fawn was brought to join him. He sat on the edge of the chair. It was warm from Ma Forrester's body. He crossed his hands in his lap. He looked furtively at the face on the pillow. A candle burned on a table at the head of the bed. When the flame flickered, it seemed that Fodder-wing's eyelids fluttered. A light breeze stirred through the room. The sheet seemed to lift, as though Fodder-wing were breathing. After a time the horror went away and he could sit back in the chair. When he leaned far back, Fodder-wing looked a little familiar. Yet it was not Fodder-wing who lay, pinched of cheek, under the candle-light. Fodder-wing was stumbling about outside in the bushes, with the raccoon at his heels. In a moment he would come into the house with his rocking gait, and Jody would hear his voice. He stole a look at the crossed, crooked hands. Their stillness was implacable. He cried to himself, soundlessly.

The wavering candle was hypnotic. His eyes blurred. He roused himself, but a moment came when his eyes would not open. Death and the silence and his sleep were one.

He awakened at daylight to a heaviness of spirit. He heard a sound of hammering. Some one had laid him across the food of the bed. He was wide awake instantly. Fodder-wing was gone. He slid from the bed and into the big room. It was empty. He went outside. Penny was nailing a cover on a fresh pine box. The Forresters stood about. Ma Forrester was crying. No one spoke to him. Penny drove the last nail.

He asked, "Ready?"

They nodded. Buck and Mill-wheel and Lem moved forward.

Buck said, "I kin tote it alone."

He swung the box to his shoulder. Pa Forrester and Gabby were missing. Buck set out toward the south hammock. Ma Forrester followed him. Mill-wheel took hold of her arm. The others dropped in behind them. The procession filed slowly to the hammock. Jody remembered that Fodder-wing had a grapevine swing here, under a live oak. He saw Pa Forrester standing beside it. They had spades in their hands. A raw hole gaped in the earth. The mounded soil beside it was dark with woodmould. The hammock was light with the dawning, for the sunrise reached out luminous fingers parallel with the earth and covered it with brightness. Buck set down the coffin and eased it into the opening. He stepped back. The Forresters hesitated.

Penny said, "The father first."

Pa Forrester lifted his spade and shovelled earth on the box. He handed the spade to Buck. Buck threw a few clods. The spade passed from one to the other of the brothers. There was a tea-cupful of earth remaining. Jody found the spade in his hands. Numb, he scooped the earth and dropped it on the mound. The Forresters looked at one another.

Pa Forrester said, "Penny, you've had Christian raising. We'd be proud, did you say somethin'."

Penny advanced to the grave and closed his eyes and lifted his face to the sunlight. The Forresters bowed their heads.

"Oh Lord. Almighty God. Hit ain't for us ignorant mortals to say what's right and what's wrong. Was ary one of us to be a-doin' of it, we'd not of brung this pore boy into the world a cripple, and his mind teched. We'd of brung him in straight and tall like his brothers, fitten to live and work and do. But in a way o' speakin', Lord, you done made it up to him. You give him a way with the wild creeturs. You give him a sort o' wisdom, made him knowin' and gentle. The birds come to him, and the varmints moved free about him, and like as not he could o' takened a she wild-cat right in his pore twisted hands.

"Now you've done seed fit to take him where bein' crookedy in mind or limb don't matter.

But Lord, hit pleasures us to think now you've done straightened out them legs and that pore bent back and them hands. Hit pleasures us to think on him, movin' around as easy as ary one. And Lord, give him a few red-birds and mebbe a squirrel and a 'coon and a 'possum to keep him comp'ny, like he had here. All of us is somehow lonesome, and we know he'll not be lonesome, do he have them leetle wild things around him, if it ain't askin' too much to put a few varmints in Heaven. Thy will be done. Amen."

The Forresters murmured "Amen." Sweat stood on their faces. They came to Penny one by one and wrung his hand. The raccoon came running and ran across the fresh-turned earth. It cried and Buck lifted it to his shoulder. The Forresters turned and trooped back to the house. They saddled Caesar and Penny mounted. He swung Jody up behind him. Jody called the fawn and it came from the bushes. Buck came from the rear of the house. He had a small wire cage in his hand. He handed it up to Jody on the horse's rump. It held Preacher, the lame red-bird.

He said, "I know your Ma wouldn't leave you keep ary o' the creeturs, but this feller'll make out on pure crumbs. Hit's for you to remember him by."

"I thank you. Good-by."

"Good-by."

Ceasar jogged down the road toward home. They did not speak. Caesar dropped into a walk and Penny did not disturb him. The sun rose high. Jody's arm ached from holding the little cage in the air. The Baxter clearing came into sight. Ma Baxter had heard the horse's hooves and was at the gate.

She called out, "Hit's enough to be fretted about one, then you both go off and stay gone."

Penny dismounted and Jody slid down.

Penny said, "Easy, Ma. We had a duty. Pore leetle ol' Fodder-wing died and we he'ped bury him."

She said, "Well — Pity 'twa'n't that great quarrelin' Lem."

Penny turned Caesar out to graze and came to the house. Breakfast had been cooked but was now cold.

He said, "Ne' mind. Jest warm the coffee."

He ate abstractedly.

He said, "I never seed a family take a thing so hard."

She said, "Don't tell me them big rough somebodies took on."

He said, "Ory, the day may come when you'll know the human heart is allus the same. Sorrer strikes the same all over. Hit makes a different kind o' mark in different places. Seems to me, times, hit ain't done nothin' to you but sharpen your tongue."

She sat down abruptly.

She said, "Seems like bein' hard is the only way I kin stand it."

He left his breakfast and went to her and stroked her hair.

"I know. Jest be a leetle mite easy on t'other feller."

Tobermory

Saki (H. H. Munro)

It was a chill, rain-washed afternoon of a late August day, that indefinite season when partridges are still in security or cold storage, and there is nothing to hunt — unless one is bounded on the north by the Bristol Channel, in which case one may lawfully gallop after fat red stags. Lady Blemley's house-party was not bounded on the north by the Bristol Channel, hence there was a full gathering of her guests round the tea-table on this particular afternoon. And, in spite of the blankness of the season and the triteness of the occasion, there was no trace in the company of that fatigued restlessness which means a dread of the pianola and a subdued hankering for auction bridge. The undisguised open-mouthed attention of the entire party was fixed on the homely negative personality of Mr. Cornelius Appin. Of all her guests, he was the one who had come to Lady Blemley with the vaguest reputation. Some one had said he was "clever," and he had got his invitation in the moderate expectation, on the part of his hostess, that some portion at least of his cleverness would be contributed to the general entertainment. Until tea-time that day she had been unable to discover in what direction, if any, his cleverness lay. He was neither a wit nor a croquet champion, a hypnotic force nor a begetter of amateur theatricals. Neither did his exterior suggest the sort of man in whom women are willing to pardon a generous measure of mental deficiency. He had subsided into mere Mr. Appin, and the Cornelius seemed a piece of transparent baptismal bluff. And now he was claiming to have launched on the world a discovery beside which the invention of gunpowder, of the printing-press, and of steam locomotion were inconsiderable trifles. Science had made bewildering strides in many directions during recent decades, but this thing seemed to belong to the domain of miracle rather than to scientific achievement.

"And do you really ask us to believe," Sir Wilfrid was saying, "that you have discovered a means for instructing animals in the art of human speech, and that dear old Tobermory has proved your first successful pupil?"

"It is a problem at which I have worked for the last seventeen years," said Mr. Appin, "but only during the last eight or nine months have I been rewarded with glimmerings of success. Of course I have experimented with thousands of animals, but latterly only with cats, those wonderful creatures which have assimilated themselves so marvellously with our civilization while retaining all their highly developed feral instincts.

Here and there among cats one comes across an outstanding superior intellect, just as one does among the ruck of human beings, and when I made the acquaintance of Tobermory a week ago I saw at once that I was in contact with a 'Beyond — cat' of extraordinary intelligence. I had gone far along the road to success in recent experiments; with Tobermory, as you call him, I have reached the goal."

Mr. Appin concluded his remarkable statement in a voice which he strove to divest of the triumphant inflection. No one said "Rats," though Clovis's lips moved in a monosyllabic contortion which probably invoked those rodents of disbelief.

"And do you mean to say," asked Miss Resker, after a slight pause, "that you have taught Tobermory to say and understand easy sentences of one syllable?"

"My dear Miss Resker," said the wonder-worker patiently, "one teaches little children and savages and backward adults in that piecemeal fashion; when one has once solved the problem of making a beginning with an animal of highly developed intelligence one has no need for those halting methods. Tobermory can speak our language with perfect correctness."

This time Clovis very distinctly said, "Beyond — rats!" Sir Wilfrid was more polite, but equally sceptical.

"Hadn't we better have the cat in and judge for ourselves?" suggested Lady Blemley.

Sir Wilfrid went in search of the animal, and the company settled themselves down to the languid expectation of witnessing some more or less adroit drawing-room ventriloquism.

In a minute Sir Wilfrid was back in the room, his face white beneath its tan and his eyes dilated with excitement.

"By Gad, it's true!"

His agitation was unmistakably genuine, and his hearers started forward in a thrill of awakened interest.

Collapsing into an armchair he continued breathlessly: "I found him dozing in the smoking — room, and called out to him to come for his tea. He blinked at me in his usual way, and I said, "Come on, Toby; don't keep us waiting'; and, by Gad! he drawled out in a most horribly natural voice that he'd come when he dashed well pleased! I nearly jumped out of my skin!"

Appin had preached to absolutely incredulous hearers; Sir Wilfrid's statement carried instant conviction. A Babel-like chorus of startled exclamation arose, amid which the scientist sat mutely enjoying the first fruit of his stupendous discovery.

In the midst of the clamour Tobermory entered the room and made his way with velvet tread and studied unconcern across to the group seated round the tea-table.

A sudden hush of awkwardness and constraint fell on the company. Somehow there seemed an element of embarrassment in addressing on equal terms a domestic cat of acknowledged dental ability.

"Will you have some milk, Tobermory?" asked Lady Blemley in a rather strained voice.

"I don't mind if I do," was the response, couched in a a tone of even indifference. A shiver of suppressed excitement went through the listeners, and Lady Blemley might be excused for pouring out the saucerful of milk rather unsteadily.

"I'm afraid I've spilt a good deal of it," she said apologetically.

"After all, it's not my Axminster," was Tobermory's rejoinder.

Another silence fell on the group, and then Miss Resker, in her best district-visitor manner, asked if the human language had been difficult to learn. Tobermory looked squarely at her for a moment and then fixed his gaze serenely on the middle distance. It was obvious that boring questions lay outside his scheme of life.

"What do you think of human intelligence?" asked Mavis Pellington lamely.

"Of whose intelligence in particular?" asked Tobermory coldly.

"Oh, well, mine for instance," said Mavis, with a feeble laugh.

"You put me in an embarrassing position," said Tobermory, whose tone and attitude certainly did not suggest a shred of embarrassment. "When your inclusion in this house-party was suggested Sir Wilfrid protested that you were the most brainless woman of his acquaintance, and that there was a wide distinction between hospitality and the care of the feeble-minded. Lady Blemley replied that your lack of brain-power was the precise quality which had earned you your invitation, as you were the only person she could think of who might be idiotic enough to buy their old car. You know, the one they call "The Envy of Sisyphus,' because it goes quite nicely up-hill if you push it."

Lady Blemley's protestations would have had greater effect if she had not casually suggested to Mavis only that morning that the car in question would be just the thing for her down at her Devonshire home.

Major Barfield plunged in heavily to effect a diversion.

"How about your carrings-on with the tortoise-shell puss up at the stables, eh?"

The moment he had said it every one realized the blunder.

"One does not usually discuss these matters in public," said Tobermory frigidly. "From a slight observation of your ways since you've been in this house I should imagine you'd find it inconvenient if I were to shift the conversation on to your own little affairs."

The panic which ensued was not confined to the Major.

"Would you like to go and see if cook has got your dinner ready?" suggested Lady Blemley hurriedly, affecting to ignore the fact that it wanted at least two hours to Tobermory's dinner-time.

"Thanks," said Tobermory, "not quite so soon after my tea. I don't want to die of indigestion."

"Cats have nine lives, you know," said Sir Wilfrid heartily.

"Possibly," answered Tobermory; "but only one liver."

"Adelaide!" said Mrs. Cornett, "do you mean to encourage that cat to go out and gossip about us in the servants' hall?"

The panic had indeed become general. A narrow ornamental balustrade ran in front of most of the bedroom windows at the Towers, and it was recalled with dismay that this had formed a favourite promenade for Tobermory at all hours, whence he could watch the pigeons — and heaven knew what else besides. If he intended to become reminiscent in his present outspoken strain the effect would be something more than disconcerting. Mrs. Cornett, who spent much time at her toilet table, and whose complexion was reputed to be of a nomadic though punctual disposition, looked as ill at ease as the Major. Miss Scrawen, who wrote fiercely sensuous poetry and led a blameless life, merely displayed irritation; if you are methodical and virtuous in private you don't necessarily want every one to know it. Bertie van Tahn, who was so depraved at seventeen that he had long ago given up trying to be any worse, turned a dull shade of gardenia white, but he did not commit the error of dashing out of the room like Odo Finsberry, a young gentleman who was understood to be reading for the Church and who was possibly disturbed at the thought of scandals he might hear concerning other people. Clovis had the presence of mind to maintain a composed exterior; privately he was calculating how long it would take to procure a box of fancy mice through the agency of the *Exchange and Mart* as a species of hush-money.

Even in the delicate situation like the present, Agnes Resker could not endure to remain too long in the background.

"Why did I ever come down here?" she asked dramatically.

Tobermory immediately accepted the opening.

"Judging by what you said to Mrs. Cornett on the croquet-lawn yesterday, you were out for food. You described the Blemleys as the dullest people to stay with that you knew, but said they were clever enough to employ a first-rate cook; otherwise they'd find it difficult to get any one to come down a second time."

"There's not a word of truth in it! I appeal to Mrs. Cornett —" exclaimed the discomfited Agnes.

"Mrs. Cornett repeated your remark afterwards to Bertie van Tahn," continued Tobermory, "and said, 'That woman is a regular Hunger Marcher; she'd go anywhere for four square meals a day,' and Bertie van Tahn said —"

At this point the chronicle mercifully ceased. Tobermory had caught a glimpse of the big yellow Tom from the Rectory working his way through the shrubbery towards the stable wing. In a flash he had vanished through the open French window.

With the disappearance of his too brilliant pupil Cornelius Appin found himself beset by a hurricane of bitter upbraiding, anxious inquiry, and frightened entreaty. The responsibility for the situation lay with him, and he must prevent matters from becoming worse. Could Tobermory impart his dangerous gift to other cats? was the first question he had to answer. It was possible, he replied, that he might have initiated his intimate friend the stable puss into his new accomplishment, but it was unlikely that his teaching could have taken a wider range as yet.

"Then," said Mrs. Cornett, "Tobermory may be a valuable cat and a great pet; but I'm sure you'll agree, Adelaide, that both he and the stable cat must be done away with without delay."

"You don't suppose I've enjoyed the last quarter of an hour, do you?" said Lady Blemley bitterly. "My husband and I are very fond of Tobermory — at least, we were before this horrible accomplishment was infused into him; but now, of course, the only thing is to have him destroyed as soon as possible."

"We can put some strychnine in the scraps he always gets at dinner-time," said Sir Wilfrid, "and I will go and drown the stable cat myself. The coachman will be very sore at losing his pet, but I'll say a very catching form of mange has broken out in both cats and we're afraid of it spreading to the kennels."

'But my great discovery!" expostulated Mr. Appin; 'after all my years of research and experiment —"

"You can go and experiment on the short-horns at the farm, who are under proper control," said Mrs. Cornett, "or the elephants at the Zoological Gardens. They're said to be highly intelligent, and they have this recommendation, that they don't come creeping about our bedrooms and under chairs, and so forth."

An archangel ecstatically proclaiming the Millennium, and then finding that it clashed unpardonably with Henley and would have to be indefinitely postponed, could hardly have felt more crestfallen than Cornelius Appin at the reception of his wonderful achievement. Public opinion, however, was against him — in fact, had the general voice been consulted on the subject it is probable that a strong minority vote would have been in favour of including him in the strychnine diet.

Defective train arrangements and a nervous desire to see matters brought to a finish prevented an immediate dispersal of the party, but dinner that evening was not a social success. Sir Wilfrid had had rather a trying time with the stable cat and subsequently with the coachmen. Agnes Resker ostentatiously limited her repast to a morsel of dry toast, which she bit as though it were a personal enemy; while Mavis Pellington maintained a vindictive silence throughout the meal. Lady Blemley kept up a flow of what she hoped was conversation, but her attention was fixed on the doorway. A plateful of carefully dosed fish scraps was in readiness on the sideboard, but sweets and savoury and dessert went their way, and no Tobermory appeared either in the dining-room or kitchen.

The sepulchral dinner was cheerful compared with the subsequent vigil in the smoking-room. Eating and drinking had at least supplied a distraction and cloak to the prevailing embarrassment. Bridge was out of the question in the general tension of nerves and tempers, and after Odo Finsberry had given a lugubrious rendering of "Mélisande in the Wood" to a frigid audience, music was tacitly avoided. At eleven the servants went to bed, announcing that the small window in the pantry had been left open as usual for Tobermory's private use. The guests read steadily through the current batch of magazines, and fell back gradually on the "Badminton Library" and bound volumes of *Punch*, Lady Blemley made periodic visits to the pantry, returning each time with an expression of listless depression which forestalled questioning.

At two o'clock Clovis broke the dominating silence.

"He won't turn up tonight. He's probably in the local newspaper office at the present moment, dictating the first instalment of his reminiscences.

Lady What's-her-name's book won't be in it. It will be the event of the day."

Having made this contribution to the general cheerfulness, Clovis went to bed. At long intervals the various members of the house-party followed his example.

The servants taking round the early tea made a uniform announcement in reply to a uniform question. Tobermory had not returned.

Breakfast was, if anything, a more unpleasant function than dinner had been, but before its conclusion the situation was relieved. Tobermory's corpse was brought in from the shrubbery, where a gardener had just discovered it. From the bites on his throat and the yellow fur which coated his claws it was evident that he had fallen in unequal combat with the big Tom from the Rectory.

By midday most of the guests had quitted the Towers, and after lunch Lady Blemley had sufficiently recovered her spirits to write an extremely nasty letter to the Rectory about the loss of her valuable pet.

Tobermory had been Appin's one successful pupil, and he was destined to have no successor. A few weeks later an elephant in the Dresden Zoological Garden, which had shown no previous signs of irritability, broke loose and killed an Englishman who had apparently been teasing it. The victim's name was variously reported in the papers as Oppin and Eppelin, but his front name was faithfully rendered Cornelius.

"If he was trying German irregular verbs on the poor beast," said Clovis, "he deserved all he got."

The Summer of the Beautiful White Horse

William Saroyan

One day back there in the good old days when I was nine and the world was full of every imaginable kind of magnificence, and life was still a delightful and mysterious dream, my cousin Mourad, who was considered crazy by everybody who knew him except me, came to my house at four in the morning and woke me up by tapping on the window of my room.

Aram, he said.

I jumped out of bed and looked out the window.

I couldn't believe what I saw.

It wasn't morning yet, but it was summer and with daybreak not many minutes around the corner of the world it was light enough for me to know I wasn't dreaming.

My cousin Mourad was sitting on a beautiful white horse.

I stuck my head out of the window and rubbed my eyes.

Yes, he said in Armenian. It's a horse. You're

not dreaming. Make it quick if you want to ride.

I knew my cousin Mourad enjoyed being alive more than anybody else who had ever fallen into the world by mistake, but this was more than even I could believe.

In the first place, my earliest memories had been memories of horses and my first longings had been longings to ride.

This was the wonderful part.

In the second place, we were poor.

This was the part that wouldn't permit me to believe what I saw.

We were poor. We had no money. Our whole tribe was poverty-stricken. Every branch of the Garoghlanian family was living in the most amazing and comical poverty in the world. Nobody could understand where we ever got money enough to keep us with food in our bellies, not even the old men of the family. Most important of all, though, we were famous for our honesty. We had been famous for our honesty for something like eleven centuries, even when we had been the wealthiest family in what we liked to think was the world. We were proud first, honest next, and after that we believed in right and wrong. None of us would take advantage of anybody in the world, let alone steal.

Consequently, even though I could *see* the horse, so magnificent; even though I could *smell* it, so lovely; even though I could *hear* it breathing, so exciting; I couldn't *believe* the horse had anything to do with my cousin Mourad or with me or with any of the other members of our family, asleep or awake, because I *knew* my cousin Mourad couldn't have bought the horse, and if he couldn't have bought it he must have *stolen* it, and I refused to believe he had stolen it.

No member of the Garoghlanian family could be a thief.

I stared first at my cousin and then at the horse. There was a pious stillness and humor in each of them which on the one hand delighted me and on the other frightened me.

Mourad, I said, where did you steal this horse?

Leap out of the window, he said, if you want to ride.

It was true, then. He *had* stolen the horse. There was no question about it. He had come to invite me to ride or not, as I chose.

Well, it seemed to me stealing a horse for a ride was not the same thing as stealing something else, such as money. For all I knew, maybe it wasn't stealing at all. If you were crazy about horses the way my cousin Mourad and I were, it wasn't stealing. It wouldn't become stealing until we offered to sell the horse, which of course I knew we would never do.

Let me put on some clothes, I said.

All right, he said, but hurry.

I leaped into my clothes.

I jumped down to the yard from the window and leaped up onto the horse behind my cousin Mourad.

That year we lived at the edge of town, on Walnut Avenue. Behind our house was the country: vineyards, orchards, irrigation ditches, and country roads. In less than three minutes we were on Olive Avenue, and then the horse began to trot. The air was new and lovely to breathe. The feel of the horse running was wonderful. My cousin Mourad, who was considered one of the craziest members of our family, began to sing. I mean, he began to roar.

Every family has a crazy streak in it somewhere, and my cousin Mourad was considered the natural descendant of the crazy streak in our tribe. Before him was our uncle Khosrove, an enormous man with a powerful head of black hair and the largest mustache in the San Joaquin Valley, a man so furious in temper, so irritable, so impatient, that he stopped anyone from talking by roaring, *It is no harm; pay no attention to it.*

That was all, no matter what anybody happened to be talking about. Once it was his own son Arak running eight blocks to the barber shop where his father was having his mustache trimmed to tell him their house was on fire. This man Khosrove sat up in the chair and roared, It is no harm; pay no attention to it. The barber said, But the boy says your house is on fire. So Khosrove roared, Enough, it is no harm, I say.

My cousin Mourad was considered the natural descendent of this man, although Mourad's father was Zorab, who was practical and nothing else. That's how it was in our tribe. A man could be the father of his son's flesh, but that did not mean that he was also the father of his spirit. The distribution of the various kinds of spirit of our tribe had been from the beginning capricious and vagrant.

We rode and my cousin Mourad sang. For all anybody knew we were still in the old country where, at least according to some of our neighbors, we belonged. We let the horse run as long as it felt like runnning.

Al last my cousin Mourad said, Get down, I want to ride alone.

Will you let me ride alone? I said.

That is up to the horse, my cousin said. Get down.

The *horse* will let me ride, I said.

We shall see, he said. Don't forget that I have a way with a horse.

Well, I said, any way you have with a horse, I have also.

For the sake of your safety, he said, let us hope so. Get down.

All right, I said, but remember you've got to let me try to ride alone.

I got down and my cousin Mourad kicked his heels into the horse and shouted, *Vazire*, run. The horse stood on its hind legs, snorted, and burst into a fury of speed that was the loveliest thing I had ever seen. My cousin Mourad raced the horse across a field of dry grass to an irrigation ditch, crossed the ditch on the horse, and five minutes later returned, dripping wet.

The sun was coming up.

Now it's my turn to ride, I said.

My cousin Mourad got off the horse.

Ride, he said.

I leaped to the back of the horse and for a moment knew the awfulest fear imaginable. The horse did not move.

Kick into his muscles, my cousin Mourad said. What are you waiting for? We've got to take him back before everybody in the world is up and about.

I kicked into the muscles of the horse. Once again it reared and snorted. Then it began to run. I didn't know what to do. Instead of running across the field to the irrigation ditch the horse ran down the road to the vineyard of Dikran Halabian where it began to leap over vines. The horse leaped over seven vines before I fell. Then it continued running.

My cousin Mourad came running down the road.

I'm not worried about you, he shouted. We've got to get that horse. You go this way and I'll go this way. If you come upon him be kindly, I'll be near.

I continued down the road and my cousin Mourad went across the field to the irrigation ditch.

It took him half an hour to find the horse and bring him back.

All right, he said, jump on. The whole world is awake now.

What will we do? I said.

Well, he said, we'll either take him back or hide him until tomorrow morning.

He didn't sound worried and I knew he'd hide him and not take him back. Not for a while, at any rate.

Where will we hide him? I said.

I know a place, he said.

How long ago did you steal this horse? I said.

It suddenly dawned on me that he had been taking these early morning rides for some time and had come for me this morning only because he knew how much I longed to ride.

Who said anything about stealing a horse? he said.

Anyhow, I said, how long ago did you begin riding every morning?

Not until this morning, he said.

Are you telling the truth? I said.

Of course not, he said, but if we are found out, that's what you're to say. I don't want both of us to be liars. All you know is that we started riding this morning.

All right, I said.

He walked the horse quietly to the barn of a deserted vineyard which at one time had been the pride of a farmer named Fetvajian. There were some oats and dry alfalfa in the barn.

We began walking home.

It wasn't easy, he said, to get the horse to behave so nicely. At first it wanted to run wild, but, as I've told you, I have a way with a horse.

I can get it to do anything *I* want it to do. Horses understand me.

How do you do it? I said.

I have an understanding with a horse, he said.

Yes, but what sort of an understanding? I said.

A simple and honest one, he said.

Well, I said, I wish I knew how to reach an understanding like that with a horse.

You're still a small boy, he said. When you get to be thirteen you'll know how to do it.

I went home and ate a hearty breakfast.

That afternoon my uncle Khosrove came to our house for coffee and cigarettes. He sat in the parlor, sipping and smoking and remembering the old country. Then another visitor arrived, a farmer named John Byro, an Assyrian who, out of loneliness, had learned to speak Armenian. My mother brought the lonely visitor coffee and tobacco, and he rolled a cigarette and sipped and smoked, and then at last, sighing sadly, he said, My white horse which was stolen last month is still gone. I cannot understand it.

My uncle Khosrove became very irritated and shouted, It's no harm. What is the loss of a horse? Haven't we all lost the homeland? What is this crying over a horse?

That may be all right for you, a city dweller to say, John Byro said, but what of my surrey? What good is a surrey without a horse?

Pay no attention to it, my uncle Khosrove roared.

I walked ten miles to get here, John Byro said.

You have legs, my uncle Khosrove roared.

My left leg pains me, the farmer said.

Pay no attention to it, my uncle shouted.

That horse cost me sixty dollars, the farmer said.

I spit on money, my uncle Khosrove said.

He got up and stalked out of the house, slamming the screen door.

My mother explained.

He has a gentle heart, she said. It is simply that he is homesick, and such a large man.

The farmer went away and I ran over to my cousin Mourad's house.

He was sitting under a peach tree, trying to repair the hurt wing of a young robin which could not fly. He was talking to the bird.

What is it? he said

The farmer, John Byro, I said. He visited our house. He wants his horse. You've had it a month. I want you to promise not to take it back until I learn to ride.

It will take a *year* to learn to ride, my cousin Mourad said.

We could keep the horse a year, I said.

My cousin Mourad leaped to his feet.

What? he roared. Are you inviting a member of the Garoghlanian family to steal? The horse must go back to its true owner.

When? I said.

In six months at the latest, he said.

He threw the bird into the air. The bird tried hard, almost fell twice, but at last flew away, high and straight.

Early every morning for two weeks my cousin Mourad and I took the horse out of the barn of the deserted vineyard where we were hiding it and rode it, and every morning the horse, when it was my turn to ride alone, leaped over grape vines and small trees and threw me and ran away. Nevertheless, I hoped in time to learn to ride the way my cousin Mourad rode.

One morning on the way to Fetvajian's deserted vineyard we ran into the farmer John Byro who was on his way to town.

Let me do the talking, my cousin Mourad said. I have a way with farmers.

Good morning, John Byro, my cousin Mourad said to the farmer.

The farmer studied the horse eagerly.

Good morning, sons of my friends, he said. What is the name of your horse?

My heart, my cousin Mourad said in Armenian.

A lovely name, John Byro said, for a lovely horse. I could swear it is the horse that was stolen from me many weeks ago. May I look into its mouth?

Of course, Mourad said.

The farmer looked into the mouth of the horse.

Tooth for tooth, he said, I would swear it *is* my horse if I didn't know your parents. The fame of your family for honesty is well known to me. Yet the horse is the twin of my horse. A suspicious man would believe his eyes instead of his heart. Good day, my young friends.

Good day, John Byro, my cousin Mourad said.

Early the following morning we took the horse to John Byro's vineyard and put it in the barn. The dogs followed us around without making a sound.

The dogs, I whispered to my cousin Mourad. I thought they would bark.

They would at somebody else, he said. I have a way with dogs.

My cousin Mourad put his arms around the horse, pressed his nose into the horse's nose, patted it, and we went away.

That afternoon John Byro came to our house in his surrey and showed my mother the horse that had been stolen and returned.

I do not know what to think, he said. The horse is stronger than ever. Better-tempered, too. I thank God.

My uncle Khosrove, who was in the parlor, became irritated and shouted, Quiet, man, quiet. Your horse has been returned. Pay no attention to it.

Coaly-Bay, the Outlaw Horse

Ernest Thompson Seton

The Wilful Beauty

ive years ago in the Bitterroot mountains of Idaho there was a beautiful little foal. His coat was bright bay; his legs, mane, and tail were glossy black — coal black and bright bay — so them called him Coaly-bay.

"Coaly-bay" sounds like "Kolibey," which is an Arab title of nobility, and those who saw the handsome colt, and did not know how he came by the name, thought he must be of Arab blood. No doubt he was, in a faraway sense; just as all our best horses have Arab blood, and once in a while it seems to come out strong and show in every part of the creature, in his frame, his power, and his wild, free roving spirit.

Coaly-bay loved to race like the wind, he gloried in his speed, his tireless legs, and when careering with the herd of colts they met a fence or ditch, it was as natural to Coaly-bay to overleap it, as it was for the others to sheer off.

So he grew up strong of limb, restless of spirit, and rebellious at any thought of restraint. Even the kindly curb of the hay-yard or the stable was unwelcome, and he soon showed that he would rather stand out all night in a driving storm than be locked in a comfortable stall where he had no vestige of the liberty he loved so well.

He became very clever at dodging the horse wrangler whose job it was to bring the horseherd to the corral. The very sight of that man set Coaly-bay agoing. He became what is known as a "Quit-the-bunch" — that is a horse of such independent mind that he will go his own way the moment he does not like the way of the herd.

So each month the colt became more set on living free, and more cunning in the means he took to win his way. Far down in his soul, too, there must have been a streak of cruelty, for he stuck at nothing and spared no one that seemed to stand between him and his one desire.

When he was three years of age, just in the perfection of his young strength and beauty, his real troubles began, for now his owner undertook to break him to ride. He was as tricky and vicious as he was handsome, and the first day's experience was a terrible battle between the horse-trainer and the beautiful colt.

But the man was skilful. He knew how to apply his power, and all the wild plunging, bucking, rearing, and rolling of the wild one had no desirable result. With all his strength the horse was hopelessly helpless in the hands of the skilful horseman, and Coaly-bay was so far mastered at length that a good rider could use him. But each time the saddle went on, he made a new fight. After a few months of this the colt seemed to realize that it was useless to resist, it simply won for him lashings and spurrings, so he pretended to reform. For a week he was ridden each day and not once did he buck, but on the last day he came home lame.

His owner turned him out to pasture. Three days later he seemed all right; he was caught and saddled. He did not buck, but within five minutes he went lame as before. Again he was turned out to pasture, and after a week, saddled, only to go lame again.

His owner did not know what to think, whether the horse really had a lame leg or was only shamming, but he took the first chance to get rid of him, and though Coaly-bay was easily worth fifty dollars, he sold him for twenty-five. The new owner felt he had a bargain, but after being ridden half a mile Coaly-bay went lame. The rider got off to examine the foot, whereupon Coaly-bay broke away and galloped back to his old pasture. Here he was caught, and the new owner, being neither gentle nor sweet, applied spur without mercy, so that the next twenty miles was covered in less than two hours and no sign of lameness appeared.

Now they were at the ranch of this new owner. Coaly-bay was led from the door of the house to the pasture, limping all the way, and then turned out. He limped over to the other horses. On one side of the pasture was the garden of a neighbor.

This man was very proud of his fine vegetables and had put a six-foot fence around the place. Yet the very night after Coaly-bay arrived, certain of the horses got into the garden somehow and did a great deal of damage. But they leaped out before daylight and no one saw them.

The gardener was furious, but the ranchman stoutly maintained that it must have been some other horses, since his were behind a six-foot fence.

Next night it happened again. The ranchman went out very early and saw all his horses in the pasture, with Coaly-bay behind them. His lameness seemed worse now instead of better. In a few days, however, the horse was seen walking all right, so the ranchman's son caught him and tried to ride him. But this seemed too good a chance to lose; all his old wickedness returned to the horse; the boy was bucked off at once and hurt. The ranchman himself now leaped into the saddle; Coaly-bay bucked for ten minutes, but finding he could not throw the man, he tried to crush his leg against a post, but the rider guarded himself well. Coaly-bay reared and threw himself backward; the rider slipped off, the horse fell, jarring heavily, and before he could rise the man was in the saddle again. The horse now ran away, plunging and bucking; he stopped short, but the rider did not go over his head, so Coaly-bay turned, seized the man's foot in his teeth, and but for heavy blows on the nose would have torn him dreadfully. It was quite clear now that Coaly-bay was an "outlaw" — that is an incurably vicious horse.

The saddle was jerked off, and he was driven, limping, into the pasture.

The raids on the garden continued, and the two men began to quarrel over it. But to prove that his horses were not guilty the ranchman asked the gardener to sit up with him and watch. That night as the moon was brightly shining they saw, not all the horses, but Coaly-bay, walk straight up to the garden fence — no sign of a limp now — easily leap over it, and proceed to gobble the finest things he could find. After they had made sure of his identity, the men ran forward. Coaly-bay cleared the fence like a Deer, lightly raced over the pasture to mix with the horseherd, and when the men came near him he had — oh, such an awful limp.

"That settles it," said the rancher. "He's a fraud, but he's a beauty, and good stuff, too."

"Yes, but it settles who took my garden truck," said the other.

"Wall, I suppose so," was the answer; "but luk a here, neighbor, you ain't lost more'n ten dollars in truck. That horse is easily worth — a hundred. Give me twenty-five dollars, take the horse, an' call it square."

"Not much I will," said the gardener. "I'm out twenty-five dollars' worth of truck; the horse ain't worth a cent more. I take him and call it even."

And so the thing was settled. The ranchman

said nothing about Coaly-bay being vicious as well as cunning, but the gardener found out, the very first time he tried to ride him, that the horse was as bad as he was beautiful.

Next day a sign appeared on the gardener's gate:

FOR SALE

First-class horse, sound and gentle. $10.00

THE BEAR BAIT

Now at this time a band of hunters came riding by. There were three mountaineers, two men from the city, and the writer of this story. The city men were going to hunt Bear. They had guns and everything needed for Bear-hunting, except bait. It is usual to buy some worthless horse or cow, drive it into the mountains where the Bears are, and kill it there. So seeing the sign up, the hunters called to the gardener: "Haven't you got a cheaper horse?"

The gardener replied: "Look at him there, ain't he a beauty? You won't find a cheaper horse if you travel a thousand miles."

"We are looking for an old Bear-bait, and five dollars is our limit," replied the hunter.

Horses were cheap and plentiful in that country; buyers were scarce. The gardener feared that Coaly-bay would escape. "Wall, if that's the best you can do, he's yourn."

The hunter handed him five dollars, then said: "Now, stranger, bargain's settled. Will you tell me why you sell this fine horse for five dollars?"

"Mighty simple. He can't be rode. He's dead lame when he's going your way and sound as a dollar going his own; no fence in the country can hold him; he's a dangerous outlaw. He's wickeder nor old Nick."

"Well, he's an almighty handsome Bear-bait," and the hunters rode on.

Coaly-bay was driven with the packhorses, and limped dreadfully on the trail. Once or twice he tried to go back, but he was easily turned by the men behind him. His limp grew worse, and toward night it was painful to see him.

The leading guide remarked: "That thar limp ain't no fake. He's got some deep-seated trouble"

Day after day the hunters rode farther into the mountains, driving the horses along and hobbling them at night. Coaly-bay went with the rest, limping along, tossing his head and his long splendid mane at every step. One of the hunters tried to ride him and nearly lost his life, for the horse seemed possessed of a demon as soon as the man was on his back.

The road grew harder as it rose. A very bad bog had to be crossed one day. Several horses were mired in it, and as the men rushed to the rescue, Coaly-bay saw his chance of escape. He wheeled in a moment and turned himself from a limping, low-headed, sorry, bad-eyed creature into a high-spirited horse. Head and tail aloft now, shaking their black streamers in the wind, he gave a joyous neigh, and, without a trace of lameness, dashed for his home one hundred miles away, threading each narrow trail with perfect certainty, though he had seen them but once before, and in a few minutes he had steamed away from their sight.

The men were furious, but one of them, saying not a word, leaped on his horse — to do what? Follow that free ranging racer? Sheer folly. Oh, no! — he knew a better plan. He knew the country. Two miles around by the trail, half a mile by the rough cut-off that he took, was Panther Gap. The runaway must pass through that, and Coaly-bay raced down the trail to find the guide below awaiting him. Tossing his head with anger, he wheeled on up the trail again, and within a few yards recovered his monotonous limp and his evil expression. He was drriven into camp, and there he vented his rage by kicking in the ribs of a harmless little packhorse.

HIS DESTINED END

This was Bear country, and the hunters resolved to end his dangerous pranks and make him useful for once. They dared not catch him, it was not really safe to go near him, but two of the guides drove him to a distant glade where Bears abounded. A thrill of pity came over me as I saw that beautiful untamable creature going away with his imitation limp.

"Ain't you coming along?" called the guide.

"No, I don't want to see him die," was the answer. Then as the tossing head was disappearing I called: "Say, fellows, I wish you would bring me that mane and tail when you come back!"

Fifteen minutes later a distant rifle crack was heard, and in my mind's eye I saw that proud head and those superb limbs, robbed of their sustaining indomitable spirit, falling flat and limp — to suffer the unsightly end of fleshly things. Poor Coaly-bay; he would not bear the yoke. Rebellious to the end, he had fought against the fate of all his kind. It seemed to me the spirit of an Eagle or a Wolf it was that dwelt behind those full bright eyes — that ordered all his wayward life.

I tried to put the tragic finish out of mind, and had not long to battle with the thought; not even one short hour, for the men came back.

Down the long trail to the west they had driven him; there was no chance for him to turn aside. He must go on, and the men behind felt safe in that.

Farther away from his old home on the Bitterroot River he had gone each time he journeyed. And now he had passed the high divide and was keeping the narrow trail that leads to the valley of Bears and on to Salmon River, and still away to the open wild Columbian Plains, limping sadly as though he knew. His glossy hide flashed back the golden sunlight, still richer than it fell, and the men behind followed like hangmen in the death train of a nobleman condemned — down the narrow trail till it opened into a little beaver meadow, with rank rich grass, a lovely mountain stream and winding Bear paths up and down the waterside.

"Guess this'll do," said the older man. "Well, here goes for a sure death or a clean miss," said the other confidently, and, waiting till the limper was out in the middle of the meadow, he gave a short, sharp whistle. Instantly Coaly-bay was alert. He swung and faced his tormentors, his noble head erect, his nostrils flaring; a picture of horse beauty — yes, of horse perfection.

The rifle was levelled, the very brain its mark, just on the cross line of the eyes and ears, that meant sure — sudden, painless death.

The rifle cracked. The great horse wheeled and dashed away. It was sudden death or miss — and the marksman *missed.*

Away went the wild horse at his famous best, nor for his eastern home, but down the unknown western trail, away and away; the pine woods hid him from the view, and left behind was the rifleman vainly trying to force the empty cartridge from his gun.

Down that trail with an inborn certainty he went, and on through the pines, then leaped a great bog, and splashed an hour later through the limpid Clearwater and on, responsive to some unknown guide that subtly called him from the farther west. And so he went till the dwindling pines gave place to scrubby cedars and these in turn were mixed with sage, and onward still, till the faraway flat plains of Salmon River were about him, and ever on, tireless as it seemed, he went, and crossed the canyon of the mighty Snake, and up again to the high wild plains where the wire fence still is not, and on, beyond the Buffalo Hump, till moving specks on the far horizon caught his eager eyes, and coming on and near, they moved and rushed aside to wheel and fact about. He lifted up his voice and called to them, the long shrill neigh of his kindred when they bugled to each other on the far Chaldean plain; and back their answer came. This way and that they wheeled and sped and caracoled, and Coaly-bay drew nearer, called and gave the countersigns his kindred know, till this they were assured — he was their kind, he was of the wild free blood that man had never tamed. And when the night came down on the purpling plain his place was in the herd as one who after many a long hard journey in the dark had found his home.

There you may see him yet, for still his strength endures, and his beauty is not less. The riders tell me they have seen him many times by Cedra. He is swift and strong among the swift ones, but it is that flowing mane and tail that mark him chiefly from afar.

There on the wild free plains of sage he lives: the stormwind smites his glossy coat at night and the winter snows are driven hard on him at times; the Wolves are there to harry all the weak ones of the herd, and in the spring the mighty Grizzly, too, may come to claim his toll. There are no luscious pastures made by man, no grain-foods; nothing but the wild hard hay, the wind and the open plains, but here at last he found the thing he craved — the one worth all the rest. Long may he roam — this is my wish, and this — that I may see him once again in all the glory of his speed with his black mane on the wind, the spur-galls gone from his flanks, and in his eye the blazing light that grew in his far-off forebears' eyes as they spurned Arabian plains to leave behind the racing wild beast and the fleet gazelle — yes, too, the driving sandstorm that over-whelmed the rest, but strove in vain on the dusty wake of the Desert's highest born.

The Slum Cat

Ernest Thompson Seton

Life I

"Meat! Meat!" came shrilling down Scrimper's Alley. Surely the Pied Piper of Hamelin was there, for it seemed that all the Cats in the neighborhood were running toward the sound, though the Dogs, it must be confessed, looked scornfully indifferent.

"Meat! Meat!" and louder; then the centre of attraction came in view — a rough, dirty little man with a push-cart; while straggling behind him were a score of Cats that joined in his cry with a sound nearly the same as his own. Every fifty yards, that is, as soon as a goodly throng of Cats was gathered, the push-cart stopped. The man with the magic voice took out of the box in his cart a skewer on which were pieces of strong-smelling boiled liver. With a long stick he pushed the pieces off. Each Cat seized on one, and wheeling, with a slight depression of the ears and a little tiger growl and glare, she rushed away with her prize to devour it in some safe retreat.

"Meat! Meat!" And still they came to get their

portions. All were well known to the meat-man. There was Castiglione's Tiger; this was Jones's Black; here was Pralitsky's "Torkershell," and this was Madame Danton's White; there sneaked Blenkinshoff's Maltee, and that climbing on the barrow was Sawyer's old Orange Billy, an impudent fraud that never had had any financial backing — all to be remembered and kept in account. This one's owner was sure pay, a dime a week; that one's doubtful. There was John Washee's Cat, that got only a small piece because John was in arrears. Then there was the saloon-keeper's collared and ribboned ratter, which got an extra lump because the "barkeep" was liberal; and the roundsman's Cat, that brought no cash, but got unusual consideration because the meat-man did. But there were others. A black Cat with a white nose came rushing confidently with the rest, only to be repulsed savagely. Alas! Pussy did not understand. She had been a pensioner of the barrow for months. Why this unkind change? It was beyond her comprehension. But the meat-man knew. Her mistress had stopped payment. The meat-man kept no books but his memory, and it never was at fault.

Outside this patrician "four hundred" about the barrow were other Cats, keeping away from the push-cart because they were not on the list, the Social Register as it were, yet fascinated by the heavenly smell and the faint possibility of accidental good luck. Among these hangers-on was a thin gray Slummer, a homeless Cat that lived by her wits — slab-sided and not over-clean. One could see at a glance that she was doing her duty by a family in some out-of-the-way corner. She kept one eye on the barrow circle and the other on the possible Dogs. She saw a score of happy Cats slink off with their delicious "daily" and their tiger-like air, but no opening for her, till a big Tom of her own class sprang on a little pensioner with intent to rob. The victim dropped the meat to defend herself against the enemy, and before the "all-powerful" could intervene, the gray Slummer saw her chance, seized the prize, and was gone.

She went through the hole in Menzie's side door and over the wall at the back, then sat down and devoured the lump of liver, licked her chops, felt absolutely happy, and set out by devious ways to the rubbish-yard, where, in the bottom of an old cracker-box, her family was awaiting her. A plaintive mewing reached her ears. She went at speed and reached the box to see a huge Black Tom-cat calmly destroying her brood. He was twice as big as she, but she went at him with all her strength, and he did as most animals will do when caught wrong-doing, he turned and ran away. Only one was left, a little thing like its mother, but of more pronounced color — gray with black spots, and a white touch on nose, ears, and tail-tip. There can be no question of the mother's grief for a few days; but that wore off, and all her care was for the survivor. That benevolence was as far as possible from the motives of the murderious old Tom there can be no doubt; but he proved a blessing in deep disguise, for both mother and Kit were visibly bettered in a short time. The daily quest for food continued. The meat-man rarely proved a success, but the ash-cans were there, and if they did not afford a meat-supply, at least they were sure to produce potato-skins that could be used to ally the gripe of hunger for another day.

One night the mother Cat smelt a wonderful smell that came from the East River at the end of the alley. A new smell always needs investigating, and when it is attractive as well as new, there is but one course open. It led Pussy to the docks a block away, and then out on a wharf, away from any cover but the night. A sudden noise, a growl and a rush, were the first notice she had that she was cut off by her old enemy, the Wharf Dog. There was only one escape. She leaped from the wharf to the vessel from which the smell came. The Dog could not follow, so when the fish-boat sailed in the morning Pussy unwilling went with her and was seen no more.

II

The Slum Kitten waited in vain for her mother. The morning came and went. She became very hungry. Toward evening a deep-laid instinct drove her forth to seek food. She slunk out of the old box, and feeling her way silently among the rubbish, she smelt everything that seemed eatable, but without finding food. At length she reached the wooden steps leading down into Jap Malee's bird-store underground. The door was open a little. She wandered into a world of rank and curious smells and a number of living things in cages all about her. A Negro was sitting idly on a box in a corner. He saw the little stranger enter and watched it curiously. It wandered past some rabbits. They paid no heed. It came to a wide-barred cage in which was a Fox. The gentleman with the bushy tail was in a far corner. He crouched low; his eyes glowed. The Kitten wandered, sniffing, up to the bars, put its head in, sniffed again, then made toward the feed-pan, to be seized in a flash by the crouching Fox. It gave a frightened "mew," but a single shake cut that short and would have ended Kitty's nine lives at once, had not the Negro come to the rescue. He had no weapon and could not get into the cage, but he spat with such copious vigor in the Fox's face that he dropped the Kitten and returned to the corner, there to sit blinking his eyes in sullen fear.

The Negro pulled Kitten out. The shake of the beast of prey seemed to have stunned the victim, really to have saved it much suffering. The Kitten seemed unharmed, but giddy. It tottered in a circle for a time, then slowly revived, and a few minutes later was purring in the Negro's lap, apparently none the worse, when Jap Malee, the bird-man, came home.

Jap was not an Oriental; he was a full-blooded

Cockney, but his eyes were such little accidental slits aslant in his round, flat face that his first name was forgotten in the highly descriptive title of "Jap." He was not especially unkind to the birds and beasts whose sales were supposed to furnish his living, but his eye was on the main chance; he knew what he wanted. He didn't want the Slum Kitten.

The Negro gave it all the food it could eat, then carried it to a distant block and dropped it in a neighboring iron-yard.

III

One full meal is as much any one needs in two or three days, and under the influence of this stored-up heat and power, Kitty was very lively. She walked around the piled-up rubbish, cast curious glances on far-away Canary-birds in cages that hung from high windows; she peeped over fences, discovered a large Dog, got quietly down again, and presently finding a sheltered place in full sunlight, she lay down and slept for an hour. A slight "sniff" awakened her, and before her stood a large Black Cat with glowing green eyes, and the thick neck and square jaws that distinguish the Tom; a scar marked his cheek, and his left ear was torn. His look was far from friendly; his ears moved backward a little, his tail twitched, and a faint, deep sound came from his throat. The Kitten innocently walked toward him. She did not remember him. He rubbed the sides of his jaws on a post, and quietly, slowly turned and disappeared. The last that she saw of him was the end of his tail-twitching from side to side; and the little Slummer had no idea that she had been as near death to-day as she had been when she ventured into the fox-cage.

As night came on the Kitten began to feel hungry. She examined carefully the long invisible colored stream that the wind is made of. She selected the most interesting of its strands, and, nose-led, followed. In the corner of the iron-yard was a box of garbage. Among this she found something that answered fairly well for food; a bucket of water under a faucet offered a chance to quench her thirst.

The night was spent chiefly in prowling about and learning the main lines of the iron-yard. The next day she passed as before, sleeping in the sun. Thus the time wore on. Sometimes she found a good meal at the garbage-box, sometimes there was nothing. Once she found the big Black Tom there, but discreetly withdrew before he saw her. The water-bucket was usually at its place, or, failing that, there were some muddy little pools on the stone below. But the garbage-box was very unreliable. Once it left her for three days without food. She searched along the high fence, and seeing a small hole, crawled through that and found herself in the open street. This was a new world, but before she had ventured far, there was a noisy, rumbling rush — a large Dog came bounding, and Kitty had barely time to run back into the hole in the fence. She was dreadfully hungry, and glad to find some potato-peelings, which gave a little respite from the hunger-pang. In the morning she did not sleep, but prowled for food. Some Sparrows chirruped in the yard. They were often there, but now they were viewed with new eyes. The steady pressure of hunger had roused the wild hunter in the Kitten; those Sparrows were game — were food. She crouched instinctively and stalked from cover to cover, but the chirpers were alert and flew in time. Not once, but many times, she tried without result except to confirm the Sparrows in the list of things to be eaten if obtainable.

On the fifth day of ill luck the Slum Kitty ventured forth into the street, desperately bent on finding food. When far from the haven hole some small boys opened fire at her with pieces of brick. She ran in fear. A Dog joined in the chase, and Kitty's position grew perilous; but an old-fashioned iron fence round a house-front was there, and she slipped in between the rails as the Dog overtook her. A woman in a window above shouted at the Dog. Then the boys dropped a piece of cat-meat down to the unfortunate; and Kitty had the most delicious meal of her life. The stoop afforded a refuge. Under this she sat patiently till nightfall came with quiet, then sneaked back like a shadow to her old iron-yard.

Thus the days went by for two months. She grew in size and strength and in an intimate knowledge of the immediate neighborhood. She made the acquaintance of Downey Street, where long rows of ash-cans were to be seen every morning. She formed her own ideas of their proprietors. The big house was to her, not a Roman Catholic mission, but a place whose garbage-tins abounded in choicest fish scrapings. She soon made the acquaintance of the meat-man, and joined in the shy fringe of Cats that formed the outer circle. She also met the Wharf Dog as well as two or three other horrors of the same class. She knew what to expect of them and how to avoid them; and she was happy in being the inventor of a new industry. Many thousand Cats have doubtless hung, in hope, about the tempting milk-cans that the early milk-man leaves on steps and window-ledges, and it was by the merest accident that Kitty found one with a broken lid and so was taught to raise it and have a satisfying drink. Bottles, of course, were beyond her, but many a can has a misfit lid, and Kitty was very painstaking in her efforts to discover the loose-jointed ones. Finally she extended her range by exploration till she achieved the heart of the next block, and farther, till once more among the barrels and boxes of the yard behind the bird-man's cellar.

The old iron-yard never had been home, she had always felt like a stranger there; but here she had a sense of ownership, and at once resented the presence of another small Cat. She approached this newcomer with threatening air. The two had got as far as snarling and spitting

when a bucket of water from an upper window
drenched them both and effectually cooled their
wrath. They fled, the newcomer over the wall,
slum Kitty under the very box where she had
been born. This whole back region appealed to
her strongly, and here again she took up her
abode. The yard had no more garbage food than
the other and no water at all, but it was
frequented by stray Rats and a few Mice of the
finest quality; these were occasionally secured,
and afforded not only a palatable meal, but were
the cause of her winning a friend.

IV

Kitty was now fully grown. She was a striking-
looking Cat of the tiger type. Her marks were
black on a very pale gray, and the four beauty-
spots of white on nose, ears, and tail-tip lent a
certain distinction. She was very expert at getting
a living, and yet she had some days of starvation
and failed in her ambition of catching a Sparrow.
She was quite alone, but a new force was coming
into her life.

She was lying in the sun one August day, when
a large Black Cat came walking along the top of
a wall in her direction. She recognized him at
once by his torn ear. She slunk into her box and
hid. He picked his way gingerly, bounded lightly
to a shed that was at the end of the yard, and
was crossing the roof when a Yellow Cat rose up.
The Black Tom glared and growled, so did the

Yellow Tom. Their tails lashed from side to side. Strong throats growled and yowled. They approached each other with ears laid back, with muscles a-tense.

"Yow — yow — ow!" said the Black One.

"Wow — w — w!" was the slightly deeper answer.

"Ya — wow — wow — wow!" said the Black One, edging up half an inch nearer.

"Yow — w — w!" was the Yellow answer, as the blond Cat rose to full height and stepped with vast dignity a whole inch forward. "Yow — w!" and he went another inch, while his tail went swish, thump, from one side to the other.

"Ya — wow — yow — w!" screamed the Black in a rising tone, and he backed the eighth of an inch, as he marked the broad, unshrinking breast before him.

Windows opened all around, human voices were heard, but the Cat scene went on.

"Yow — yow — ow!" rumbled the Yellow Peril, his voice deepening as the other's rose. "Yow!" and he advanced another step.

Now their noses were but three inches apart; they stood side-wise, both ready to clinch, but each waiting for the other. They glared for three minutes in silence and like statues, except that each tail-tip was twisting.

The Yellow began again. "Yow — ow — ow!" in deep tone.

"Ya — a — a — a — a!" screamed the Black, with intent to strike terror by his yell; but he retreated one sixteenth of an inch. The Yellow walked up a long half-inch; their whiskers were mixing now; another advance, and their noses almost touched.

"Yo — w — w!" said Yellow, like a deep moan.

"Ya — a — a — a — a — a — a!" screamed the Black, but he retreated a thirty-second of an inch, and the Yellow Warrior closed and clinched like a demon.

Oh, how they rolled and bit and tore, especially the Yellow One!

How they pitched and gripped and hugged, but especially the Yellow One!

Over and over, sometimes one on top, sometimes another, but mostly the Yellow One; and farther till they rolled off the roof, amid cheers from all the windows. They lost not a second in that fall to the junk-yard; they tore and clawed all the way down, but especially the Yellow One. And when they struck the ground, still fighting, the one on top was chiefly the Yellow One; and before they separated both had had as much as they wanted, especially the Black One! He scaled a wall and, bleeding and growling, disappeared, while the news was passed from window to window that Cayley's Nig had been licked at last by Orange Billy.

Either the Yellow Cat was a very clever seeker, or else Slum Kitty did not hide very hard; but he discovered her among the boxes, and she made no attempt to get away, probably because she had witnessed the fight. There is nothing like success in warfare to win the female heart, and thereafter the Yellow Tom and Kitty became very good friends, not sharing each other's lives or food — Cats do not do that way much — but recognizing each other as entitled to special friendly privileges.

V

September had gone. October's shortening days were on when an event took place in the old cracker-box. If Orange Billy had come he would have seen five little Kittens curled up in the embrace of their mother, the little Slum Cat. It was a wonderful thing for her. She felt all the elation an animal mother can feel, all the delight, and she loved them and licked them with a tenderness that must have been a surprise to herself, had she had the power to think of such things.

She had added a joy to her joyless life, but she had also added a care and a heavy weight to her heavy load. All her strength was taken now to find food. The burden increased as the offspring grew up big enough to scramble about the boxes, which they did daily during her absence after they were six weeks old. That troubles go in flocks and luck in streaks is well known in Slumland. Kitty had had three encounters with Dogs, and had been stoned by Malee's Negro during a two days' starve. Then the tide turned.

The very next morning she found a full milk-can without a lid, successfully robbed a barrow pensioner, and found a big fishhead, all within two hours. She had just returned with that perfect peace which comes only of a full stomach, when she saw a little brown creature in her junk-yard. Hunting memories came back in strength; she didn't know what it was, but she had killed and eaten several Mice, and this was evidently a big Mouse with bobtail and large ears. Kitty stalked it with elaborate but unnecessary caution; the little Rabbit simply sat up and looked faintly amused. He did not try to run, and Kitty sprang on him and bore him off. As she was not hungry, she carried him to the cracker-box and dropped him among the Kittens. He was not much hurt. He got over his fright, and since he could not get out of the box, he snuggled among the Kittens, and when they began to take their evening meal he very soon decided to join them. The old Cat was puzzled. The hunter instinct had been dominant, but absence of hunger had saved the Rabbit and given the maternal instinct a chance to appear. The result was that the Rabbit became a member of the family, and was thenceforth guarded and fed with the kittens.

Two weeks went by. The Kittens romped much among the boxes during their mother's absence. The Rabbit could not get out of the box. Jap Malee, seeing the Kittens about the back yard, told the Negro to shoot them. This he was doing one morning with a 22-calibre rifle.

He had shot one after another and seen them drop from sight into the crannies of the lumber-pile, when the old Cat came running along the wall from the dock, carrying a small Wharf Rat. He had been ready to shoot her, too, but the sight of that Rat changed his plans; a rat-catching Cat was worthy to live. It happened to be the very first one she had ever caught, but it saved her life. She threaded the lumber-maze to the cracker-box and was probably puzzled to find that there were no Kittens to come at her call, and the Rabbit would not partake of the Rat. Pussy curled up to nurse the Rabbit, but she called from time to time to summon the Kittens. Guided by that call, the Negro crawled quietly to the place, and peering down into the cracker-box, saw, to his intense surprise, that it contained the old Cat, a live Rabbit, and a dead Rat.

The mother Cat laid back her ears and snarled. The Negro withdrew, but a minute later a board was dropped on the opening of the cracker-box, and the den with its tenants, dead and alive, was lifted into the bird-cellar.

"Say, boss, look a-hyar — hyar's where de little Rabbit got to wot we lost. Yo' sho t'ought Ah stoled him for de 'tater-bake."

Kitty and Bunny were carefully put in a large wire cage and exhibited as a happy family till a few days later, when the Rabbit took sick and died.

Pussy had never been happy in the cage. She had enough to eat and drink, but she craved her freedom — would likely have gotten "death or liberty" now, but that during the four days' captivity she had so cleaned and slicked her fur that her unusual coloring was seen, and Jap decided to keep her.

Life II

VI

Jap Malee was as disreputable a little Cockney bantam as ever sold cheap Canary-birds in a cellar. He was extremely poor, and the Negro lived with him because the "Henglishman" was willing to share bed and board, and otherwise admit a perfect equality that few Americans conceded. Jap was perfectly honest according to his lights, but he hadn't any lights; and it was well known that his chief revenue was derived from storing and restoring stolen Dogs and Cats. The half-dozen Canaries were mere blinds. Yet Jap believed in himself. "Hi tell you, Sammy, me boy, you'll see me with 'orses of my own yet," he would say, when some trifling success inflated his dirty little chest. He was not without ambition, in a weak, flabby, once-in-a-while way, and he sometimes wished to be known as a fancier. Indeed, he had once gone the wild length of offering a Cat for exhibition at the Knicker-bocker High Society Cat and Pet Show, with three not over-clear objects: first, to gratify his ambition; second, to secure the exhibitors free pass; and, third, "well, you kneow, one 'as to kneow the valuable Cats, you kneow, when one goes a-catting." But this was a society show, the exhibitor had to be introduced, and his miserable alleged half-Persian was scornfully rejected. The "Lost and Found" columns of the papers were the only ones of interest to Jap, but he had noticed and saved a clipping about "breeding for fur." This was stuck on the wall of his den, and under its influence he set about what seemed a cruel experiment with the Slum Cat. First, he soaked her dirty fur with stuff to kill the two or three kinds of creepers she wore; and, when it had done its work, he washed her thoroughly in soap and warm water, in spite of her teeth, claws, and yowls. Kitty was savagely indignant, but a warm, and happy glow spread over her as she dried off in a cage near the stove, and her fur began to fluff out with wonderful softness and whiteness. Jap and his assistant were much pleased with the result, and Kitty ought to have been. But this was preparatory: now for the experiment. "Nothing is so good for growing fur as plenty of oily food and continued exposure to cold weather," said the clipping. Winter was at hand, and Jap Malee put Kitty's cage out in the yard, protected only from the rain and the direct wind, and fed her with all the oil-cake and fish-heads she could eat. In a week a change began to show. She was rapidly getting fat and sleek — she had nothing to do but get fat and dress her fur. Her cage was kept clean, and nature responded to the chill weather and the oily food by making Kitty's coat thicker and glossier every day, so that by midwinter she was an unusually beautiful Cat in the fullest and finest of fur, with markings that were at least a rarity. Jap was much pleased with the result of the experimient, and as a very little success had a wonderful effect on him, he began to dream of the paths of glory. Why not send the Slum Cat to the show now coming on? The failure of the year before made him more careful as to details. " 'T won't do, ye kneow, Sammy, to henter 'er as a tramp Cat, ye kneow," he observed to his help; "but it kin be arranged to suit the Knickerbockers. Nothink like a good noime, ye kneow. Ye see now it had orter be 'Royal' somethink or other — nothink goes with the Knickerbockers like 'Royal' any-think. Now 'Royal Dick,' or 'Royal Sam,' 'ow's that? But 'owld on; them's Tom names. Oi say, Sammy, wot's the noime of that island where ye wuz born?"

"Analostan Island, sah, was my native vicinity, sah."

"Oi say, now, that's good, ye kneow. 'Royal Analostan,' by Jove! The onliest pedigreed 'Royal Analostan' in the 'ole sheow, ye kneow. Ain't that foine?" and they mingled their cackles.

"But we'll 'ave to 'ave a pedigree, ye kneow." So a very long fake pedigree on the recognized lines was prepared. One dark afternoon Sam, in a borrowed silk hat, delivered the Cat and the pedigree at the show door. The darkey did the honors. He had been a Sixth Avenue barber, and he could put on more pomp and lofty hauteur in five minutes than Jap Malee could have displayed in a lifetime, and this, doubtless, was one reason for the respectful reception awarded the Royal Analostan at the Cat Show.

Jap was very proud to be an exhibitor; but he had all a Cockney's reverence for the upper class, and when on the opening day he went to the door, he was overpowered to see the array of carriages and silk hats. The gate-man looked at him sharply, but passed him on his ticket, doubtless taking him for stable-boy to some exhibitor. The hall had velvet carpets before the long rows of cages. Jap, in his small cunning, was sneaking down the side rows, glancing at the Cats of all kinds, noting the blue ribbons and the reds, peering about but not daring to ask for his own exhibit, only trembling to think what the gorgeous gathering of fashion would say if they discovered the trick he was playing on them. He had passed all around the outer aisles and seen many prize-winners, but no sign of Slum Kitty. The inner aisles were more crowded. He picked his way down them, but still no Kitty, and he decided that it was a mistake; the judges had rejected the Cat later. Never mind; he had his exhibitor's ticket, and now knew where several valuable Persians and Angoras were to be found.

In the middle of the centre aisle were the high-class Cats. A great throng was there. The passage was roped, and two policemen were in place to keep the crowd moving. Jap wriggled in among them; he was too short to see over, and though the richly gowned folks shrunk from his shabby old clothes, he could not get near; but he gathered from the remarks that the gem of the show was there.

"Oh, isn't she a beauty!" said one tall woman.

"What distinction!" was the reply.

"One cannot mistake the air that comes only from ages of the most refined surroundings."

"How I should like to own that superb creature!"

"Such dignity — such repose!"

"She has an authentic pedigree nearly back to the Pharaohs, I hear"; and poor, dirty little Jap marvelled at his own cheek in sending his Slum Cat into such company.

"Excuse me, madame." The director of the show now appeared, edging his way through the crowd. "The artist of the *Sporting Element* is here, under orders to sketch the 'pearl of the show' for immediate use. May I ask you to stand a little aside? That's it; thank you."

"Oh, Mr. Director, cannot you persuade him to sell that beautiful creature?"

"Hm, I don't know," was the reply. "I understand he is a man of ample means and not at all approachable; but I'll try, I'll try, madame. He was quite unwilling to exhibit his treasure at all, so I understand from his butler. Here, you, keep out of the way," growled the director, as the shabby little man eagerly pushed between the artist and the blue-blooded Cat. But the disreputable one wanted to know where valuable Cats were to be found. He came near enough to get a glimpse of the cage, and there read a placard which announced that "The blue ribbon and *gold medal* of the Knickerbocker High Society Cat and Pet Show" had been awarded to the "thoroughbred, pedigreed Royal Analostan, imported and exhibited by J. Malee, Esq., the well-known fancier. (Not for sale.)" Jap caught his breath and stared again. Yes, surely; there, high in a gilded cage, on velvet cushions, with four policemen for guards, her fur bright black and pale gray, her bluish eyes slightly closed, was his Slum Kitty, looking the picture of a Cat bored to death with a lot of fuss that she likes as little as she understands it.

VII

Jap Malee lingered around that cage, taking in the remarks, for hours — drinking a draught of glory such as he had never known in life before and rarely glimpsed in his dreams. But he saw that it would be wise for him to remain unknown; his "butler" must do all the business.

It was Slum Kitty who made that show a success. Each day her value went up in her owner's eyes. He did not know what prices had been given for Cats, and thought that he was touching a record pitch when his "butler" gave the director authority to sell the Analostan for

407

one hundred dollars.

This is how it came about that the Slum Cat found herself transferred from the show to a Fifth Avenue mansion. She evinced a most unaccountable wildness at first. Her objection to petting, however, was explained on the ground of her aristocratic dislike of familiarity. Her retreat from the Lap-dog onto the centre of the dinner-table was understood to express a deep-rooted though mistaken idea of avoiding a defiling touch. Her assaults on a pet Canary were condoned for the reason that in her native Orient she had been used to despotic example. The patrician way in which she would get the cover off a milk-can was especially applauded. Her dislike of her silk-lined basket, and her frequent dashes against the plate-glass windows, were easily understood: the basket was too plain, and plate-glass was not used in her royal home. Her spotting of the carpet evidenced her Eastern modes of thought. The failure of her several attempts to catch Sparrows in the high-walled back yard was new proof of the royal impotency of her bringing up; while her frequent wallowings in the garbage-can were understood to be the manifestation of a little pardonable high-born eccentricity. She was fed and pampered, shown and praised; but she was not happy. Kitty was homesick! She clawed at that blue ribbon round her neck till she got it off; she jumped against the plate-glass because that seeemd the road to outside; she avoided people and Dogs because they had always proved hostile and cruel; and she would sit and gaze on the roofs and back yards at the other side of the window, wishing she could be among them for a change.

But she was strictly watched, was never allowed outside — so that all the happy garbage-can moments occurred while these receptacles of joy were indoors. One night in March, however, as they were set out a-row for the early scavenger, the Royal Analostan saw her chance, slipped out of the door, and was lost to view.

Of course there was a grand stir; but Pussy neither knew nor cared anything about that — her one thought was to go home. It may have been chance that took her back in the direction of Gramercy Grange Hill, but she did arrive there after sundry small adventures. And now what? She was not at home, and she had cut off her living. She was beginning to be hungry, and yet she had a peculiar sense of happiness. She cowered in a front garden for some time. A raw east wind had been rising, and now it came to her with a particularly friendly message; man would have called it an unpleasant smell of the docks, but to Pussy it was welcome tidings from home. She trotted down the long street due east, threading the rails of front gardens, stopping like a statue for an instant, or crossing the street in search of the darkest side, and came at length to the docks and to the water. But the place was strange. She could go north or south. Something turned her southward; and, dodging among docks and Dogs, carts and Cats, crooked arms of the bay and straight board fences, she got, in an hour or two, among familiar scenes and smells; and, before the sun came up, she had crawled back weary and foot-sore through the same old hole in the same old fence and over a wall to her junk-yard back of the bird-cellar — yes, back into the very cracker-box where she was born.

Oh, if the Fifth Avenue family could only have seen her in her native Orient!

After a long rest she came quietly down from the cracker-box toward the steps leading to the cellar, engaged in her old-time pursuit of seeking for eatables. The door opened, and there stood the Negro. He shouted to the bird-man inside:

"Say, boss, come hyar. Ef dere ain't dat dar Royal Ankalostan am comed back!"

Jap came in time to see the Cat jumping the wall. They called loudly and in the most seductive, wheedling tones: "Pussy, Pussy, poor Pussy! Come, Pussy!" But Pussy was not prepossessed in their favor, and disappeared to forage in her old-time haunts.

The Royal Analostan had been a windfall for Jap — had been the means of adding many comforts to the cellar and several prisoners to the cages. It was now of the utmost importance to recapture her majesty. Stale meat-offal and other infallible lures were put out till Pussy, urged by the re-established hunger-pinch, crept up to a large fish-head in a box-trap; the Negro, in watching, pulled the string that dropped the lid, and, a minute later, the Analostan was once more among the prisoners in the cellar. Meanwhile Jap had been watching the "Lost and Found" column. There it was, "$25 reward," etc. That night Mr. Malee's butler called at the Fifth Avenue mansion with the missing cat. "Mr. Malee's compliments, sah. De Royal Analostan had recurred in her recent proprietor's vicinity and residence, sah. Mr. Malee had pleasure in recuperating the Royal Analostan, sah." Of course, Mr. Malee could not be rewarded, but the butler was open to any offer, and plainly showed that he expected the promised reward and something more.

Kitty was guarded very carefully after that; but so far from being disgusted with the old life of starving and glad of her ease, she became wilder and more dissatisfied.

VIII

The spring was doing its New York best. The dirty little English Sparrows were tumbling over each other in their gutter brawls, Cats yowled all night in the areas, and the Fifth Avenue family were thinking of their country residence. They packed up, closed house, and moved off to their summer home, some fifty miles away, and Pussy, in a basket, went with them.

"Just what she needed: a change of air and scene to wean her away from her former owners and make her happy."

The basket was lifted into a Rumble-shaker. New sounds and passing smells were entered and left. A turn in the course was made. Then a roaring of many feet, more swinging of the basket; a short pause, another change of direction, then some clicks, some bangs, a long shrill whistle, and door-bells of a very big front door; a rumbling, a whizzing, an unpleasant smell, a hideous smell, a growing horrible, hateful choking smell, a deadly, gripping, poisonous stench, with roaring that drowned poor Kitty's yowls, and just as it neared the point where endurance ceased, there was relief. She heard clicks and clacks. There was light; there was air. Then a man's voice called, "All out for 125th Street," though of course to Kitty it was a mere human bellow. The roaring almost ceased — did cease. Later the rackety-bang was renewed with plenty of sounds and shakes, though not the poisonous gas; a long, hollow, booming roar with a pleasant dock smell was quickly passed, and then there was a succession of jolts, roars, jars, stops, clicks, clacks, smells, jumps, shakes, more smells, more shakes — big shakes, little shakes — gases, smokes, screeches, door-bells, tremblings, roars, thunders, and some new smells, raps, taps, heavings, rumblings, and more smells, but all without any of the feel that the direction is changed. When at last it stopped, the sun came twinkling through the basket-lid. The Royal Cat was lifted into a Rumble-shaker of the old familiar style, and, swerving aside from their past course, very soon the noises of its wheels were grittings and rattlings; a new and horrible sound was added — the barking of Dogs, big and little and dreadfully close. The basket was lifted, and Slum Kitty had reached her country home.

Every one was officiously kind. They wanted to please the Royal Cat, but somehow none of them did, except, possibly, the big, fat cook that Kitty discovered on wandering into the kitchen. This unctuous person smelt more like a slum than anything she had met for months, and the Royal Analostan was proportionately attracted. The cook, when she learned that fears were entertained about the Cat staying, said: "Shure, she'd 'tind to thot; wanst a Cat licks her futs, shure she's at home." So she deftly caught the unapproachable royalty in her apron, and committed the horrible sacrilege of greasing the soles of her feet with pot-grease. Of course Kitty resented it — she resented everything in the place; but on being set down she began to dress her paws and found evident satisfaction in that grease. She licked all four feet for an hour, and the cook triumphantly announced that now "shure she'd be apt to shtay." And stay she did, but she showed a most surprising and disgusting preference for the kitchen, the cook, and the garbage-pail.

The family, though distressed by these distinguished peculiarities, were glad to see the Royal Analostan more contented and approachable. They gave her more liberty after a week or two.

413

They guarded her from every menace. The Dogs were taught to respect her. No man or boy about the place would have dreamed of throwing a stone at the famous pedigreed Cat. She had all the food she wanted, but still she was not happy. She was hankering for many things, she scarcely knew what. She had everthing — yes, but she wanted something else. Plenty to eat and drink — yes, but milk does not taste the same when you can go and drink all you want from a saucer; it has to be stolen out of a tin pail when you are belly-pinched with hunger and thirst, or it does not have the tang — it isn't milk.

Yes, there *was* a junk-yard back of the house and beside it and around it too, a big one, but it was everywhere poisoned and polluted with roses. The very Horses and Dogs had the wrong smells; the whole country round was a repellent desert of lifeless, disgusting gardens and hay-fields, without a single tenement or smoke-stack in sight. How she did hate it all! There was only one sweet-smelling shrub in the whole horrible place, and that was in a neglected corner. She did enjoy nipping that and rolling in the leaves; it was a bright spot in the grounds; but the only one, for she had not found a rotten fish-head nor seen a genuine garbage-can since she came, and altogether it was the most unlovely, unnattractive, unsmellable spot she had ever known. She would surely have gone that first night had she had the liberty. The liberty was weeks in coming, and, meanwhile, her affinity with the cook had developed as a bond to keep her; but one day after a summer of discontent a succession of things happened to stir anew the slum instinct of the royal prisoner.

A great bundle of stuff from the docks had reached the country mansion. What it contained was of little moment, but it was rich with a score of the most piquant and winsome of dock and slum smells. The chords of memory surely dwell in the nose, and Pussy's past was conjured up with dangerous force. Next day the cook "left" through some trouble over this very bundle. It was the cutting of cables, and that evening the youngest boy of the house, a horrid little American with no proper appreciation of royalty, was tying a tin to the blue-blooded one's tail, doubtless in furtherance of some altruistic project, when Pussy resented the liberty with a paw that wore five big fish-hooks for the occasion. The howl of downtrodden America roused America's mother. The deft and womanly blow that she aimed with her book was miraculously avoided, and Pussy took flight, up-stairs, of course. A hunted Rat runs down-stairs, a hunted Dog goes on the level, a hunted Cat runs up. She hid in the garret, baffled discovery, and waited till night came. Then, gliding down-stairs, she tried each screen-door in turn, till she found one unlatched, and escaped into the black August night. Pitch-black to man's eyes, it was simply gray to her, and she glided through the disgusting shrubbery and flower-beds, took a final nip at that one little bush that had been an attractive spot in the garden, and boldly took her back track of the spring.

How could she take a back track that she never saw? There is in all animals some sense of direction. It is very low in man and very high in Horses, but Cats have a large gift, and this mysterious guide took her westward, not clearly and definitely, but with a general impulse that was made definite simply because the road was easy to travel. In an hour she had covered two miles and reached the Hudson River. Her nose had told her many times that the course was true. Smell after smell came back, just as a man after walking a mile in a strange street may not recall a single feature, but will remember, on seeing it again, "Why, yes, I saw that before." So Kitty's main guide was the sense of direction, but it was her nose that kept reassuring her, "Yes, now you are right — we passed this place last spring."

At the river was the railroad. She could not go on the water; she must go north or south. This was a case where her sense of direction was clear; it said, "Go south," and Kitty trotted down the foot-path between the iron rails and the fence.

Life III

IX

Cats can go very fast up a tree or over a wall, but when it comes to the long steady trot that reels off mile after mile, hour after hour, it is not the cat-hop, but the dog-trot, that counts. Although the travelling was good and the path direct, an hour had gone before two miles were put between her and the Hades of roses. She was tired and a little foot-sore. She was thinking of rest when a Dog came running to the fence near by, and broke out into such a horrible barking close to her ear that Pussy leaped in terror. She ran as hard as she could down the path, at the same time watching to see if the Dog should succeed in passing the fence. No, not yet! but he ran close by it, growling horribly, while Pussy skipped along on the safe side. The barking of the Dog grew into a low rumble — a louder rumble and roaring — a terrifying thunder. A light shone. Kitty glanced back to see, not the Dog, but a huge Black Thing with a blazing red eye coming on, yowling and spitting like a yard full of Cats. She put forth all her powers to run, made such time as she had never made before, but dared not leap the fence. She was running like a Dog, was flying, but all in vain; the monstrous pursuer overtook her, but missed her in the darkness, and hurried past to be lost in the night, while Kitty crouched gasping for breath, half a mile nearer home since that Dog began to bark.

This was her first encounter with the strange monster, strange to her eyes only; her nose seemed to know him and told her this was another landmark on the home trail. But Pussy lost much of her fear of this kind. She learned that they were very stupid and could not find her if she slipped quietly under a fence and lay still. Before morning she had encountered several of them, but escaped unharmed from all.

About sunrise she reached a nice little slum on her home trail, and was lucky enough to find several unsterilized, eatables in an ash-heap. She spent the day around a stable where were two Dogs and a number of small boys, that between them came near ending her career. It was so very like home; but she had no idea of staying there. She was driven by the old craving, and next evening set out as before. She had seen the one-eyed Thunder-rollers all day going by, and was getting used to them, so travelled steadily all that night. The next day was spent in a barn where she caught a Mouse, and the next night was like the last, except that a Dog she encountered drove her backward on her trail for a long way. Several times she was misled by angling roads, and wandered far astray; but in time she wandered back again to her general southward course. The days were passed in skulking under barns and hiding from Dogs and small boys, and the nights in limping along the track, for she was getting foot-sore; but on she went, mile after mile, southward, ever southward — Dogs, boys, Roarers, hunger — Dogs, boys, Roarers, hunger — yet on and onward still she went, and her nose from time to time cheered her by confidently reporting. "There surely is a smell we passed last spring."

X

So, a week went by, and Pussy, dirty, ribbonless, foot-sore, and weary, arrived at the Harlem Bridge. Though it was enveloped in delicious smells, she did not like the look of that bridge. For half the night she wandered up and down the shore without discovering any other means of going south, excepting some other bridges, or anything of interest except that here the men were as dangerous as the boys. Somehow she had to come back to it; not only its smells were familiar, but from time to time, when a One-eye ran over it, there was that peculiar rumbling roar that was a sensation in the springtime trip. The calm of the late night was abroad when she leaped to the timber stringer and glided out over the water. She had got less than a third of the way across when a thundering One-eye came roaring at her from the opposite end. She was much frightened, but knowing their stupidity and blindness, she dropped to a low side beam and there crouched in hiding. Of course the stupid Monster missed her and passed on, and all would have been well, but it turned back, or another just like it came suddenly spitting behind her. Pussy leaped to the long track and made for the home shore. She might have got there had not a third of the Red-eyed Terrors come screeching at her from between two foes. There was nothing for it but a desperate leap from the timbers into — she didn't know what. Down, down, down — plop, splash, plunge into the deep water, not cold, for it was August, but oh, so horrible! She spluttered and coughed when she came to the top, glanced around to see if the Monsters were swimming after her, and struck out for shore. She had never learned to swim, and yet she swam, for the simple reason that a Cat's position and actions in swimming are the same as her position and actions in walking. She had fallen into a place she did not like; naturally she tried to *walk* out, and the result was that she swam ashore. Which shore? The homelove never fails: the south side was the only shore for her, the one nearest home. She scrambled out all dripping wet, up the muddy bank and through coal-piles and dust-heaps, looking as black, dirty and unroyal is it was possible for a Cat to look.

Once the shock was over, the Royal-pedigreed Slummer began to feel better for the plunge. A genial glow without from the bath, a genial sense of triumph within, for had she not outwitted three of the big Terrors?

Her nose, her memory, and her instinct of direction inclined her to get on the track again; but the place was infested with those Thunder-rollers, and prudence led her to turn aside and follow the river-bank with its musky home-reminders; and thus she was spared the unspeakable horrors of the tunnel.

She was over three days learning the manifold

dangers and complexities of the East river docks. Once she got by mistake on a ferry-boat and was carried over to Long Island; but she took an early boat back. At length on the third night she reached familiar ground, the place she had passed the night of her first escape. From that her course was sure and rapid. She knew just where she was going and how to get there. She knew even the more prominent features in the Dog-scape now. She went faster, felt happier. In a little while surely she would be curled up in her native Orient — the old junk-yard. Another turn, and the block was in sight.

But — what! It was gone! Kitty couldn't believe her eyes; but she must, for the sun was not yet up. There where once had stood or leaned or slouched or straggled the houses of the block, was a great broken wilderness of stone, lumber, and holes in the ground.

Kitty walked all around it. She knew by the bearings and by the local color of the pavement that she was in her home, that there had lived the bird-man, and there was the old junk-yard; but all were gone, completely gone, taking their familiar odors with them, and Pussy turned sick at heart in the utter hopelessness of the case. Her place-love was her master-mood. She had given up all to come to a home that no longer existed, and for once her sturdy little heart was cast down. She wandered over the silent heaps of rubbish and found neither consolation nor eatables. The ruin had taken in several of the blocks and reached back from the water. It was not a fire; Kitty had seen one of those things. This looked more like the work of a flock of the Red-eyed Monsters. Pussy knew nothing of the great bridge that was to rise from this very spot.

When the sun came up she sought for cover. An adjoining block still stood with little change, and the Royal Analostan retired to that. She knew some of its trails; but once there, was unpleasantly surprised to find the place swarming with Cats that, like herself, were driven from their old grounds, and when the garbage-cans came out there were several Slummers at each. It meant a famine in the land, and Pussy, after standing it a few days, was reduced to seeking her other home on Fifth Avenue. She got there to find it shut up and deserted. She waited about for a day; had an unpleasant experience with a big man in a blue coat, and next night returned to the crowded slum.

September and October wore away. Many of the Cats died of starvation or were too weak to escape their natural enemies. But Kitty, young and strong, still lived.

Great changes had come over the ruined blocks. Though silent on the night when she first saw them, they were crowded with noisy workmen all day. A tall buiilding, well advanced on her arrival, was completed at the end of October, and Slum Kitty, driven by hunger, went sneaking up to a pail that a Negro had set outside. The pail, unfortunately, was not for garbage; it was a

422

new thing in that region: a scrubbing pail. A sad disappointment, but it had a sense of comfort — there were traces of a familiar touch on the handle. While she was studying it, the Negro elevator-boy came out again. In spite of his blue clothes, his odorous person confirmed the good impression of the handle. Kitty had retreated across the street. He gazed at her.

"Sho ef dat don't look like de Royal Ankalostan! Hyar, Pussy, Pussy, Pu-s-s-s-s-y! Co-o-o-o-m-e, Pu-u-s-sym hyar! I 'spec's she's sho hungry."

Hungry! She hadn't had a real meal for months. The Negro went into the building and reappeared with a portion of his own lunch.

"Hyar, Pussy, Puss, Puss, Puss!" It seemed very good, but Pussy had her doubts of the man. At length he laid the meat on the pavement and went back to the door. Slum Kitty came forward very warily; sniffed at the meat, seized it, and fled like a little Tigress to eat her prize in peace.

Life IV

XI

This was the beginning of a new era. Pussy came to the door of the building now whenever pinched by hunger, and the good feeling for the Negro grew. She had never understood that man before. He had always seemed hostile. Now he was her friend, the only one she had.

One week she had a streak of luck. Seven good meals on seven successive days; and right on the top of the last meal she found a juicy dead Rat, the genuine thing, a perfect windfall. She had never killed a full-grown rat in all her lives, but seized the prize and ran off to hide it for future use. She was crossing the street in front of the new building when an old enemy appeared — the Wharf Dog — and Kitty retreated, naturally enough, to the door where she had a friend. Just as she neared it, he opened the door for a well-dressed man to come out, and both saw the Cat with her prize.

"Hello! Look at that for a Cat!"

"Yes, sah," answered the Negro. "Dat's ma Cat, sah; she's a terror on Rats, sah! hez 'em about cleaned up, sah; dat's why she's so thin."

"Well, don't let her starve," said the man with the air of the landlord. "Can't you feed her?"

"De liver meat-man comes reg'lar, sah; quatah dollar a week, sah," said the Negro, fully realizing that he was entitled to the extra fifteen cents for "the idea."

"That's all right. I'll stand it."

XII

"M-e-a-t! M-e-a-t!" is heard the magnetic, cat-conjuring cry of the old liver-man, as his barrow is pushed up the glorified Scrimper's Alley, and Cats come crowding, as of yore, to receive their due.

There are Cats black, white, yellow, and gray to be remembered, and, above all, there are

424

owners to be remembered. As the barrow rounds the corner near the new building it makes a newly scheduled stop.

"Hyar, you get out o' the road, you common trash," cries the liver-man, and he waves his wand to make way for the little gray Cat with blue eyes and white nose. She receives an unusually large portion, for Sam is wisely dividing the returns evenly; and Slum Kitty retreats with her "daily" into shelter of the great building, to which she is regularly attached. She has entered into her fourth life with prospects of happiness never before dreamed of. Everything was against her at first; now everything seems to be coming her way. It is very doubtful that her mind was broadened by travel, but she knew what she wanted and she got it. She has achieved her long-time great ambition by catching, not a Sparrow, but two of them, while they were clinched in mortal combat in the gutter.

There is no reason to suppose that she ever caught another Rat; but the Negro secures a dead one when he can, for purposes of exhibition, lest her pension be imperilled. The dead one is left in the hall till the proprietor comes: then it is apologetically swept away. "Well, drat dat Cat, sah; dat Royal Ankalostan blood, sah, is terrors on Rats."

She has had several broods since. The Negro thinks the Yellow Tom is the father of some of them, and no doubt the Negro is right.

He has sold her a number of times with a

perfectly clear conscience, knowing quite well that it is only a question of a few days before the Royal Analostan comes back again. Doubtless he is saving the money for some honorable ambition. She has learned to tolerate the elevator, and even to ride up and down on it. The Negro stoutly maintains that once, when she heard the meat-man, while she was on the top floor, she managed to press the button that called the elevator to take her down.

She is sleek and beautiful again. She is not only one of the four hundred that form the inner circle about the liver-barrow, but she is recognized as the star pensioner among them. The liver-man is positively respectful. Not even the cream-and-chicken fed Cat of the pawn-broker's wife has such a position as the Royal Analostan. But in spite of her prosperity, her social position, her royal name and fake pedigree, the greatest pleasure of her life is to slip out and go a-slumming in the gloaming, for now, as in her previous lives, she is at heart, and likely to be, nothing but a dirty little Slum Cat.

Brute Neighbors*

Henry David Thoreau

The mice which haunted my house were not the common ones,which are said to have been introduced into the country, but a wild native kind not found in the village. I sent one to a distinguished naturalist, and it interested him much. When I was building, one of these had its nest underneath the house, and before I had laid the second floor, and swept out the shavings, would come out regularly at lunch times and pick up the crums at my feet. It probably had never seen a man before; and it soon became quite familiar, and would run over my shoes and up my clothes. It could readily ascend the sides of the room by short impulses, like a squirrel, which it resembled in its motions. At length, as I leaned with my elbow on the bench one day, it ran up my clothes, and along my sleeve, and round and round the paper which held my dinner, while I kept the latter close, and dodged and played at bo-peep with it; and when

*This selection comes from *Walden*, Thoreau's master-piece about his experiment of living in nature, in a shack beside the New England pond.

427

at last I held still a piece of cheese between my thumb and finger, it came and nibbled it, sitting in my hand, and afterward cleaned its face and paws, like a fly, and walked away.

A phoebe soon built in my shed, and a robin for protection in a pine which grew against the house. In June the partridge, *(Tetrao unbellus,)* which is so shy a bird, led her brood past my windows, from the woods in the rear to the front of my house, clucking and calling to them like a hen, and in all her behavior proving herself the hen of the woods. The young suddenly disperse on your approach, at a signal from the mother, as if a whirlwind had swept them away, and they so exactly resemble the dried leaves and twigs that many a traveller has placed his foot in the midst of a brood, and heard the whir of the old bird as she flew off, and her anxious calls and mewing, or seen her trail her wings to attract his attention, without suspecting their neighborhood. The parent will sometimes roll and spin round before you in such dishabille, that you cannot, for a few moments, detect what kind of creature it is. The young squat still and flat, often running their heads under a leaf, and mind only their mother's directions given from a distance, nor will your approach make them run again and betray themselves. You may even tread on them, or have your eyes on them for a minute, without discovering them. I have held them in my open hand at such a time, and still their only care, obedient to their mother and their instinct, was to squat there without fear or trembling. So perfect is this instinct, that once, when I had laid them on the leaves again, and one accidentally fell on its side, it was found with the rest in exactly the same position ten minutes afterward. They are not callow like the young of most birds, but more perfectly developed and precocious even than chickens. The remarkably adult yet innocent expression of their open and serene eyes is very memorable. All intelligence seems reflected in them. They suggest not merely the purity of infancy, but a wisdom clarified by experience. Such an eye was not born when the bird was, but is coeval with the sky it reflects. The woods do not yield another such a gem. The traveller does not often look into such a limpid well. The ignorant or reckless sportsman often shoots the parent at such a time, and leaves these innocents to fall a prey to some prowling beast or bird, or gradually mingle with the decaying leaves which they so much resemble. It is said that when hatched by a hen they will direct disperse on some alarm, and so are lost, for they never hear the mother's call which gathers them again. These were my hens and chickens.

It is remarkable how many creatures live wild and free though secret in the woods, and still sustain themselves in the neighborhood of towns, suspected by hunters only. How retired the otter manages to live here! He grows to be four feet long, as big as a small boy, perhaps without any human being getting a glimpse of him. I formerly saw the raccoon in the woods behind where my house is built, and probably still heard their whinnering at night. Commonly I rested an hour or two in the shade at noon, after planting, and ate my lunch, and read a little by a spring which was the source of a swamp and of a brook, oozing from under Brister's Hill, half a mile from my field. The approach to this was through a succession of descending grassy hollows, full of young pitchpines, into a larger wood about the swamp. There, in a very secluded and shaded spot, under a spreading white-pine, there was yet a clean firm sward to sit on. I had dug out the spring and made a well of clear gray water, where I could dip up a pailful without roiling it, and thither I went for this purpose almost every day in midsummer, when the pond was warmest. Thither too the wood-cock led her brood, to probe the mud for worms, flying but a foot above them down the bank, while they ran in a troop beneath; but at last, spying me, she would leave her young and circle round and round me, nearer and nearer till within four or five feet, pretending broken wings and legs, to attract my attention, and get off her young, who would already have taken up their march, with faint wiry peep, single file through the swamp, as she directed. Or I heard the peep of the young when I could not see the parent bird. There too the turtledoves sat over the spring, or fluttered from bough to bough of the soft white-pines over my head; or the red squirrel, coursing down the nearest bough, was particularly familiar and inquisitive. You only need sit still long enough in some attractive spot in the woods that all its inhabitants may exhibit themselves to you by turns.

I was witness to events of a less peaceful character. One day when I went out to my wood-pile, or rather my pile of stumps, I observed two large ants, the one red, the other much larger, nearly half an inch long, and black, fiercely contending with one another. Having once got hold they never let go, but struggled and wrestled and rolled on the chips incessantly. Looking farther, I was surprised to find that the chips were covered with such combatants, that it was not a *duellum*, but a *bellum*, a war between two races of ants, the red always pitted against the black, and frequently two red ones to one black. The legions of these Myrmidons covered all the hills and vales in my woodyard, and the ground was already strewn with the dead and dying, both red and black. It was the only battle which I have ever witnessed, the only battle-field I ever trod while the battle was raging; internecine war; the red republicans on the one hand, and the black imperialists on the other. On every side they were engaged in deadly combat, yet without any noise that I could hear, and human soldiers never fought so resolutely. I watched a couple that were fast locked in each other's embraces, in a little sunny valley amid the chips, now at noon-day prepared to fight till the sun went down, or life went out. The smaller red champion

431

had fastened himself like a vice to his adversary's front, and through all the tumblings on that field for an instant ceased to gnaw at one of his feelers near the root, having already caused the other to go by the board; while the stronger black one dashed him from side to side, and, as I saw on looking nearer, had already divested him of several of his members. They fought with more pertinacity than bull-dogs. Neither manifested the least disposition to retreat. It was evident that their battlecry was Conquer or die. In the mean while there came along a single red ant on the hill-side of this valley, evidently full of excitement, who either had despatched his foe, or had not yet taken part in the battle; probably the latter, for he had lost none of his limbs; whose mother had charged him to return with his shield or upon it. Or perchance he was some Achilles, who had nourished his wrath apart, and had now come to avenge or rescue his Patroclus. He saw this unequal combat from afar, — for the blacks were nearly twice the size of the red, — he drew near with rapid pace till he stood on his guard within half an inch of the combatants; then, watching his opportunity, he sprang upon the black warrior, and commenced his operations near the root of his right fore-leg, leaving the foe to select among his own members; and so there were three united for life, as if a new kind of attraction had been invented which put all other locks and cements to shame. I should not have wondered by this time to find that they had their respective musical bands stationed on some eminent chip, and playing their national airs the while, to excite the slow and cheer the dying combatants. I was myself excited somewhat even as if they had been men. The more you think of it, the less the difference. And certainly there is not the fight recorded in Concord history, at least, if in the history of America, that will bear a moment's comparison with this, whether for the numbers engaged in it, or for the patriotism and heroism displayed. For numbers and for carnage it was an Austerlitz or Dresden. Concord Fight! Two killed on the patriots' side, and Luther Blanchard wounded! Why here every ant was a Buttrick, — "Fire! for God's sake fire!" — and thousands shared the fate of Davis and Hosmer. There was not one hireling there. I have no doubt that it was a principle they fought for, as much as our ancestors, and not to avoid a three-penny tax on their tea; and the results of this battle will be as important and memorable to those whom it concerns as those of the battle of Bunker Hill, at least.

I took up the chip on which the three I have particularly described were struggling, carried it into my house, and placed it under a tumbler on my window-sill, in order to see the issue. Holding a microscope to the first-mentioned red ant, I saw that, though he was assiduously gnawing at the near fore-leg of his enemy, having severed his remaining feeler, his own breast was all torn away, exposing what vitals he had there to the jaws of the black warrior, whose breastplate was apparently too thick for him to pierce; and the dark carbuncles of the sufferer's eyes shone with ferocity such as war only could excite. They struggled half an hour longer under the tumbler, and when I looked again the black soldier had severed the heads of his foes from their bodies, and the still living heads were hanging on either side of him like ghastly trophies at his saddle-bow, still apparently as firmly fastened as ever, and he was endeavoring with feeble struggles, being without feelers and with only the remnant of a leg, and I know not how many other wounds, to divest himself of them; which at length, after half an hour more, he accomplished. I raised the glass, and he went off over the window-sill in that crippled state. Whether he finally survived that combat, and spent the remainder of his days in some Hotel des Invalides, I do not know; but I thought that his industry would not be worth much thereafter. I never learned which party was victorious, nor the cause of the war; but I felt for the rest of that day as if I had had my feelings excited and harrowed by witnessing the struggle, the ferocity and carnage, of a human battle before my door.

Kirby and Spence tell us that the battles of ants have long been celebrated and the date of them recorded, though they say that Huber is the only modern author who appears to have witnessed them. "Æneas Sylvius," say they, "after giving a very circumstantial account of one contested with great obstinacy by a great and small species on the trunk of a pear tree," adds that " 'This action was fought in the pontificate of Eugenius the Fourth, in the presence of Nicholas Pistoriensis, an eminent lawyer, who related the whole history of the battle with the greatest fidelity.' A similar engagement between great and small ants is recorded by Olaus Magnus, in which the small ones, being victorious, are said to have buried the bodies of their own soldiers, but left those of their giant enemies a prey to the birds. This event happened previous to the expulsion of the tyrant Christiern the Second from Sweden." The battle which I witnessed took place in the Presidency of Polk, five years before the passage of Webster's Fugitive-Slave Bill.

Many a village Bose, fit only to course a mud-turtle in a victualling cellar, sported his heavy quarters in the woods, without the knowledge of his master, and ineffectually smelled at old fox burrows and woodchucks' holes; led perchance by some slight cur which nimbly threaded the wood, and might still inspire a natural terror in its denizens; — now far behind his guide, barking like a canine bull toward some small squirrel which had treed itself for scrutiny, then, cantering off, bending the bushes with his weight, imaging that he is on the track of some stray member of the jerbilla family. Once I was surprised to see a cat walking along the stony shore of the pond, for they rarely wander so far from home. The surprise was mutual. Nevertheless the most domestic cat, which has lain on a rug all her days, appears quite at home in the woods, and, by her sly and stealthy behavior, proves herself more native there than the regular inhabitants. Once, when berrying, I met with a cat with young kittens in the woods, quite wild, and they all, like their mother, had their backs up and were fiercely spitting at me. A few years before I lived in the woods there was what was called a "winged cat" in one of the farm-houses in Lincoln nearest the pond, Mr. Gillian Baker's. When I called to see her in June, 1842, she was gone a-hunting in the woods, as was her wont, (I am not sure whether it was a male or female, and so use the more common pronoun), but her mistress told me that she came into the neighborhood a little more than a year before, in April, and was finally taken into their house; that she was of a dark brownish-gray color, with a white spot on her throat, and white feet, and had a large bushy tail like a fox; that in the winter the fur grew thick and flatted out along her sides, forming strips ten or twelve inches long by two and a half wide, and under her chin like a muff, the upper side loose, the under matted like felt, and in the spring these appendages dropped off. They gave me a pair of her "wings," which I keep still. There is no appearance of a membrane about them. Some thought it was part flying-squirrel or some other wild animal, which is not impossible, for, according to naturalists, prolific hybrids

436

have been produced by the union of the marten and domestic cat. This would have been the right kind of cat for me to keep, if I had kept any; for why should not a poet's cat be winged as well as his horse?

In the fall the loon (*Colymbus glacialis*) came, as usual, to moult and bathe in the pond, making the woods ring with his wild laughter before I had risen. At rumor of his arrival all the Mill-dam sportsmen are on the alert, in gigs and on foot, two by two and three by three, with patent rifles and conical balls and spy-glasses. They come rustling through the woods like autumn leaves, at least ten men to one loon. Some station themselves on this side of the pond, some on that, for the poor bird cannot be omnipresent; if he dive here he must come up there. But now the kind October wind rises, rustling the leaves and rippling the surface of the water, so that no loon can be heard or seen, though his foes sweep the pond with spy-glasses, and make the woods resound with their discharges. The waves generously rise and dash angrily, taking sides with all waterfowl, and our sportsmen must beat a retreat to town and shop and unfinished jobs. But they were too often successful. When I went to get a pail of water early in the morning I frequently saw this stately bird sailing out of my cove within a few rods. If I endeavored to overtake him in a boat, in order to see how he could manœuvre, he would dive and be completely lost, so that I did not discover him again, sometimes, till the latter part of the day. But I was more than a match for him on the surface. He commonly went off in a rain.

As I was paddling along the north shore one very calm October afternoon, for such days especially they settle on to the lakes, like the milkweed down, having looked in vain over the pond for a loon, suddenly one, sailing out from the shore toward the middle a few rods in front of me, set up his wild laugh and betrayed himself. I pursued with a paddle and he dived, but when he came up I was nearer than before. He dived again, but I miscalculated the direction he would take, and we were fifty rods apart when he came to the surface this time, for I had helped to widen the interval; and again he laughed long and loud, and with more reason than before. He manœuvred so cunningly that I could not get within half a dozen rods of him. Each time, when he came to the surface, turning his head this way and that, he coolly surveyed the water and the land, and apparently chose his course so that he might come up where there was the widest expanse of water and at the greatest distance from the boat. It was surprising how quickly he made up his mind and put his resolve into execution. He led me at once to the widest part of the pond, and could not be driven from it. While he was thinking one thing in his brain, I was endeavoring to divine his thought in mine. It was a pretty game, played on the smooth surface of the pond, a man against a loon.

Suddenly your adversary's checker disappears beneath the board, and the problem is to place yours nearest to where his will appear again. Sometimes he would come up unexpectedly on the opposite side of me, having apparently passed directly under the boat. So long-winded was he and so unweariable, that when he had swum farthest he would immediately plunge again, nevertheless; and then no wit could divine where in the deep pond; beneath the smooth surface, he might be speeding his way like a fish, for he had time and ability to visit the bottom of the pond in its deepest part. It is said that loons have been caught in the New York lakes eighty feet beneath the surface, with hooks set for trout, — though Walden is deeper than that. How surprised must the fishes be to see this ungainly visitor from another sphere speeding his way amid their schools! Yet he appeared to know his course as surely under water as on the surface, and swam much faster there. Once or twice I saw a ripple where he approached the surface, just put his head out to reconnoitre, and instantly dived again. I found that it was as well for me to rest on my oars and wait his reappearing as to endeavor to calculate where he would rise; for again and again, when I was straining my eyes over the surface one way, I would suddenly be startled by his unearthly laugh behind me. But why, after displaying so much cunning, did he invariably betray himself the moment he came up by that loud laugh? Did not his white breast enough betray him? He was indeed a silly loon, I thought. I could commonly hear the plash of the water when he came up, and so also detected him. But after an hour he seemed as fresh as ever, dived as willingly and swam yet farther than at first. It was surprising to see how serenely he sailed off with unruffled breast when he came to the surface, doing all the work with his webbed feet beneath. His usual note was this demoniac laughter, yet somewhat like that of a water-fowl; but occasionally, when he had balked me most successfully and come up a long way off, he uttered a long-drawn unearthly howl, probably more like that of a wolf than any bird; as when a beast puts his muzzle to the ground and deliberately howls. This was his looning, — perhaps the wildest sound that is ever heard here, making the woods ring far and wide. I concluded that he laughed in derision of my efforts, confident of his own resources. Though the sky was by this time overcast, the pond was so smooth that I could see where he broke the surface when I did not hear him. His white breast, the stillness of the air, and the smoothness of the water were all against him. At length, having come up fifty rods off, he uttered one of those prolonged howls, as if calling on the god of loons to aid him, and immediately there came a wind from the east and rippled the surface, and filled the whole air with misty rain, and I was impressed as if it were the prayer of the loon answered, and his god was angry with me; and so I left him disappearing far away on the tumultuous surface.

For hours, in fall days, I watched the ducks cunningly tack and veer and hold the middle of the pond, far from the sportsman; tricks which they will have less need to practise in Louisiana bayous. When compelled to rise they would sometimes circle round and round and over the pond at a considerable height, from which they could easily see to other ponds and the river, like black motes in the sky; and, when I thought they had gone off thither long since, they would settle down by a slanting flight of a quarter of a mile on to a distant part which was left free; but what beside safety they got by sailing in the middle of Walden I do not know, unless they love its water for the same reason that I do.

Snapshot of a Dog

James Thurber

I ran across a dim photograph of him the other day, going through some old things. He's been dead twenty-five years. His name was Rex (my two brothers and I named him when we were in our early teens) and he was a bull terrier. "An American bull terrier," we used to say proudly; none of your English bulls. He had one brindle eye that sometimes made him look like a clown and sometimes reminded you of a politician with derby hat and cigar. The rest of him was white except for a brindle saddle that always seemed to be slipping off and a brindle stocking on a hind leg. Nevertheless, there was a nobility about him. He was big and muscular and beautifully made. He never lost his dignity even when trying to accomplish the extravagant tasks my brothers and myself used to set for him. One of these was the bringing of a ten-foot wooden rail into the yard through the back gate. We would throw it out into the alley and tell him to go get it. Rex was as powerful as a wrestler, and there were not many things that he couldn't manage somehow to get hold of with his great jaws and lift or drag to wherever he wanted to put them, or wherever we wanted them put. He could catch the rail at the balance and lift it clear of the ground and trot with great confidence towards the gate. Of course, since the gate was only four feet wide or so, he couldn't bring the rail in broadside. He found that out when he got a few terrific jolts, but he wouldn't give up. He finally figured out how to do it, by dragging the rail, holding on to one end, growling. He got a great, wagging satisfaction out of his work. We used to bet kids who had never seen Rex in action that he could catch a baseball thrown as high as they could throw it. He almost never let us down. Rex could hold a baseball with ease in his mouth, in one cheek, as if it were a chew of tobacco.

He was a tremendous fighter, but he never started fights. I don't believe he liked to get into them, despite the fact that he came from a line of fighters. He never went for another dog's throat, but for one of its ears (that teaches a dog a lesson), and he would get his grip, close his eyes, and hold on. He could hold on for hours. His longest fight lasted from dusk until almost pitch-dark, one Sunday. It was fought in East Main Street in Columbus with a large, snarly nondescript that belonged to a big colored man. When Rex finally got his ear grip the brief whirlwind of snarling turned to screeching. It was frightening to listen to and to watch. The Negro boldly picked the dogs up somehow and began swinging them round his head, and finally let them fly like a hammer throw, but although they landed ten feet away with a great plump, Rex still held on.

The two dogs eventually worked their way to the middle of the car tracks, and after a while two or three streetcars were held up by the fight. A motorman tried to pry Rex's jaws open with a switch rod; somebody lighted a fire and made a torch of a stick and held that to Rex's tail, but he paid no attention. In the end, all the residents and storekeepers in the neighbourhood were on hand, shouting this, suggesting that. Rex's joy of battle, when battle was joined, was almost tranquil. He had a kind of pleasant expression during fights, not a vicious one, his eyes closed in what would have seemed to be sleep had it not been for the turmoil of the struggle. The Oak Street Fire Department finally had to be sent for — I don't know why nobody thought of it sooner. Five or six pieces of apparatus arrived, followed by a battalion chief. A hose was attached and a powerful stream of water was turned on the dogs. Rex held on for several moments more while the torrent buffeted him about like a log in a freshet. He was a hundred yards away from where the fight started when he finally let go.

The story of that Homeric fight got all around town, and some of our relatives looked upon the incident as a blot on the family name. They insisted that we get rid of Rex, but we were very happy with him, and nobody could have made us give him up. We would have left town with him first, along any road there was to go. It would have been different, perhaps, if he'd ever started fights, or looked for trouble. But he had a gentle disposition. He never bit a person in the ten strenuous years that he lived, not even growled at anyone except prowlers. He killed cats, that is true, but quickly and neatly and without especial malice, the way men kill certain animals. It was the only thing he did that we could never cure him of doing. He never killed, or even chased, a squirrel. I don't know why. He had his own philosophy about such things. He never ran barking after wagons or automobiles. He didn't seem to see the idea in pursuing something you couldn't catch, or something you couldn't do anything with, even if you did catch it. A wagon was one of the things he couldn't tug along with his mighty jaws, and he knew it. Wagons, therefore, were not a part of his world.

Swimming was his favorite recreation. The first time he ever saw a body of water (Alum Creek), he trotted nervously along the steep bank for a while, fell to barking wildly, and finally plunged in from a height of eight feet or more. I shall always remember that shining, virgin dive. Then he swam upstream and back just for the pleasure of it, like a man. It was fun to see him battle upstream against a stiff current, struggling and growling every foot of the way. He had as much fun in the water as any person I have known. You didn't have to throw a stick in the water to get him to go in. Of course, he would bring back a stick to you if you did throw one in. He would even have brought back a piano if you had thrown one in.

That reminds me of the night, way after midnight, when he went a-roving in the light of the moon and brought back a small chest of drawers that he found somewhere — how far from the house nobody ever knew; since it was Rex, it could easily have been half a mile. There were no drawers in the chest when he got it home, and it wasn't a good one — he hadn't taken it out of anybody's house; it was just an old cheap piece that somebody had abandoned on a trash heap. Still, it was something he wanted, probably because it presented a nice problem in transportation. It tested his mettle. We first knew about his achievement when, deep in the night, we heard him trying to get the chest up on to the porch. It sounded as if two or three people were trying to tear the house down. We came downstairs and turned on the porch light. Rex was on the top step trying to pull the thing up, but it had caught somehow and he was just holding his own till dawn if we hadn't helped him. The next day we carted the chest miles away and threw it out. If we had thrown it out in a nearby alley he would have brought it home again, as a small token of his integrity in such matters. After all, he had been taught to carry heavy wooden objects about, and he was proud of his prowess.

I am glad Rex never saw a trained police dog

jump. He was just an amateur jumper himself, but the most daring and tenacious I have ever seen. He would take on any fence we pointed out to him. Six feet was easy for him, and he could do eight by making a tremendous leap and hauling himself over finally by his paws, grunting and straining; but he lived and died without knowing that twelve- and sixteen-foot walls were too much for him. Frequently, after letting him try to go over one for a while, we would have to carry him home. He would never have given up trying.

There was in his world no such thing as the impossible. Even death couldn't beat him down. He died, it is true, but only, as one of his admirers said, after "straight-arming the death angel" for more than an hour. Late one afternoon he wandered home, too slowly and too uncertainly to be the Rex that had trotted briskly, homeward up our avenue for ten years. I think we all knew when he came through the gate that he was dying. He had apparently taken a terrible beating, probably from the owner of some dog that he had got into a fight with. His head and body were scarred. His heavy collar with the teeth marks of many a battle on it was awry; some of the big brass studs in it were sprung loose from the leather. He licked at our hands and, staggering, fell, but got up again. We could see that he was looking for someone. One of his three masters was not home. He did not get home for an hour. During that hour the bull terrier fought against death as he had fought against the cold strong current of Alum Creek, as he had fought to climb twelve-foot walls. When the person he was waiting for did come through the gate, whistling, ceasing to whistle, Rex walked a few wobbly paces towards him, touched his hand with his muzzle, and fell down again. This time he didn't get up.

The Celebrated Jumping Frog of Calaveras County

Mark Twain

In compliance with the request of a friend of mine, who wrote me from the East, I called on good-natured, garrulous old Simon Wheeler, and inquired after my friend's friend, Leonidas W. Smiley, as requested to do, and I hereunto append the result. I have a lurking suspicion that *Leonidas W.* Smiley is a myth; that my friend never knew such a personage; and that he only conjectured that if I asked old Wheeler about him, it would remind him of his infamous *Jim* Smiley, and he would go to work and bore me to death with some exasperating reminiscence of him as long and as tedious as it should be useless to me. If that was the design, it succeeded.

I found Simon Wheeler dozing comfortably by the barroom stove of the dilapidated tavern in the decayed mining camp of Angel's, and I noticed that he was fat and bald-headed, and had an expression of winning gentleness and simplicity upon his tranquil countenance. He roused up, and gave me good-day. I told him a friend of mine had commissioned me to make some inquiries about a cherished companion of his boyhood named *Leonidas W. Smiley* — *Rev. Leonidas W.* Smiley, a young minister of the Gospel, who he had heard was at one time a resident of Angel's Camp. I added that if Mr. Wheeler could tell me anything about this Rev. Leonidas W. Smiley, I would feel under many obligations to him.

Simon Wheeler backed me into a corner and blockaded me there with his chair, and then sat down and reeled off the monotonous narrative which follows this paragraph. He never smiled, he never frowned, he never changed his voice from the gentle-flowing key to which he turned his initial sentence, he never betrayed the slightest suspicion of enthusiasm; but all through the interminable narrative there ran a vein of impressive earnestness and sincerity, which showed me plainly that, so far from his imagining that there was anything ridiculous or funny about his story, he regarded it as a really important matter, and admired its two heroes as men of transcendent genius in *finesse*. I let him go on in his own way, and never interrupted him once.

"Rev. Leonidas W. H'm, Reverend Le — well, there was a feller here once by the name of *Jim* Smiley, in the winter of '49 — or may be it was the spring of '50 — I don't recollect exactly, somehow, though what makes me think it was one or the other is because I remember the big flume warn't finished when he first come to the camp; but any way, he was the curiosest man about always betting on anything that turned up you ever see, if he could get anybody to bet on the other side; and if he couldn't he'd change sides. Any way that suited the other man would suit *him* — any way just so's he got a bet, *he* was satisfied. But still he was lucky, uncommon lucky; he most always come out winner. He was always ready and laying for a chance; there couldn't be no solit'ry thing mentioned but that feller'd offer to bet on it, and take any side you please, as I was just telling you. If there was a horse-race, you'd find him flush or you'd find him busted at the end of it; if there was a dog-fight, he'd bet on it; if there was a cat-fight, he'd bet on it; if there was a chicken-fight, he'd bet on it; why, if there was two birds setting on a fence, he would bet you which one would fly first; or if there was a camp-meeting, he would be there reg'lar to bet on Parson Walker, which he judged to be the best exhorter about here, and so he was too, and a good man. If he even see a straddle-bug start to go anywheres, he would bet you how long it would take him to get to — to wherever he was going to, and if you took him up, he would foller that straddle-bug to Mexico but what he would find out where he was bound for and how long he was on the road. Lots of the boys here has seen that Smiley, and can tell you about him. Why, it never made no difference to *him* — he'd bet on *any* thing — the dangdest feller. Parson Walker's wife laid very sick once, for a good while, and it seemed as if they warn't going to save her; but one morning he come in, and Smiley up and asked him how she was, and he said she was considable better — thank the Lord for his inf'nite mercy — and coming on so smart that with the blessing of Prov'dence she'd get well yet; and Smiley, before he thought, says, "Well, I'll resk two-and-a-half she don't anyway."

Thish-yer Smiley had a mare — the boys called her the fifteen-minute nag, but that was only in fun, you know, because of course she was faster than that — and he used to win money on that horse, for all she was so slow and always had the asthma, or the distemper, or the consumption, or something of that kind. They used to give her two or three hundred yards start, and then pass her under way; but always at the fag end of the race she'd get excited and desperate like, and come cavorting and straddling up, and scattering her legs around limber, sometimes in the air, and sometimes out to one side among the fences, and kicking up m-o-r-e dust and raising m-o-r-e racket with her coughing and sneezing and blowing her nose — and *always* fetch up at the stand just about a neck ahead, as near as you could cipher it down.

And he had a little small bull-pup, that to look at him you'd think he warn't worth a cent but to set around and look ornery and lay for a chance to steal something. But as soon as money was up on him he was a different dog; his under-jaw'd begin to stick out like the fo'castle of a steamboat, and his teeth would uncover and shine like the furnaces. And a dog might tackle him and bully-rag him, and bite him, and throw him over his shoulder two or three times, and Andrew Jackson — which was the name of the pup — Andrew Jackson would never let on but what *he* was satisfied, and hadn't expected nothing else — and the bets being doubled and doubled on the other side all the time, till the money was all up; and then all of a sudden he would grab that other dog jest by the j'int of his hind leg and freeze to it — not chaw, you understand, but only just grip and hang on till they throwed up the sponge, if it was a year. Smiley always come out winner on that pup, till he harnessed a dog once that didn't have no hind legs, because they'd been sawed off in a circular saw, and when the thing had gone along far enough, and the money was all up, and he come to make a snatch for his pet holt, he see in a minute how he'd been imposed on, and how the other dog had him in the door, so to speak, and he 'peared surprised, and then he looked sorter discouraged-like, and didn't try no more to win the fight, and so he got shucked out bad. He give Smiley a look, as much as to say his heart was broke, and it was *his* fault, for putting up a dog that hadn't no hind legs for him to take holt of, which was his main dependence in a fight, and then he limped off a piece and laid down and died. It was a good pup, was that Andrew Jackson, and would have made a name for hisself if he'd lived, for the stuff was in him and he had genius — I know it, because he hadn't no opportunities to speak of, and it don't stand to reason that a dog could make such a fight as he could under them circumstances if he hadn't no talent. It always makes me feel sorry when I think of that last fight of his'n, and the way it turned out.

Well, thish-yer Smiley had rat-tarriers, and chicken cocks, and tomcats and all them kind of things, till you couldn't rest, and you couldn't fetch nothing for him to bet on but he'd match you. He ketched a frog one day, and took him home, and said he cal'lated to educate him; and so he never done nothing for three months but set in his back yard and learn that frog to jump. And you bet you he *did* learn him, too. He'd give him a little punch behind and the next minute you'd see that frog to jump. And you bet you he *did* learn him, too. He'd give him a little punch behind, and the next minute you'd see that frog whirling in the air like a doughnut — see him turn one summerset, or may be a couple, if he got a good start, and come down flat-footed and all right, like a cat. He got him up so in the matter of ketching flies, and kep' him in practice so constant, that he'd nail a fly every time as fur as he could see him. Smiley said all a frog wanted was education, and he could do 'most anything — and I believe him. Why, I've seen him set Dan'l Webster down here on this floor — Dan'l, Webster was the name of the frog — and sing out, "Flies, Dan'l, flies!" and quicker'n you could wink he'd spring straight up and snake a fly off'n the counter there, and flop down on the floor ag'in as solid as a gob of mud, and fall to scratching the side of his head with his hind foot as indifferent as if he hadn't no idea he'd been doin' any more'n any frog might do. You never see a frog so modest and straightfor'ard as he was, for all he was so gifted. And when it come to fair and square jumping on a dead level, he could get over more ground at one straddle than any animal of his breed you ever see. Jumping on a dead level was his strong suit, you understand; and when it come to that, Smiley would ante up money on him as long as he had a red. Smiley was monstrous proud of his frog, and well he might be, for fellers that had traveled and been everywheres all said he laid over any frog that ever *they* see.

Well, Smiley kep' the beast in a little lattice box, and he used to fetch him down town sometimes and lay for a bet. One day a feller — a stranger in the camp, he was — come acrost him with his box, and says:

"What might it be that you've got in the box?"

And Smiley says, sorter indifferent-like, "It might be a parrot, or it might be a canary, maybe, but it ain't — it's only just a frog."

And the feller took it, and looked at it careful, and turned it round this way and that, and says, "H'm — so 'tis. Well, what's *he* good for?"

"Well," Smiley says, easy and careless, "he's good enough for *one* thing — he can outjump any frog in Calaveras county."

The feller took the box again, and took another long, particular look, and give it back to Smiley, and says, very deliberate, "Well," he says, "I don't see no p'ints about that frog that's any better'n any other frog."

"Maybe you don't," Smiley says. "Maybe you understand frogs and maybe you don't understand 'em; maybe you've had experience, and maybe you ain't only a amature, as it were. Anyways, I've got *my* opinion, and I'll resk forty dollars that he can outjump any frog in Calaveras county."

And the feller studied a minute, and then says, kinder sad like, "Well, I'm only a stranger here, and I ain't got no frog; but if I had a frog, I'd bet you."

And then Smiley says, "That's all right — that's all right — if you'll hold my box a minute, I'll go and get you a frog." And so the feller took the box, and put up his forty dollars along with Smiley's, and set down to wait.

So he set there a good while thinking and thinking to hisself, and then he got the frog out and prized his mouth open and took a teaspoon and filled him full of quail shot — filled him pretty near up to his chin — and set him on the floor. Smiley he went to the swamp and slopped around in the mud for a long time, and finally he ketched a frog, and fetched him in, and give him to this feller, and says:

"Now, if you're ready, set him alongside of

Dan'l, with his fore-paws just even with Dan'l's, and I'll give the word." Then he says, "One — two — three — *git!*" and him and the feller touched up the frogs from behind, and the new frog hopped off lively, but Dan'l give a heave, and hysted up his shoulders — so — like a Frenchman, but it warn't no use — he couldn't budge; he was planted as solid as a church, and he couldn't no more stir than if he was anchored out. Smiley was a good deal surprised, and he was disgusted too, but he didn't have no idea what the matter was, of course.

The feller took the money and started away; and when he was going out the door, he sorter jerked his thumb over his shoulder — so — at Dan'l, and says again, very deliberate, "Well," he says, "*I* don't see no p'ints about that frog that's any better'n any other frog."

Smiley he stood scratching his head and looking down at Dan'l a long time, and at last he says, "I do wonder what in the nation that frog throw'd off for — I wonder if there ain't something the matter with him — he 'pears to look mighty baggy, somehow." And he ketched Dan'l by the nap of the neck, and hefted him, and says, "Why blame my cats if he don't weigh five pound!" and turned him upside down and he belched out a double handful of shot. And then he see how it was, and he was the maddest man — he set the frog down and took out after that feller, but he never ketched him. And —"

[Here Simon Wheeler heard his name called

457

from the front yard, and got up to see what was wanted.] And turning to me as he moved away, he said: "Just set where you are, stranger, and rest easy — I ain't going to be gone a second."

But, by your leave, I did not think that a continuation of the history of the enterprising vagabond *Jim* Smiley would be likely to afford me much information concerning the Rev. *Leonidas W*. Smiley, and so I started away.

At the door I met the sociable Wheeler returning, and he button-holed me and re-commenced:

"Well, thish-yer Smiley had a yaller one-eyed cow that didn't have no tail, only just a short stump like a bannanner, and —"

However, lacking both time and inclination, I did not wait to hear about the afflicted cow, but took my leave.

I Ride a Bucking Horse

Mark Twain

I resolved to have a horse to ride. I had never seen such wild, free, magnificent horsemanship outside of a circus as these picturesquely-clad Mexicans, Californians, and Mexicanized Americans displayed in Carson streets every day. How they rode! Leaning just gently forward out of the perpendicular, easy and nonchalant, with broad slouch-hat brim blown square up in front, and long *riata* swinging above the head, they swept through the town like the wind! The next minute they were only a sailing puff of dust on the far desert. If they trotted, they sat up gallantly and gracefully, and seemed part of the horse; did not go jiggering up and down after the silly Miss-Nancy fashion of the riding-schools. I had quickly learned to tell a horse from a cow, and was full of anxiety to learn more. I was resolved to buy a horse.

While the thought was rankling in my mind, the auctioneer came scurrying through the plaza on a black beast that had as many humps and corners on him as a dromedary, and was necessarily uncomely; but he was "going, going, at twenty-two! — horse, saddle and bridle at twenty-two dollars, gentlemen!" and I could hardly resist.

A man whom I did not know (he turned out to be the auctioneer's brother) noticed the wistful look in my eye, and observed that that was a very remarkable horse to be going at such a price, and added that the saddle alone was worth the money. It was a Spanish saddle, with ponderous *tapidaros* and furnished with the ungainly sole-leather covering with the unspellable name. I said I had half a notion to bid. Then this keen-eyed person appeared to me to be "taking my measure"; but I dismissed suspicion when he spoke, for his manner was full of guileless candor and truthfulness. Said he:

"I know that horse — know him well. You are a stranger, I take it, and so you might think he was an American horse, maybe, but I assure you he is not. He is nothing of the kind; but — excuse my speaking in a low voice, other people being near — he is, without the shadow of a doubt, a Genuine Mexican Plug!"

I did not know what a Genuine Mexican Plug was, but there was something about this man's way of saying it, that made me swear inwardly that I would own a Genuine Mexican Plug, or die.

"Has he any other — er — advantages?" I inquired, suppressing what eagerness I could.

He hooked his forefinger in the pocket of my army-shirt, led me to one side, and breathed in my ear impressively these words:

460

"He can out-buck anything in America!"

"Twenty-seven!" I shouted, in a frenzy.

"And sold!" said the auctioneer, and passed over the Genuine Mexican Plug to me.

I could scarcely contain my exultation. I paid the money, and put the animal in a neighboring livery-stable to dine and rest himself.

In the afternoon I brought the creature into the plaza, and certain citizens held him by the head, and others by the tail, while I mounted him. As soon as they let go, he placed all his feet in a bunch together, lowered his back, and then suddenly arched it upward, and shot me straight into the air a matter of three or four feet! I came as straight down again, lit in the saddle, went instantly up again, came down almost on the high pommel, shot up again, and came down on the horse's neck — all in the space of three or four seconds. Then he rose and stood almost straight up on his hind feet, and I, clasping his lean neck desperately, slid back into the saddle, and held on. He came down, and immediately hoisted his heels into the air, delivering a vicious kick at the sky, and stood on his fore feet. And then down he came once more, and began the original exercise of shooting me straight up again.

The third time I went up I heard a stranger say: "Oh, *don't* he buck, though!"

While I was up, somebody struck the horse a sounding thwack with a leathern strap, and when I arrived again the Genuine Mexican Plug was not there. A Californian youth chased him up

461

and caught him, and asked if he might have a ride. I granted him that luxury. He mounted the Genuine, got lifted into the air once, but sent his spurs home as he descended, and the horse darted away like a telegram. He soared over three fences like a bird, and disappeared down the road towards the Washoe Valley.

I sat down on a stone with a sigh, and by natural impulse one of my hands sought my forehead, and the other the base of my stomach. I believe I never appreciated, till then, the poverty of human machinery — for I still needed a hand or two to place elsewhere. Pen cannot describe how I was jolted up. Imagination cannot conceive how disjointed I was — how internally, externally and universally I was unsettled, mixed up, and ruptured. There was a sympathetic crowd around me, though.

One elderly-looking comforter said:

"Stranger, you've been taken in. Everybody in this camp knows that horse. Any child, any Injun, could have told you that he'd buck; he is the very worst devil to buck on the continent of America. You hear *me*. I'm Curry. *Old* Curry. Old *Abe* Curry. And moreover, he is a simon-pure, out-and-out genuine d — d Mexican plug, and an uncommon mean one at that, too. Why, you turnip, if you had laid low and kept dark, there's chances to buy an *American* horse for mighty little more than you paid for that bloody old foreign relic."

I gave no sign; but I made up my mind that

if the auctioneer's brother's funeral took place while I was in the Territory I would postpone all other recreations and attend it.

After a gallop of sixteen miles, the Californian youth and the Genuine Mexican Plug came tearing into town again, shedding foam-flakes like the spume-spray that drives before a typhoon, and, with one final skip over a wheelbarrow and a Chinaman, cast anchor in front of the "ranch."

Such panting and blowing! Such spreading and contracting of the red equine nostrils, and glaring of the wild equine eye! But was the imperial beast subjugated? Indeed, he was not. His lordship the Speaker of the House thought he was, and mounted him to go down to the Capitol; but the first dash the creature made was over a pile of telegraph poles half as high as a church; and his time to the Capitol — one mile and three quarters — remains unbeaten to this day. But then he took an advantage — he left out the mile, and only did the three-quarters. That is to say, he made a straight cut across lots, preferring fences and ditches to a crooked road; and when the Speaker got to the Capitol he said he had been in the air so much he felt as if he had made the trip on a comet.

In the evening the Speaker came home afoot for exercise, and got the Genuine towed back behind a quartz wagon. The next day I loaned the animal to the Clerk of the House to go down to the Dana silver mine, six miles, and he walked back for exercise, and got the horse towed.

463

Everybody I loaned him to always walked back; they never could get enough exercise any other way. Still, I continued to loan him to anybody who was willing to borrow him, my idea being to get him crippled, and throw him on the borrower's hands, or killed, and make the borrower pay for him. But somehow nothing ever happened to him. He took chances that no other horse ever took and survived, he always came out safe. It was his daily habit to try experiments that had always before been considered impossible, but he always got through. Sometimes he miscalculated a little, and did not get his rider through intact, but *he* always got through himself. Of course I had tried to sell him; but that was a stretch of simplicity which met with little sympathy. The auctioneer stormed up and down the streets on him for four days, dispersing the populace, interrupting business and destroying children, and never got a bid — at least never any but the eighteen-dollar one he hired a notoriously substanceless bummer to make. The people only smiled pleasantly, and restrained their desire to buy, if they had any. Then the auctioneer brought in his bill, and I withdrew the horse from the market. We tried to trade him off at private vendue next, offering him at a sacrifice for second-hand tombstones, old iron, temperance tracts — any kind of property. But holders were stiff, and we retired from the market again. I never tried to ride the horse any more. Walking was good enough exercise for a man like me, that had nothing the matter with him except ruptures, internal injuries, and such things. Finally I tried to *give* him away. But it was a failure. Parties said earthquakes were handy enough on the Pacific coast — they did not wish to own one. As a last resort I offered him to the Governor for the use of the "Brigade." His face lit up eagerly at first, but toned down again, and he said the thing would be too palpable.

Just then the livery stable man brought in his bill for six weeks' keeping — stall-room for the horse, fifteen dollars; hay for the horse, two hundred and fifty! The Genuine Mexican Plug had eaten a ton of the article, and the man said he would have eaten a hundred if he had let him.

I will remark here, in all seriousness, that the regular price of hay during that year and a part of the next was really two hundred and fifty dollars a ton. during a part of the previous year it had sold at five hundred a ton, in gold, and during the winter before that there was such a scarcity of the article that in several instances small quantities had brought eight hundred dollars a ton in coin! The consequence might be guessed without my telling it: people turned their stock loose to starve, and before the spring arrived Carson and Eagle Valleys were almost literally carpeted with their carcasses! Any old settler there will verify these statements.

I managed to pay the livery bill, and that same day I gave the Genuine Mexican Plug to a passing

Arkansas emigrant whom fortune delivered into my hand. If this ever meets his eye, he will doubtless remember the donation.

Now whoever has the luck to ride a real Mexican plug will recognize the animal depicted in this chapter, and hardly consider him exaggerated — but the uninitiated will feel justified in regarding his portrait as a fancy sketch, perhaps.

The Geese

E. B. White

Allen Cove, July 9, 1971

To give a clear account of what took place in the barnyard early in the morning on that last Sunday in June, I will have to go back more than a year in time, but a year is nothing to me these days. Besides, I intend to be quick about it, and not dawdle.

I have had a pair of elderly gray geese — a goose and a gander — living on this place for a number of years, and they have been my friends. "Companions" would be a better word; geese are friends with no one, they badmouth everybody and everything. But they are companionable once you get used to their ingratitude and their false accusations. Early in the spring, a year ago, as soon as the ice went out of the pond, my goose started to lay. She laid three eggs in about a week's time and then died. I found her halfway down the lane that connects the barnyard with the pasture. There were no marks on her — she lay with wings partly outspread, and with her neck forward in the grass, pointing downhill. Geese are rarely sick, and I think this goose's time had come and she had simply died of old age. I had noticed that her step had slowed on her trips back from the pond to the barn where her nest was. I had never known her age, and so had nothing else to go on. We buried her in our private graveyard, and I felt sad at losing an acquaintance of such long standing — long standing and loud shouting.

Her legacy, of course, was the three eggs. I knew they were good eggs and did not like to pitch them out. It seemed to me that the least I could do for my departed companion was to see that the eggs she had left in my care were hatched. I checked my hen pen to find out whether we had a broody, but there was none. During the next few days, I scoured the neighborhood for a broody hen, with no success. Years ago, if you needed a broody hen, almost any barn or henhouse would yield one. But today broodiness is considered unacceptable in a hen; the modern hen is an egg-laying machine, and her natural tendency to sit on eggs in springtime has been bred out of her. Besides, not many people keep hens anymore — when they want a dozen eggs, they don't go to the barn, they go to the First National.

Days went by. My gander, the widower, lived a solitary life — nobody to swap gossip with, nobody to protect. He seemed dazed. The three eggs were not getting any younger, and I myself felt dazed — restless and unfulfilled. I had stored the eggs down cellar in the arch where it is cool, and every time I went down there for something they seemed silently to reproach me. My plight had become known around town, and one day a friend phoned and said he would lend me an incubator designed for hatching the eggs of waterfowl. I brought the thing home, cleaned it up, plugged it in, and sat down to read the directions. After studying them, I realized that if I were to tend eggs in that incubator, I would have to withdraw from the world for thirty days — give up everything, just as a broody goose does. Obsessed though I was with the notion of bringing life into three eggs, I wasn't quite prepared to pay the price.

Instead, I abandoned the idea of incubation and decided to settle the matter by acquiring three ready-made goslings, as a memorial to the goose and a gift for the lonely gander. I drove up the road about five miles and dropped in on Irving Closson. I knew Irving had geese; he has everything — even a sawmill. I found him shoeing a very old horse in the doorway of his barn, and I stood and watched for a while. Hens and geese wandered about the yard, and a turkey tom circled me, wings adroop, strutting. The horse, with one forefoot between the man's kees, seemed to have difficulty balancing himself on three legs but was quiet and sober, almost asleep. When I asked Irving if he planned to put shoes on the horse's hind feet, too, he said, "No, it's hard work for me, and he doesn't use those hind legs much anyway." Then I brought up the question of goslings, and he took me into the barn and showed me a sitting goose. He said he thought she was covering more than twenty eggs and should bring off her goslings in a couple of weeks and I could buy a few if I wanted. I said I would like three.

I took to calling at Irving's every few days — it is about the pleasantest place to visit anywhere around. At last, I was rewarded: I pulled into the driveway one morning and saw a goose surrounded by green goslings. She had been staked out, like a cow. Irving had simply tied a piece of string to one leg and fastened the other end to a peg in the ground. She was a pretty goose — not as large as my old one had been, and with a more slender neck. She appeared to be a cross-bred bird, two-toned gray, with white markings — a sort of particolored goose. The goslings had the cheerful, bright innocent look that all baby geese have. We scooped up three and tossed them into a box, and I paid Irving and carried them home.

My next concern was how to introduce these small creatures to their foster father, my old gander. I thought about this all the way home. I've had just enough experience with domesticated animals and birds to know that they are a bundle of eccentricities and crotchets, and I was not at all sure what sort of reception three strange youngsters would get from a gander who was full of sorrows and suspicions. (I once saw a gander, taken by surprise, seize a newly hatched gosling and hurl it the length of the barn floor.) I had an uneasy feeling that my three little charges might be dead within the hour, victims of a griefcrazed old fool. I decided to go slow. I fixed a makeshift pen for the goslings in the barn, arranged so that they would be separated from the gander but visible to him, and he would be visible to them. The old fellow, when he heard youthful voices, hustled right in to find out what was going on. He studied the scene in silence and with the greatest attention. I could not tell whether the look in his eye was one of malice or affection — a goose's eye is a small round enigma. After observing this introductory scene for a while, I left and went into the house.

Half an hour later, I heard a commotion in the barnyard: the gander was in full cry. I hustled out. The goslings, impatient with life indoors, had escaped from their hastily constructed enclosure in the barn and had joined their foster father in the barnyard. The cries I had heard were his screams of welcome — the old bird was delighted with the turn that events had taken. His period of mourning was over, he now had interesting and useful work to do, and he threw himself into the role of father with immense satisfaction and zeal, hissing at me with renewed malevolence, shepherding the three children here and there, and running interference against real and imaginary enemies. My fears were laid to rest. In the rush of emotion that seized him at finding himself the head of a family, his thoughts turned immediately to the pond, and I watched admiringly as he guided the goslings down the long, tortuous course through the weedy lane and on down across the rough pasture between blueberry knolls and granite boulders. It was a sight to see him hold the heifers at bay so the procession could pass safely. Summer was upon us, the pond was alive again. I brought the three eggs up from the cellar and dispatched them to the town dump.

At first, I did not know the sex of my three goslings. But nothing on two legs grows any faster than a young goose, and by early fall it was obvious that I had drawn one male and two females. You tell the sex of a goose by its demeanor and its stance — the way it holds itself, its general approach to life. A gander carries his head high and affects a threatening attitude. Females go about with necks in a graceful arch and are less aggressive. My two young females looked like their mother, parti-colored. The young male was quite different. He feathered out white all over except for his wings, which were a very light, pearly gray. Afloat on the pond, he looked almost like a swan, with his tall, thin white neck and his cocked-up white tail — a real dandy, full of pompous thoughts and surly gestures.

Winter is a time of waiting, for man and goose. Last winter was a long wait, the pasture deep in drifts, the lane barricaded, the pond inaccessible and frozen. Life centered in the barn and the barnyard. When the time for mating came, conditions were unfavorable, and this was upsetting to the old gander. Geese like a body of water for their coupling; it doesn't have to be a large body of water — just any wet place in which a goose can become partly submerged. My old gander, studying the calendar, inflamed by passion, unable to get to the pond, showed signs of desperation. On several occasions, he tried to manage with a ten-quart pail of water that stood in the barnyard. He would chivvy one of his young foster daughters over to the pail, seize her by the nape, and hold her head under water while he made his attempt. It was never a success and usually ended up looking more like a comedy tumbling act than like coitus. One got the feeling during the water-pail routine that the gander had been consulting one of the modern sex manuals describing peculiar positions. Anyway, I noticed two things: the old fellow confined his attentions to one of the two young geese and let the other alone, and he never allowed his foster son to approach either of the girls — he was very stict about that, and the handsome young male lived all spring in a state of ostracism.

Evenutally, the pond opened up, the happy band wended its way down across the melting snows, and the breeding season was officially opened. My pond is visible from the house, but it is at quite a distance. I am not a voyeur and do not spend my time watching the sex antics of geese or anything else. But I try to keep reasonably well posted on all the creatures around the place, and it was apparent that the young gander was not allowed by his foster father to enjoy the privileges of the pond and that the old gander's attentions continued to be directed to just one of the young geese. I shall call her Liz to make this tale easier to tell.

Both geese were soon laying. Liz made her nest in the barn cellar; her sister, Apathy, made hers in the tie-ups on the main floor of the barn. It was the end of April or the beginning of May. Still awfully cold — a reluctant spring.

Apathy laid three eggs, then quit. I marked them with a pencil and left them for the time being in the nest she had constructed. I made a mental note that they were infertile. Liz, unlike her sister, went right on laying, and became a laying fool. She dallied each morning at the pond with her foster father, and she laid and laid and laid, like a commercial hen. I dutifully marked the eggs as they arrived — 1, 2, 3, and so on. When she had accumulated a clutch of fifteen, I decided she had all she could cover. From then on, I took to removing the oldest egg from the nest each time a new egg was deposited. I also removed Apathy's three eggs from *her* nest, discarded them, and began substituting the purloined eggs from the barn cellar — the ones that rightfully belonged to Liz. Thus I gradually contrived to assemble a nest of fertile eggs for each bird, all of them laid by the fanatical Liz.

During the last week in May, Apathy, having produced only three eggs of her own but having acquired ten through the kind offices of her sister and me, became broody and began to sit. Liz, with a tally of twenty-five eggs, ten of them stolen, showed not the slightest desire to sit. Laying was her thing. She laid and laid, while the other goose sat and sat. The old gander, marveling at what he had wrought, showed a great deal of interest in both nests. The young gander was impressed but subdued. I continued to remove the early eggs from Liz's nest, holding her to a clutch of fifteen and discarding the extras. In late June, having produced forty-one eggs, ten of which were under Apathy, she at last sat down.

I had marked Apathy's hatching date on my desk calendar. On the night before the goslings were due to arrive, when I made my rounds before going to bed, I looked in on her. She hissed, as usual, and ran her neck out. When I shone my light at her, two tiny green heads were visible, thrusting their way through the feathers. The goslings were here — a few hours ahead of schedule. My heart leapt up. Outside, in the barnyard, both ganders stood vigil. They knew very well what was up: ganders take an enormous interest in family affairs and are deeply impressed by the miracle of the egg-that-becomes-goose. I shut the door against them and went to bed.

Next morning, Sunday, I rose early and went straight to the barn to see what the night had brought. Apathy was sitting quietly while five goslings teetered about on the slopes of the nest.

One of them, as I watched, strayed from the others, and, not being able to find his way back, began sending out cries for help. They were the kind of distress signal any anxious father would instantly respond to. Suddenly, I heard sounds of a rumble outside in the barnyard where the ganders were — loud sounds of scuffling. I ran out. A fierce fight was in progress — it was no mere skirmish, it was the real thing. The young gander had grabbed the old one by the stern, his white head buried in feathers right where it would hurt the most, and was running him around the yard, punishing him at every turn — thrusting him on ahead and beating him unmercifully with his wings. It was an awesome sight, these two great male birds locked in combat, slugging it out — not for the favors of a female but for the dubious privilege of assuming the responsibilities of parenthood. The young male had suffered all spring the indignities of a restricted life at the pond; now he had turned, at last, against the old one, as though to get even. Round and round, over rocks and through weeds, they raced, struggling and tripping, the old one in full retreat and in apparent pain. It was a beautiful late-June morning, with fair-weather clouds and a light wind going, the grasses long in the orchard — the kind of morning that always carries for me overtones of summer sadness, I don't know why. Overhead, three swallows circled at low altitude, pursuing one white feather, the coveted trophy of nesting time. They were like three tiny fighter planes giving air support to the battle that raged below. For a moment, I thought of climbing the fence and trying to separate the combatants, but instead I just watched. The engagement was soon over. Plunging desperately down the lane,the old gander sank to the ground. The young one let go, turned, and walked back, screaming in triumph, to the door behind which his newly won family were waiting: a strange family indeed — the sister who was not even the mother of the babies, and the babies who were not even his own get.

When I was sure the fight was over, I climbed the fence and closed the barnyard gate, effectively separating victor from vanquished. The old gander had risen to his feet. He was in almost the same spot in the lane where his first wife had died mysteriously more than a year ago. I watched as he threaded his way slowly down the narrow path between clumps of thistles and daisies. His head was barely visible above the grasses, but his broken spirit was plain to any eye. When he reached the pasture bars, he hesitated, then painfully squatted and eased himself under the bottom bar and into the pasture, where he sat down on the cropped sward in the bright sun. I felt very deeply his sorrow and his defeat. As things go in the animal kingdom, he is about my age, and when he lowered himself to creep under the bar, I could feel in my own bones his pain at bending down so far. Two hours later, he was still sitting there, the sun by this time quite hot.

I had seen his likes often enough on the benches of the treeless main street of a Florida city — spent old males, motionless in the glare of the day.

Toward the end of the morning, he walked back up the lane as far as the gate, and there he stood all afternoon, his head and orange bill looking like the head of a great snake. The goose and her goslings had emerged into the barnyard. Through the space between the boards of the gate, the old fellow watched the enchanting scene: the goslings taking their frequent drinks of water, climbing in and out of the shallow pan for their first swim, closely guarded by the handsome young gander, shepherded by the pretty young goose.

After supper, I went into the tie-ups and pulled the five remaining, unhatched eggs from the nest and thought about the five lifeless chicks inside the eggs — the unlucky ones, the ones that lacked what it takes to break out of an egg into the light of a fine June morning. I put the eggs in a basket and set the basket with some other miscellany consigned to the dump. I don't know anything sadder than a summer's day.

The Story of Webster

P. G. Wodehouse

'Cats are not dogs!'

There is only one place where you can hear good things like that thrown off quite casually in the general run of conversation and that is the bar parlour of the Angler's Rest. It was there, as we sat grouped about the fire, that a thoughtful Pint of Bitter had made the statement just recorded.

Although the talk up to this point had been dealing with Einstein's Theory of Relativity, we readily adjusted our minds to cope with the new topic. Regular attendance at the nightly sessions over which Mr Mulliner presides with such unfailing dignity and geniality tends to produce mental nimbleness. In our little circle I have known an argument on the Final Destination of the Soul to change inside forty seconds into one concerning the best method of preserving the juiciness of bacon fat.

'Cats,' proceeded the Pint of Bitter, 'are selfish. A man waits on a cat hand and foot for weeks, humouring its lightest whim, and then it goes and leaves him flat because it has found a place down the road where the fish is more frequent.'

'What I've got against cats,' said a Lemon Sour, speaking feelingly, as one brooding on a private grievance, 'is their unreliability. They lack candour and are not square shooters. You get your cat and you call him Thomas or George, as the case may be. So far, so good. Then one morning you wake up and find six kittens in the hat-box and you have to reopen the whole matter, approaching it from an entirely different angle.'

'If you want to know what's the trouble with cats,' said a red-faced man with glassy eyes, who had been rapping on the table for his fourth whisky, 'they've got no tact. That's what's the trouble with them. I remember a friend of mine had a cat. Made quite a pet of that cat, he did. And what occurred? What was the outcome? One night he came home rather late and was feeling for the keyhole with his corkscrew; and, believe me or not, his cat selected that precise moment to jump on the back of his neck out of a tree. No tact.'

Mr. Mulliner shook his head.

'I grant you all this,' he said, 'but still, in my opinion, you have not got to the root of the matter. The real objection to the great majority of cats is their insufferable air of superiority. Cats, as a class, have never completely got over the snootiness caused by the fact that in Ancient Egypt they were worshipped as gods. This makes them too prone to set themselves up as critics and censors of the frail and erring human beings whose lot they share. They stare rebukingly.

They view with concern. And on a sensitive man this often has the worst effects, inducing an inferiority complex of the gravest kind. It is odd that the conversation should have taken this turn,' said Mr. Mulliner, sipping his hot Scotch and lemon, 'for I was thinking only this afternoon of the rather strange case of my cousin Edward's son, Lancelot.'

'I knew a cat —' began a Small Bass.

My cousin Edward's son, Lancelot (said Mr. Mulliner) was at the time of which I speak, a comely youth of some twenty-five summers. Orphaned at an early age, he had been brought up in the home of his Uncle Theodore, the saintly Dean of Bolsover; and it was a great shock to that good man when Lancelot, on attaining his majority, wrote from London to inform him that he had taken a studio in Bott Street, Chelsea, and proposed to remain in the metropolis and become an artist.

The Dean's opinion of artists was low. As a prominent member of the Bolsover Watch Committee, it had recently been his distasteful duty to be present at a private showing of the super-super-film, *Palettes of Passion;* and he replied to his newphew's communication with a vibrant letter in which he emphasized the grievous pain it gave him to think that one of his flesh and blood should deliberately be embarking on a career which must inevitably lead sooner or later to the painting of Russian princesses lying on divans in the semi-nude with their arms round tame jaguars. He urged Lancelot to return and become a curate while there was yet time.

But Lancelot was firm. he deplored the rift between himself and a relative whom he had always respected; but he was dashed if he meant to go back to an environment where his individuality had been stifled and his soul confined in chains. And for four years there was silence between uncle and nephew.

During these years Lancelot had made progress in his chosen profession. At the time at which this story opens, his prospects seemed bright. He was painting the portrait of Brenda, only daughter of Mr and Mrs B. B. Carberry-Pirbright, of 11 Maxton Square, South Kensington, which meant thirty pounds in his sock on delivery. He had learned to cook eggs and bacon. He had practically mastered the ukulele. And, in addition, he was engaged to be married to a fearless young *vers libre* poetess of the name of Gladys Bingley, better known as The Sweet Singer of Garbidge Mews, Fulham — a charming girl who looked like a penwiper.

It seemed to Lancelot that life was very full and beautiful. He lived joyously in the present, giving no thought to the past.

But how true it is that the past is inextricably mixed up with the present and that we can never tell when it may spring some delayed bomb beneath our feet. One afternoon, as he sat making a few small alterations in the portrait of Brenda Carberry-Pirbright, his fiancée entered.

He had been expecting her to call, for today she was going off for a three weeks' holiday to the South of France, and she had promised to look in on her way to the station. He laid down his brush and gazed at her with a yearning affection, thinking for the thousandth time how he worshipped every spot of ink on her nose. Standing there in the doorway with her bobbed hair sticking out in every direction like a golliwog's, she made a picture that seemed to speak to his very depths.

'Hullo, Reptile!" he said lovingly.

'What ho, Worm!' said Gladys, maidenly devotion shining through the monocle which she wore in her left eye. 'I can stay just half an hour.'

'Oh, well, half an hour soon passes,' said Lancelot. 'What's that you've got there?'

'A letter, ass. What did you think it was?'

'Where did you get it?'

'I found the postman outside.'

Lancelot took the envelope from her and examined it.

'Gosh!' he said.

'What's the matter?'

'It's from my Uncle Theodore.'

'I didn't know you had an Uncle Theodore.'

'Of course I have. I've had him for years.'

'What's he writing to you about?'

'If you'll kindly keep quiet for two seconds, if you know how,' said Lancelot, 'I'll tell you.'

And in a clear voice which, like that of all the Mulliners, however distant from the main branch,

483

was beautifully modulated, he read as follows:

> The Deanery,
> Bolsover, Wilts.

My dear Lancelot,

As you have, no doubt, already learned from your *Church Times*, I have been offered and have accepted the vacant Bishopric of Bongo-Bongo, in West Africa. I sail immediately to take up my new duties, which I trust will be blessed.

In these circumstances it becomes necessary for me to find a good home for my cat Webster. It is, alas, out of the question that he should accompany me, as the rigours of the climate and the lack of essential comforts might well sap a constitution which has never been robust.

I am dispatching him, therefore, to your address, my dear boy, in a straw-lined hamper, in the full confidence that you will prove a kindly and conscientious host.

With cordial good wishes,

> Your affectionate uncle,
> THEODORE BONGO-
> BONGO

For some moments after he had finished reading this communication, a thoughtful silence prevailed in the studio. Finally Gladys spoke.

'Of all the nerve!' she said. 'I wouldn't do it.'
'Why not?'

'What do you want with a cat?'

Lancelot reflected.

'It is true,' he said, 'that, given a free hand, I would prefer not to have my studio turned into a cattery or cat-bin. But consider the special circumstances. Relations between Uncle Theodore and self have for the last few years been a bit strained. In fact, you might say we had definitely parted brass rags. It looks to me as if he were coming round. I should describe this letter as more or less what you might call an olive-branch. If I lush this cat up satisfactorily, shall I not be in a position later on to make a swift touch?'

'He is rich, this bean?' said Gladys, interested.

'Extremely.'

'Then,' said Gladys, 'consider my objections withdrawn. A good stout cheque from a grateful cat-fancier would undoubtedly come in very handy. We might be able to get married this year.'

'Exactly,' said Lancelot. 'A pretty loathsome prospect, of course; but still, as we've arranged to do it, the sooner we get it over, the better, what?

'Absolutely.'

'Then that's settled. I accept custody of cat.'

'It's the only thing to do,' said Gladys. 'Meanwhile, can you lend me a comb? Have you such a thing in your bedroom?'

'What do you want with a comb?'

'I got some soup in my hair at lunch. I won't be a minute.'

She hurried out, and Lancelot, taking up the letter again, found that he had omitted to read a continuation of it on the back page.

It was to the following effect:

PS. In establishing Webster in your home, I am actuated by another motive than the simple desire to see to it that my faithful friend and companion is adequately provided for.

From both a moral and educative standpoint, I am convinced that Webster's society will prove of inestimable value to you. His advent, indeed, I venture to hope, will be a turning-point in your life. Thrown, as you must be, incessantly among loose and immoral Bohemians, you will find in this cat an example of upright conduct which cannot but act as an antidote to the poison cup of temptation which is, no doubt, hourly pressed to your lips.

PPS. Cream only at midday, and fish not more than three times a week.

He was reading these words for the second time, when the front doorbell rang and he found a man on the steps with a hamper. A discreet mew from within revealed its contents, and Lancelot, carrying it into the studio, cut the strings.

'Hi!' he bellowed, going to the door.

'What's up?' shrieked his betrothed from above.

'That cat's come.'

'All right. I'll be down in a jiffy.'

Lancelot returned to the studio.

'What ho, Webster!' he said cheerily. 'How's the boy?'

The cat did not reply. It was sitting with bent head, performing that wash and brush up which a journey by rail renders so necessary.

In order to facilitate these toilet operations, it had raised its left leg and holding it rigidly in the air. And there flashed into Lancelot's mind an old superstition handed on to him, for what it was worth, by one of the nurses of his infancy. If, this woman had said, you creep up to a cat when its leg is in the air and give it a pull, then you make a wish and your wish comes true in thirty days.

It was a pretty fancy, and it seemed to Lancelot that the theory might as well be put to the test. He advanced warily, therefore, and was in the act of extending his fingers for the pull, when Webster, lowering the leg, turned and raised his eyes.

He looked at Lancelot. And suddenly with sickening force there came to Lancelot the realization of the unpardonable liberty he had been about to take.

Until this moment, though the postcript to his uncle's letter should have warned him, Lancelot Mulliner had had no suspicion of what manner of cat this was that he had taken into his home. Now, for the first time, he saw him steadily and saw him whole.

Webster was very large and very black and very composed. He conveyed the impression of being a cat of deep reserves. Descendant of a long line of ecclesiastical ancestors who had conducted their decorous courtships beneath the shadow of cathedrals and on the back walls of bishops' palaces, he had that exquisite pose which one sees in high dignitaries of the Church. His eyes were clear and steady, and seemed to pierce to the very roots of the young man's soul, filling him with a sense of guilt.

Once, long ago, in his hot childhood, Lancelot, spending his summer holidays at the deanery, had been so far carried away by ginger-beer and original sin as to plug a senior canon in the leg with his air-gun — only to discover, on turning, that a visiting archdeacon had been a spectator of the entire incident from his immediate rear. As he had felt then, when meeting the archdeacon's eye, so did he feel now as Webster's gaze played silently upon him.

Webster, it is true, had not actually raised his eyebrows. But this, Lancelot felt, was simply because he hadn't any.

He backed, blushing.

'Sorry!' he muttered.

There was a pause. Webster continued his steady scrutiny. Lancelot edged towards the door.

'Er — excuse me — just a moment . . .' he mumbled. And, sidling from the room, he ran distractedly upstairs.

'I say,' said Lancelot.

'Now what?' asked Gladys.

'Have you finished with the mirror?'

488

'Why?'

'Well, I — er — I thought,' said Lancelot, 'that I might as well have a shave.'

The girl looked at him, astonished.

'Shave? Why, you shaved only the day before yesterday.'

'I know. But, all the same . . . I mean to say, it seems only respectful. That cat, I mean.'

'What about him?'

'Well, he seems to expect it, somehow. Nothing actually said, don't you know, but you cou'd tell by his manner. I thought a quick shave and perhaps change into my blue serge suit —'

'He's probably thirsty. Why don't you give him some milk?'

'Could one, do you think?' said Lancelot doubtful. 'I mean, I hardly seem to know him well enough.' He paused. 'I say, old girl,' he went on, with a touch of hesitation.

'Hullo?'

'I know you won't mind my mentioning it, but you've got a few spots of ink on your nose.'

'Of course I have. I always have spots of ink on my nose.'

'Well . . . you don't think . . . a quick scrub with a bit of pumice-stone . . . I mean to say, you know how important first impressions are . . .'

The girl stared.

'Lancelot Mulliner,' she said, 'if you think I'm going to skin my nose to the bone just to please a mangy cat —'

'Sh!' cried Lancelot, in agony.'

'Here, let me go down and look at him,' said Gladys petulantly.

As they re-entered the studio, Webster was gazing with an air of quiet distaste at an illustration from *La Vie Parisienne* which adorned one of the walls. Lancelot tore it down hastily.

Gladys looked at Webster in an unfriendly way.

'So that's the blighter!'

'Sh!'

'If you want to know what I think,' said Gladys, 'that cat's been living too high. Doing himself a dashed sight too well. You'd better cut his rations down a bit.'

In substance, her criticism was not unjustified. Certainly, there was about Webster more than a suspicion of *embonpoint*. He had that air of portly well-being which we associate with those who dwell in cathedral closes. But Lancelot winced uncomfortably. He had so hoped that Gladys would make a good impression, and here she was, starting right off by saying the tactless thing.

He longed to explain to Webster that it was only her way; that in the Bohemian circles of which she was such an ornament genial chaff of a personal order was accepted and, indeed, relished. But it was too late. The mischief had been done. Webster turned in a pointed manner and withdrew silently behind the chesterfield.

Gladys, all unconscious, was making preparations for departure.

'Well, bung-oh,' she said lightly. "See you in three weeks. I suppose you and that cat'll both be out on the tiles the moment by back's turned.'

'Please! Please!' moaned Lancelot. 'Please!'

He had caught sight of the tip of a black tail protruding from behind the chesterfield. It was twitching slightly, and Lancelot could read it like a book. With a sickening sense of dismay, he knew that Webster had formed a snap judgement of his finacée and condemned her as frivolous and unworthy.

It was some ten days later that Barnard Worple, the neo-Vorticist sculptor, lunching at the Puce Ptarmigan, ran into Rodney Scollop, the powerful young surrealist. And after talking for a while of their art:

'What's all this I hear about Lancelot Mulliner?' asked Worple. 'There's a wild story going about that he was seen shaved in the middle of the week. Nothing in it, I suppose?'

Scollop looked grave. He had been on the point of mentioning Lancelot himself, for he loved the lad and was deeply exercised about him.

'It is perfectly true,' he said.

'It sounds incredible.'

Scollop leaned forward. His fine face was troubled.

'Shall I tell you something, Worple?'

'What?'

'I know for an absolute fact,' said Scollop, 'that Lancelot Mulliner now shaves every morning.'

Worple pushed aside the spaghetti which he was wreathing about him and through the gap stared at his companion.

'Every morning?'

'Every single morning. I looked in on him myself the other day, and there he was, neatly dressed in blue serge and shaved to the core. And, what is more, I got the distinct impression that he had used talcum powder afterwards.'

'You don't mean that!'

'I do. And shall I tell you something else? There was a book lying open on the table. He tried to hide it, but he wasn't quick enough. It was one of those etiquette books!'

'An etiquette book!'

'*Polite Behaviour*, by Constance, Lady Bodbank.'

Worple unwound a stray tendril of spaghetti from about his left ear. He was deeply agitated. Like Scollop, he loved Lancelot.

'He'll be dressing for dinner next!' he exclaimed.

'I have every reason to believe,' said Scollop gravely, 'that he does dress for dinner. At any rate, a man closely resembling him was seen furtively buying three stiff collars and a black tie at Hope Brothers in the King's Road last Tuesday.'

Worple pushed his chair back, and rose. His manner was determined.

'Scollop,' he said, 'we are friends of Mulliner's, you and I. It is evident from what you tell me that subversive influences are at work and that never has he needed our friendship more. Shall we not go round and see him immediately?'

'It was what I was about to suggest myself,' said Rodney Scollop.

Twenty minutes later they were in Lancelot's studio, and with a significant glance Scollop drew his companion's notice to their host's appearance. Lancelot Mulliner was neatly, even foppishly, dressed in blue serge with creases down the trouser-legs, and his chin, Worple saw with a pang, gleamed smoothly in the afternoon light.

At the sight of his friends' cigars, Lancelot exhibited unmistakable concern.

'You don't mind throwing those away, I'm sure,' he said pleadingly.

Rodney Scollop drew himself up a little haughtily.

'And since when,' he asked, 'have the best fourpenny cigars in Chelsea not been good enough for you?'

Lancelot hastened to soothe him.

'It isn't me,' he exclaimed. 'It's Webster. My cat. I happen to know he objects to tobacco smoke. I had to give up my pipe in deference to his views.'

Bernard Worple snorted.

'Are you trying to tell us,' he sneered, 'that Lancelot Mulliner allows himself to be dictated to by a blasted cat?'

'Hush!' cried Lancelot, trembling. 'If you

know how he disapproves of strong language!'

'Where is this cat?' asked Rodney Scollop. 'Is that the animal?' he said, pointing out of the window to where, in the yard, a tough-looking Tom with tattered ears stood mewing in a hard-boiled way out of the corner of its mouth.

'Good heavens, no!' said Lancelot. 'That is an alley cat which comes round here from time to time to lunch at the dustbin. Webster is quite different. Webster has a natural dignity and repose of manner. Webster is a cat who prides himself on always being well turned out and whose high principles and lofty ideals shine from his eyes like beacon fires . . ." And then suddenly, with an abrupt change of manner, Lancelot broke down and in a low voice added: 'Curse him! Curse him! Curse him! Curse him!'

Worple looked at Scollop. Scollop looked at Worple.

'Come, old man,' said Scollop, laying a gentle hand on Lancelot's bowed shoulder. 'We are your friends. Confide in us.'

'Tell us all,' said Worple. 'What's the matter?'

Lancelot uttered a bitter, mirthless laugh.

'You want to know what's the matter? Listen, then. I'm cat-pecked!'

'Cat-pecked?'

'You've heard of men being hen-pecked, haven't you?' said Lancelot with a touch of irritation. 'Well, I'm cat-pecked.'

And in broken accents he told his story. He sketched the history of his association with

Webster from the latter's first entry into the studio. Confident now that the animal was not within earshot, he unbosomed himself without reserve.

'It's something in the beast's eye,' he said in a shaking voice. 'Something hypnotic. He casts a spell upon me. He gazes at me and disapproves. Little by little, bit by bit, I am degenerating under his influence from a wholesome, self-respecting artist into . . . well, I don't know what you call it. Suffice it to say that I have given up smoking, that I have ceased to wear carpet slippers and go about without a collar, that I never dream of sitting down to my frugal evening meal without dressing, and' — he choked — 'I have sold my ukulele.'

'Not that!' said Worple, paling.

'Yes,' said Lancelot. 'I felt he considered it frivolous.'

There was a long silence.

'Mulliner,' said Scollop, 'this is more serious than I had supposed. We must brood upon your case.'

'It may be possible,' said Worple, 'to find a way out.'

Lancelot shook his head hopelessly.

'There is no way out. I have explored every avenue. The only thing that could possibly free me from this intolerable bondage would be if once — just once — I could catch that cat unbending. If once — merely once — it would lapse in my presence from its austere dignity for but a single instant, I feel that the spell would be broken. But what hope is there of that? cried Lancelot passionately. 'You were pointing just now to that alley cat in the yard. There stands one who has strained every nerve and spared no effort to break down Webster's inhuman self-control. I have heard that animal say things to him which you would think no cat with red blood in its veins would suffer for an instant. And Webster merely looks at him like a Suffragan Bishop eyeing an erring choirboy and turns his head and falls into a refreshing sleep.'

He broke off with a dry sob. Worple, always an optimist, attempted in his kindly way to minimize the tragedy.

'Ah, well,' he said. 'It's bad, of course, but still, I suppose there is no actual harm in shaving and dressing for dinner and so on. Many great artists . . . Whistler, for example —'

'Wait!' cried Lancelot. 'you have not heard the worst.'

He rose feverishly, and, going to the easel, disclosed the portrait of Brenda Carberry-Pirbright.

'Take a look at that,' he said, 'and tell me what you think of her.'

His two friends surveyed the face before them in silence. Miss Carberry-Pirbright was a young woman of prim and glacial aspect. One sought in vain for her reasons for wanting to have her portrait painted. It would be a most unpleasant thing to have about any house.

Scollop broke the silence.

'Friend of yours?'

'I can't stand the sight of her,' said Lancelot vehemently.

'Then,' said Scollop, 'I may speak frankly. I think she's a pill.'

'A blister,' said Worple.

'A boil and a disease,' said Scollop, summing up.

Lancelot laughed hackingly.

'You have described her to a nicety. She stands for everything most alien to my artist soul. She gives me a pain in the neck. I'm going to marry her.'

'What!' cried Scollop.

'But you're going to marry Gladys Bingley,' said Worple.

'Webster thinks not,' said Lancelot bitterly. 'At their first meeting he weighed Gladys in the balance and found her wanting. And the moment he saw Brenda Carberry-Pirbright he stuck his tail up at right angles, uttered a cordial gargle, and rubbed his head against her leg. Then turning, he looked at me. I could read that glance. I knew what was in his mind. From that moment he has been doing everything in his power to arrange the match.'

'But, Mulliner,' said Worple, always eager to point out the bright side, 'why should this girl want to marry a wretched, scrubby, hard-up footler like you? Have courage, Mulliner. It is simply a question of time before you repel and sicken her.'

Lancelot shook his head.

'No,' he said. 'You speak like a true friend, Worple, but you do not understand. Old Ma Carberry-Pirbright, this exhibit's mother, who chaperons her at the sittings, discovered at an early date my relationship to my Uncle Theodore, who, as you know, has got it in gobs. She knows well enough that some day I shall be a rich man. She used to know my Uncle Theodore when he was Vicar of St Botoloph's in Knightsbridge, and from the very first she assumed towards me the repellent chumminess of an old family friend. She was always trying to lure me to her At Homes, her Sunday luncheons, her little dinners. Once she actually suggested that I should escort her and her beastly daughter to the Royal Academy.'

He laughed bitterly. The mordant witticisms of Lancelot Mulliner at the expense of the Royal Academy were quoted from Tite Street in the south to Holland Park in the north and eastward as far as Bloomsbury.

'To all these overtures,' resumed Lancelot, 'I remained firmly unresponsive. My attitude was from the start one of frigid aloofness. I did not actually say in so many words that I would rather be dead in a ditch than at one of her At Homes, but my manner indicated it. And I was just beginning to think I had choked her off when in crashed Webster and upset everything. Do you know how many times I have been to that infernal house in the last week? Five. Webster seemed to wish it. I tell you, I am a lost man.'

He buried his face in his hands. Scollop touched Worple on the arm, and together the two men stole silently out.

'Bad!' said Worple.

'Very bad,' said Scollop.

'It seems incredible.'

'Oh, no. Cases of this kind are, alas, by no means uncommon among those who, like Mulliner, possess to a marked degree the highly-strung, ultra-sensitive artistic temperament. A friend of mine, a rhythmical interior decorator, once rashly consented to put his aunt's parrot up at his studio while she was away visiting friends in the north of England. She was a woman of strong evangelical views, which the bird had imbibed from her. It had a way of putting its head on one side, making a nose like someone drawing a cork from a bottle, and asking my friend if he was saved. To cut a long story short, I happened to call on him a month later and he had installed a harmonium in his studio and was singing hymns, ancient and modern, in a rich tenor, while the parrot, standing on one leg on its perch, took the bass. A very sad affair. We were all much upset about it.'

Worple shuddered.

'You appal me, Scollop! Is there nothing we can do?'

Rodney Scollop considered for a moment.

'We might wire Gladys Bingley to come home

at once. She might possibly reason with the unhappy man. A woman's gentle influence . . . Yes, we could do that. Look in at the post office on your way home and send Gladys a telegram. I'll owe you for my half of it.'

In the studio they had left, Lancelot Mulliner was staring dumbly at a black shape which had just entered the room. He had the appearance of a man with his back to the wall.

'No!' he was crying. 'No! I'm dashed if I do!'

Webster continued to look at him.

'Why should I?' demanded Lancelot weakly.

Webster's gaze did not flicker.

'Oh, all right,' said Lancelot sullenly.

He passed from the room with leaden feet, and, proceeding upstairs, changed into morning clothes and a top hat. Then, with a gardenia in his buttonhole, he made his way to 11 Maxton Square, where Mrs Carberry-Pirbright was giving one of her intimate little teas ('just a few friends') to meet Clara Throckmorton Stooge, authoress of *A Strong Man's Kiss*.

Gladys Bingley was lunching at her hotel in Antibes when Worple's telegram arrived. It occasioned her the gravest concern.

Exactly what it was all about she was unable to gather, for emotion had made Bernard Worple rather incoherent. There were moments, reading it, when she fancied that Lancelot had met with a serious accident; others when the solution seemed to be that he had sprained his brain to

500

such an extent that rival lunatic asylums were competing eagerly for his custom; others, again, when Worple appeared to be suggesting that he had gone into partnershp with his cat to start a harem. But one fact emerged clearly. Her loved one was in serious trouble of some kind, and his best friends were agreed that only her immediate return could save him.

Gladys did not hesitate. Within half an hour of the receipt of the telegram she had packed her trunk, removed a piece of asparagus from her right eyebrow, and was negotiating for accommodation on the first train going north.

Arriving in London, her first impulse was to go straight to Lancelot. But a natural feminine curiosity urged her, before doing so, to call upon Bernard Worple and have light thrown on some of the more abstruse passages in the telegram.

Worple, in his capacity of author, may have tended towards obscurity, but, when confining himself to the spoken word, he told a plain story well and clearly. Five minutes of his society enabled Gladys to obtain a firm grasp on the salient factrs, and there appeared on her face that grim, tight-lipped expression which is seen only on the faces of fiancées who have come back from a short holiday to discover that their dear one has been straying in their absence from the straight and narrow path.

'Brenda Carberry-Pirbright, eh?' said Gladys, with ominous calm. 'I'll give him Brenda Carberry-Pirbright! My gosh, if one can't go off

501

to Antibes for the merest breather without having one's betrothed getting it up his nose and starting to act like a Mormon Elder, it begins to look a pretty tough world for a girl.'

Kind-hearted Bernard Worple did his best.

'I blame the cat,' he said. 'Lancelot, to my mind, is more sinned against than sinning. I consider him to be acting under undue influence or duress.'

'How like a man!' said Gladys. 'Shoving it all off on to an innocent cat!'

'Lancelot says it has a sort of something in its eye.'

'Well, when I meet Lancelot,' said Gladys, 'he'll find that I have a sort of something in my eye.'

She went out, breathing flame quietly through her nostrils. Worple, saddened, heaved a sigh and resumed his neo-Vorticist sculpting.

It was some five minutes later that Gladys, passing through Maxton Square on her way to Bott Street, stopped suddenly in her tracks. The sight she had seen was enough to make any fiancée do so.

Along the pavement leading to No 11 two figures were advancing. Or three, if you counted a morose-looking dog of a semi-dachshund nature which preceded them, attached to a leash. One of the figures was that of Lancelot Mulliner, natty in grey herring-bone tweed and a new Homburg hat. It was he who held the leash. The other Gladys recognized from the portraits which she had seen on Lancelot's easel as that modern Du Barry, that notorious wrecker of homes and breaker-up of love-nests, Brenda Carberry-Pirbright.

The next moment they had mounted the steps of No 11, and had gone in to tea, possibly with a little music.

It was perhaps an hour and a half later that Lancelot, having wrenched himself with difficulty from the lair of the Philistines, sped homeward in a swift taxi. As always after an extended *tête-à-tête* with Miss Carberry-Pirbright, he felt dazed and bewildered, as if he had been swimming in a sea of glue and had swallowed a good deal of it. All he could think of clearly was that he wanted a drink and that the materials for that drink were in the cupboard behind the chesterfield in his studio.

He paid the cab and charged in with his tongue rattling dryly against his front teeth. And there before him was Gladys Bingley, whom he had supposed far, far away.

'You!' exclaimed Lancelot.

'Yes, me!' said Gladys.

Her long vigil had not helped to restore the girl's equanimity. Since arriving at the studio she had had leisure to tap her foot three thousand, one hundred and forty-two times on the carpet, and the number of bitter smiles which had flitted across her face was nine hundred and eleven. She was about ready for the battle of the century.

She rose and faced him, all the woman in her

flashing from her eyes.

'Well, you Casanova!' she said.

'You who?' said Lancelot.

'Don't say "Yoo-hoo!" to me!' cried Gladys. 'Keep that for your Brenda Carberry-Pirbright. Yes, I know all about it, Lancelot Don Juan Henry the Eighth Mulliner! I saw you with her just now. I hear that you and she are inseparable. Bernard Worple says you said you were going to marry her.'

'You mustn't believe everything a neo-Vorticist sculptor tells you,' quavered Lancelot.

'I'll bet you're going back to dinner there tonight,' said Gladys.

She had spoken at a venture, basing the charge purely on a possessive cock of the head which she had noticed in Brenda Carberry-Pirbright at their recent encounter. There, she had said to herself at the time, had gone a girl who was about to invite — or had just invited — Lancelot Mulliner to dine quietly and take her to the pictures afterwards. But the shot went home. Lancelot hung his head.

'There was some talk of it,' he admitted.

'Ah!' exclaimed Gladys.

Lancelot's eyes were haggard.

'I don't want to go,' he pleaded. 'Honestly, I don't. But Webster insists.'

'Webster!'

'Yes, Webster. If I attempt to evade the appointment, he will sit in front of me and look at me.'

'Tchah!'

'Well, he will. Ask him for yourself.'

Gladys tapped her foot six times in rapid succession on the carpet, bringing the total to three thousand, one hundred and forty-eight. Her manner had changed and was now dangerously calm.

'Lancelot Mulliner,' she said, 'you have your choice. Me, on the one hand, Brenda Carberry-Pirbright on the other. I offer you a home where you will be able to smoke in bed, spill the ashes on the floor, wear pyjamas and carpet slippers all day and shave only on Sunday mornings. From her, what have you to hope? A house in South Kinsington — possibly the Brompton Road — probably with her mother living with you. A life that will be one long round of stiff collars and tight shoes, of morning coats and top hats.'

Lancelot quivered, but she went on remorselessly.

'You will be at home on alternate Thursdays, and will be expected to hand the cucumber sandwiches. Every day you will air the dog, till you become a confirmed dog-airer. You will dine out in Bayswater and go for the summer to Bournemouth or Dinard. Choose well, Lancelot Mulliner! I will leave you to think it over. But one last word. If by seven-thirty on the dot you have not presented yourself at 6a Garbidge Mews ready to take me out to dinner at the Ham and Beef, I shall know what to think and shall act accordingly.'

And brushing the cigarette ashes from her chin, the girl strode haughtily from the room.

'Gladys!' cried Lancelot.

But she had gone.

For some minutes Lancelot Mulliner remained where he was, stunned. Then, insistently, there came to him the recollection that he had not had that drink. He rushed to the cupboard and produced the bottle. He uncorked it, and was pouring out a lavish stream, when a movement on the floor below him attracted his attention.

Webster was standing there, looking up at him. And in his eyes was that familiar expression of quiet rebuke.

'Scarcely what I have been accustomed to at the Deanery,' he seemed to be saying.

Lancelot stood paralysed. The feeling of being bound hand and foot, of being caught in a snare from which there was no escape, had become more poignant than ever. The bottle fell from his nerveless fingers and rolled across the floor, spilling its contents in an amber river, but he was too heavy in spirit to notice it. With a gesture such as Job might have made on discovering a new boil, he crossed to the window and stood looking moodily out.

Then, turning with a sigh, he looked at Webster again — and, looking, stood spellbound.

The spectacle which he beheld was of a kind to stun a stronger man than Lancelot Mulliner. At first, he shrank from believing his eyes. Then, slowly, came the realization that what he saw was no mere figment of a disordered imagination. This unbelievable thing was actually happening.

Webster sat crouched upon the floor beside the widening pool of whisky. But it was not horror and disgust that had caused him to crouch. He was crouched because, crouching, he could get nearer to the stuff and obtain crisper action. His tongue was moving in and out like a piston.

And then abruptly, for one fleeting instant, he stopped lapping and glanced up at Lancelot, and across his face there flitted a quick smile — so genial, so intimate, so full of jovial camaraderie, that the young man found himself automatically smiling back, and not only smiling but winking. And in answer to that wink Webster winked too — a whole-hearted, roguish wink that said as plainly as if he had spoken the words:

'How long has this been going on?'

Then with a slight hiccough he turned back to the task of getting his drink before it soaked the floor.

Into the murky soul of Lancelot Mulliner there poured a sudden flood of sunshine. It was as if a great burden had been lifted from his shoulders. The intolerable obsession of the last two weeks had ceased to oppress him, and he felt a free man. At the eleventh hour the reprieve had come. Webster, that seeming pillar of austere virtue, was one of the boys, after all. Never again would Lancelot quail beneath his eye. He had the goods on him.

Webster, like the stag at eve, had now drunk his fill. He had left the pool of alcohol and was walking round in slow, meditative circles. From time to time he mewed tentatively, as if he were trying to say 'British Constitution'. His failure to articulate the syllables appeared to tickle him, for at the end of each attempt he would utter a slow, amused chuckle. It was about this moment that he suddenly broke into a rhythmic dance, not unlike the old Saraband.

It was an interesting spectacle, and at any other time Lancelot would have watched it raptly. But now he was busy at his desk, writing a brief note to Mrs Carberry-Pirbright, the burden of which was that if she thought he was coming within a mile of her foul house that night or any other night she had vastly underrated the dodging powers of Lancelot Mulliner.

And what of Webster? The Demon Rum now had him in an iron grip. A lifetime of abstinence had rendered him a ready victim to the fatal fluid. He had now reached the stage when geniality gives way to belligerence. The rather foolish smile had gone from his face, and in its stead there lowered a fighting frown. For a few moments he stood on his hind legs, looking about him for a suitable adversary: then, losing all vestiges of self-control, he ran five times round the room at a high rate of speed and, falling foul of a small footstool, attacked it with the utmost ferocity, sparing neither tooth nor claw.

But Lancelot did not see him. Lancelot was

not there. Lancelot was out in Bott Street, hailing a cab.

'6a Garbidge Mews, Fulham,' said Lancelot to the driver.

The Paradise of Cats

Emile Zola

An aunt bequeathed me an Angora cat, which is certainly the most stupid animal I know of. This is what my cat related to me, one winter night, before the warm embers.

I

I was then two years old, and I was certainly the fattest and most simple cat any one could have seen. Even at that tender age I displayed all the presumption of an animal that scorns the attractions of the fireside. And yet what gratitude I owed to Providence for having placed me with your aunt! The worthy woman idolised me. I had a regular bedroom at the bottom of a cupboard, with a feather pillow and a triple-folded rug. The food was as good as the bed; no bread or soup, nothing but meat, good underdone meat.

Well! amidst all these comforts, I had but one wish, but one dream, to slip out by the half-open window, and run away on to the tiles. Caresses appeared to me insipid, the softness of my bed disgusted me, I was so fat that I felt sick, and from morn till eve I experienced the weariness of being happy.

I must tell you that by straining my neck I had perceived the opposite roof from the window. That day four cats were fighting there. With bristling coats and tails in the air, they were rolling on the blue slates, in the full sun, amidst oaths of joy. I had never witnessed such an extraordinary sight. From that moment my convictions were settled. Real happiness was upon that roof, in front of that window which the people of the house so carefully closed. I found the proof of this in the way in which they shut the doors of the cupboards where the meat was hidden.

I made up my mind to fly. I felt sure there were other things in life than underdone meat. There was the unknown, the ideal. One day they forgot to close the kitchen window. I sprang on to a small roof beneath it.

II

How beautiful the roofs were! They were bordered by broad gutters exhaling delicious odours. I followed those gutters in raptures of delight, my feet sinking into fine mud, which was deliciously warm and soft. I fancied I was walking on velvet. And the generous heat of the sun melted my fat.

I will not conceal from you the fact that I was trembling in every limb. My delight was mingled with terror. I remember, particularly, experiencing a terrible shock that almost made me tumble down into the street. Three cats came rolling over from the top of a house towards me, mewing most frightfully, and as I was on the point of fainting away, they called me a silly thing, and said they were mewing for fun. I began mewing with them. It was charming. The jolly fellows had none of my stupid fat. When I slipped on the sheets of zinc heated by the burning sun, they laughed at me. An old tom, who was one of the band, showed me particular friendship. He offered to teach me a thing or two, and I gratefully accepted. Ah! Your aunt's cat's meat was far from my thoughts! I drank in the gutters, and never had sugared milk seemed so sweet to me. Everything appeared nice and beautiful. A she-cat passed by, a charming she-cat, the sight of her gave me a feeling I had never experienced before. Hitherto, I had only seen these exquisite creatures, with such delightfully supple backbones in my dreams. I and my three companions rushed forward to meet the newcomer. I was in front of the others, and was about to pay my respects to the bewitching thing, when one of my comrades cruelly bit my neck. I cried out with pain.

"Bah!" said the old tom, leading me away; "you will meet with stranger adventures than that."

III

After an hour's walk I felt as hungry as a wolf.

"What do you eat on the roofs?" I inquired of my friend the tom.

512

"What you can find," he answered shrewdly.

This reply caused me some embarrassment, for though I carefully searched I found nothing. At last I perceived a young work-girl in a garret preparing her lunch. A beautiful chop of a tasty red colour was lying on a table under the window.

"There's the very thing I want," I thought, in all simplicity.

And I sprang on to the table and took the chop. But the work-girl, having seen me, struck me a fearful blow with a broom on the spine, and I fled, uttering a dreadful oath.

"You are fresh from your village then?" said the tom. "Meat that is on tables is there for the purpose of being longed for at a distance. You must search in the gutters."

I could never understand that kitchen meat did not belong to cats. My stomach was beginning to get seriously angry. The tom put me completely to despair by telling me it would be necessary to wait until night. Then we would go down into the street and turn over the heaps of muck. Wait until night! He said it quietly, like a hardened philosopher. I felt myself fainting at the mere thought of this prolonged fast.

IV

Night came slowly, a foggy night that chilled me to the bones. It soon began to rain, a fine, penetrating rain, driven by sudden gusts of wind. We went down along the glazed roof of a staircase.

How ugly the street appeared to me! It was no longer that nice heat, that beautiful sun, those roofs white with light where one rolled about so deliciously. My paws slipped on the greasy stones. I sorrowfully recalled to memory my triple blanket and feather pillow.

We were hardly in the street when my friend the tom began to tremble. He made himself small, very small, and ran stealthily along beside the houses, telling me to follow as rapidly as possible. He rushed in at the first street door he came to, and purred with satisfaction as he sought refuge there. When I questioned him as to the motive of his flight, he answered:

"Did you see that man with a basket on his back and a stick with an iron hook at the end?"

"Yes."

"Well! if he had seen us he would have knocked us on the heads and roasted us!"

"Roasted us!" I exclaimed. "Then the street is not ours? One can't eat, but one's eaten!"

V

However, the boxes of kitchen refuse had been emptied before the street doors. I rummaged in the heaps in despair. I came across two or three bare bones that had been lying among the cinders, and I then understood what a succulent dish fresh cat's meat made. My friend the tom scratched artistically among the muck. He made me run about until morning, inspecting each heap, and without showing the least hurry. I was out in the rain for more than ten hours, shivering in every limb. Cursed street, cursed liberty, and how I regretted my prison!

At dawn the tom, seeing I was staggering said to me with a strange air:

"Have you had enough of it?"

"Oh yes," I answered.

"Do you want to go home?"

"I do indeed; but how shall I find the house?"

"Come along. This morning, when I saw you come out, I understood that a fat cat like you was not made for the lively delights of liberty. I know your place of abode and will take you to the door."

The worthy tom said this very quietly. When we had arrived, he bid me "Good-bye," without betraying the least emotion.

"No," I exclaimed, "we will not leave each other so. You must accompany me. We will share the same bed and the same food. My mistress is a good woman —"

He would not allow me to finish my sentence.

"Hold your tongue," he said sharply, "you are a simpleton. Your effeminate existence would kill me. Your life of plenty is good for bastard cats. Free cats would never purchase your cat's meat and feather pillow at the price of a prison. Good-bye."

And he returned up on to the roofs, where I saw his long outline quiver with joy in the rays of the rising sun.

When I got in, your aunt took the whip and gave me a thrashing which I received with profound delight. I tasted in full measure the pleasure of being beaten and being warm. Whist she was striking me, I thought with rapture of the meat she would give me afterwards.

Index of Titles and Authors

The publishers hope that this
Large Print Book has brought
you pleasurable reading.
Each title is designed to make
the text as easy to see as possible.
G. K. Hall Large Print Books
are available from your library and
your local bookstore. Or, you can
receive information by mail on
upcoming and current Large Print Books
and order directly from the publishers.
Just send your name and address to:

G. K. Hall & Co.
70 Lincoln Street
Boston, Mass. 02111

or call, toll-free:

1-800-343-2806

A note on the text
Large print edition designed by
Bernadette Montalvo
Composed in 16 pt Plantin
on a Mergenthaler Linotron 202
by Modern Graphics, Inc.